Collins

GCSE Maths
2 tier-higher
for Edexcel A

YEAR 11

BRIAN SPEED

KEITH GORDON

KEVIN EVANS

William Collins' dream of knowledge for all began with the publication of his first book in 1819. A self-educated mill worker, he not only enriched millions of lives, but also founded a flourishing publishing house. Today, staying true to this spirit, Collins books are packed with inspiration, innovation and a practical expertise. They place you at the centre of a world of possibility and give you exactly what you need to explore it.

Collins. Do more.

Published by Collins
An imprint of HarperCollins*Publishers*
77–85 Fulham Palace Road
Hammersmith
London
W6 8JB

Browse the complete Collins catalogue at
www.collinseducation.com

© HarperCollins*Publishers* Limited 2006

10 9 8 7 6 5 4 3 2 1
ISBN-13 978-0-00-725682-2
ISBN-10 0-00-725682-5

The author asserts his moral right to be identified as the author of this work.

Commissioned by Marie Taylor, Vicky Butt and Michael Cotter

Project managed by Penny Fowler

Edited by Marian Bond and Paul Sterner

Answer checker: Amanda Whyte

Internal design by JPD

Cover design by JPD

Cover illustration by Andy Parker, JPD

Page make-up and indexing by Gray Publishing

Page make-up of Really Useful Maths! spreads by EMC Design

Illustrations by Gray Publishing, EMC Design, Peters and Zabransky, Peter Cornwell, Bob Lea (Artists Partners), Martin Sanders (Beehive Illustration) and Laszlo Veres (Beehive Illustration)

Production by Natasha Buckland

Printed and bound in Hong Kong by Printing Express Ltd.

Acknowledgements

With special thanks to Lynn and Greg Byrd

The Publishers gratefully acknowledge the following for permission to reproduce copyright material. Whilst every effort has been made to trace the copyright holders, in cases where this has been unsuccessful or if any have inadvertently been overlooked, the Publishers will be pleased to make the necessary arrangements at the first opportunity.

Edexcel material reproduced with permission of Edexcel Limited. Edexcel Ltd accepts no responsibility whatsoever for the accuracy or method of working in the answers given.

Grade bar photos © 2006 JupiterImages Corporation

© 2006 JupiterImages Corporation, p1, p53, p147, p157, p169, p181, p197, p211

© Sergeo Syd / Istock, p23

© PCL / Alamy, p75

© Michal Galazka / Istock, p117

© SuperStock / Alamy, p166

© Penny Fowler, p223

CONTENTS

Welcome to Collins GCSE Maths, the easiest way to learn and succeed in Mathematics. This textbook uses a stimulating approach that really appeals to students. Here are some of the key features of the textbook, to explain why.

Each chapter of the textbook begins with an **Overview**. The Overview lists the Sections you will encounter in the chapter, the key ideas you will learn, and shows how these ideas relate to, and build upon, each other. The Overview also highlights what you should already know, and if you're not sure, there is a short Quick Check activity to test yourself and recap.

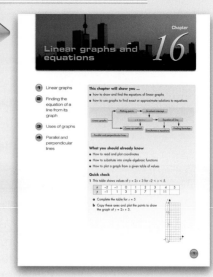

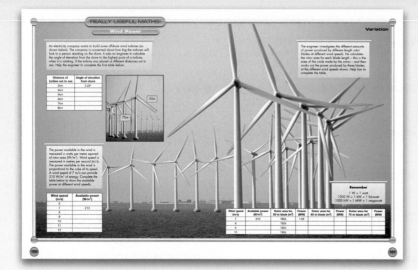

Maths can be useful to us every day of our lives, so look out for these **Really Useful Maths!** pages. These double page spreads use big, bright illustrations to depict real-life situations, and present a short series of real-world problems for you to practice your latest mathematical skills on.

Each **Section** begins first by explaining what mathematical ideas you are aiming to learn, and then lists the key words you will meet and use. The ideas are clearly explained, and this is followed by several examples showing how they can be applied to real problems. Then it's your turn to work through the exercises and improve your skills. Notice the different coloured panels along the outside of the exercise pages. These show the equivalent exam grade of the questions you are working on, so you can always tell how well you are doing.

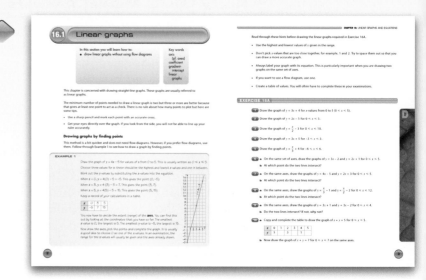

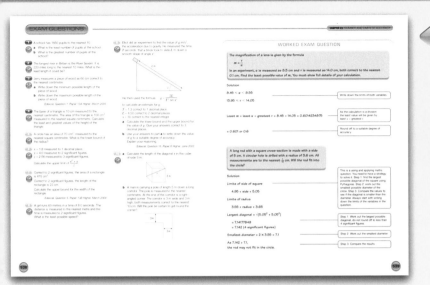

Every chapter in this textbook contains lots of **Exam Questions**. These provide ideal preparation for your examinations. Each exam question section also concludes with a fully worked example. Compare this with your own work, and pay special attention to the examiner's comments, which will ensure you understand how to score maximum marks.

Throughout the textbook you will find **Activities** – highlighted in the green panels – designed to challenge your thinking and improve your understanding.

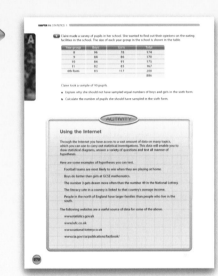

Review the **Grade Yourself** pages at the very end of the chapter. This will show what exam grade you are currently working at. Doublecheck **What you should now know** to confirm that you have the knowledge you need to progress.

Working through these sections in the right way should mean you achieve your very best in GCSE Maths. Remember though, if you get stuck, answers to all the questions are at the back of the book (except the exam question answers which your teacher has).

We do hope you enjoy using Collins GCSE Maths, and wish you every good luck in your studies!

Brian Speed, Keith Gordon, Kevin Evans

ICONS

 You may use your calculator for this question

 You should not use your calculator for this question

 Indicates a Using and Applying Mathematics question

 Indicates a Proof question

Linear graphs and equations

1 Linear graphs

2 Finding the equation of a line from its graph

3 Uses of graphs

4 Parallel and perpendicular lines

This chapter will show you ...

- how to draw and find the equations of linear graphs
- how to use graphs to find exact or approximate solutions to equations

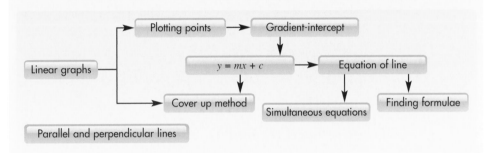

What you should already know

- How to read and plot coordinates
- How to substitute into simple algebraic functions
- How to plot a graph from a given table of values

Quick check

1 This table shows values of $y = 2x + 3$ for $-2 \leqslant x \leqslant 5$.

x	−2	−1	0	1	2	3	4	5
y	−1	1	3	5	7	9	11	

a Complete the table for $x = 5$

b Copy these axes and plot the points to draw the graph of $y = 2x + 3$.

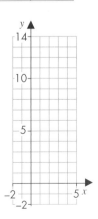

Linear graphs

In this section you will learn how to:

- draw linear graphs without using flow diagrams

Key words

axis
  (pl: axes)
coefficient
gradient-
  intercept
linear
  graphs

This chapter is concerned with drawing straight-line graphs. These graphs are usually referred to as **linear graphs**.

The minimum number of points needed to draw a linear graph is two but three or more are better because that gives at least one point to act as a check. There is no rule about how many points to plot but here are some tips.

- Use a sharp pencil and mark each point with an accurate cross.

- Get your eyes directly over the graph. If you look from the side, you will not be able to line up your ruler accurately.

Drawing graphs by finding points

This method is a bit quicker and does not need flow diagrams. However, if you prefer flow diagrams, use them. Follow through Example 1 to see how to draw a graph by finding points.

EXAMPLE 1

Draw the graph of $y = 4x - 5$ for values of x from 0 to 5. This is usually written as $0 \leqslant x \leqslant 5$.

Choose three values for x: these should be the highest and lowest x-values and one in between.

Work out the y-values by substituting the x-values into the equation.

When $x = 0$, $y = 4(0) - 5 = -5$. This gives the point $(0, -5)$.

When $x = 3$, $y = 4(3) - 5 = 7$. This gives the point $(3, 7)$.

When $x = 5$, $y = 4(5) - 5 = 15$. This gives the point $(5, 15)$.

Keep a record of your calculations in a table.

x	0	3	5
y	−5	7	15

You now have to decide the extent (range) of the **axes**. You can find this out by looking at the coordinates that you have so far. The smallest x-value is 0, the largest is 5. The smallest y-value is −5, the largest is 15.

Now draw the axes, plot the points and complete the graph. It is usually a good idea to choose 0 as one of the x-values. In an examination, the range for the x-values will usually be given and the axes already drawn.

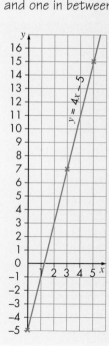

Read through these hints before drawing the linear graphs required in Exercise 16A.

● Use the highest and lowest values of x given in the range.

● Don't pick x-values that are too close together, for example, 1 and 2. Try to space them out so that you can draw a more accurate graph.

● Always label your graph with its equation. This is particularly important when you are drawing two graphs on the same set of axes.

● If you want to use a flow diagram, use one.

● Create a table of values. You will often have to complete these in your examinations.

EXERCISE 16A

1 Draw the graph of $y = 3x + 4$ for x-values from 0 to 5 ($0 \leqslant x \leqslant 5$).

2 Draw the graph of $y = 2x - 5$ for $0 \leqslant x \leqslant 5$.

3 Draw the graph of $y = \dfrac{x}{2} - 3$ for $0 \leqslant x \leqslant 10$.

4 Draw the graph of $y = 3x + 5$ for $-3 \leqslant x \leqslant 3$.

5 Draw the graph of $y = \dfrac{x}{3} + 4$ for $-6 \leqslant x \leqslant 6$.

6 **a** On the same set of axes, draw the graphs of $y = 3x - 2$ and $y = 2x + 1$ for $0 \leqslant x \leqslant 5$.

  b At which point do the two lines intersect?

7 **a** On the same axes, draw the graphs of $y = 4x - 5$ and $y = 2x + 3$ for $0 \leqslant x \leqslant 5$.

  b At which point do the two lines intersect?

8 **a** On the same axes, draw the graphs of $y = \dfrac{x}{3} - 1$ and $y = \dfrac{x}{2} - 2$ for $0 \leqslant x \leqslant 12$.

  b At which point do the two lines intersect?

9 **a** On the same axes, draw the graphs of $y = 3x + 1$ and $y = 3x - 2$ for $0 \leqslant x \leqslant 4$.

  b Do the two lines intersect? If not, why not?

10 **a** Copy and complete the table to draw the graph of $x + y = 5$ for $0 \leqslant x \leqslant 5$.

x	0	1	2	3	4	5
y	5		3		1	

  b Now draw the graph of $x + y = 7$ for $0 \leqslant x \leqslant 7$ on the same axes.

Gradient

The slope of a line is called its gradient. The steeper the slope of the line, the larger the value of the gradient.

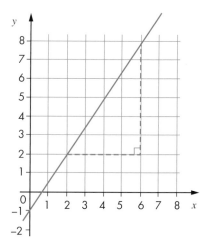

The gradient of the line shown here can be measured by drawing, as large as possible, a right-angled triangle which has part of the line as its hypotenuse (sloping side). The gradient is then given by:

$$\text{gradient} = \frac{\text{distance measured up}}{\text{distance measured along}}$$

$$= \frac{\text{difference on } y\text{-axis}}{\text{difference on } x\text{-axis}}$$

For example, to measure the steepness of the line in the next figure, you first draw a right-angled triangle whose hypotenuse is part of this line. It does not matter where you draw the triangle but it makes the calculations much easier if you choose a sensible place. This usually means using existing grid lines, so that you avoid fractional values.

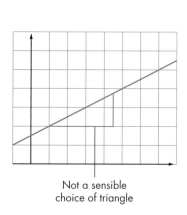

Not a sensible choice of triangle

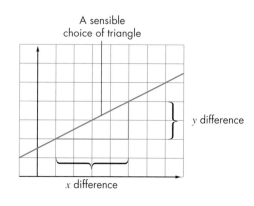

A sensible choice of triangle

y difference

x difference

After you have drawn the triangle, you measure (or count) how many squares there are on the vertical side. This is the difference between your *y*-coordinates. In the case above, this is 2.

You then measure (or count) how many squares there are on the horizontal side. This is the difference between your *x*-coordinates. In the case above, this is 4.

To work out the gradient, you do the following calculation.

$$\text{gradient} = \frac{\text{difference of the } y\text{-coordinates}}{\text{difference of the } x\text{-coordinates}} = \frac{2}{4} = \frac{1}{2} \text{ or } 0.5$$

Note that the value of the gradient is not affected by where the triangle is drawn. As we are calculating the ratio of two sides of the triangle, the gradient will always be the same wherever we draw the triangle.

Remember: When a line slopes down from left to right, the gradient is negative, so a minus sign must be placed in front of the calculated fraction.

EXAMPLE 2

Find the gradient of each of these lines.

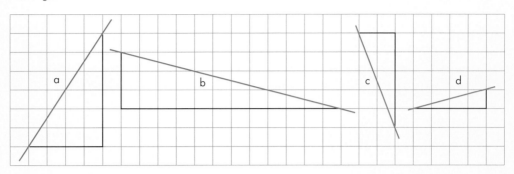

In each case, a sensible choice of triangle has already been made.

a y difference = 6, x difference = 4   Gradient = $6 \div 4 = \dfrac{3}{2} = 1.5$

b y difference = 3, x difference = 12   Line slopes down left to right,

so gradient = $-(3 \div 12) = -\dfrac{1}{4} = -0.25$

c y difference = 5, x difference = 2   Line slopes down from left to right,

so gradient = $-(5 \div 2) = -\dfrac{5}{2} = -2.5$

d y difference = 1, x difference = 4   Gradient = $1 \div 4 = \dfrac{1}{4} = 0.25$

Drawing a line with a certain gradient

To draw a line with a certain gradient, you reverse the process described above. That is, you first draw the right-angled triangle using the given gradient. For example, take a gradient of 2.

Start at a convenient point (A in the diagrams below). A gradient of 2 means for an x-step of 1 the y-step must be 2 (because 2 is the fraction $\frac{2}{1}$). So, move one square across and two squares up, and mark a dot.

Repeat this as many times as you like and draw the line. You can also move one square back and two squares down, which gives the same gradient, as the third diagram shows.

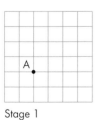

Stage 1

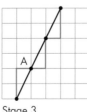

Stage 2

Stage 3

EXAMPLE 3

Draw lines with these gradients.   **a** $\frac{1}{3}$ **b** -3 **c** $-\frac{1}{4}$

a This is a fractional gradient which has a y-step of 1 and an x-step of 3. Move three squares across and one square up every time.

b This is a negative gradient, so for every one square across, move three squares down.

c This is also a negative gradient and it is a fraction. So for every four squares across, move one square down.

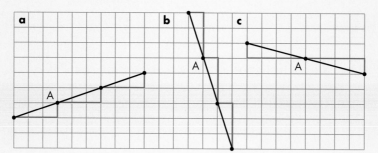

EXERCISE 16B

1 Find the gradient of each of these lines.

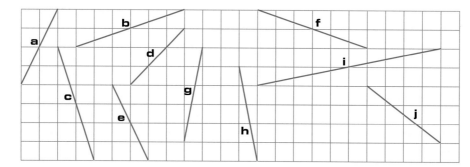

2 Draw lines with these gradients.

  a 4   **b** $\frac{2}{3}$ **c** -2 **d** $-\frac{4}{5}$ **e** 6   **f** -6

3 Find the gradient of each of these lines. What is special about these lines?

  a

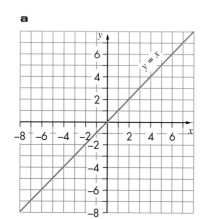

  b

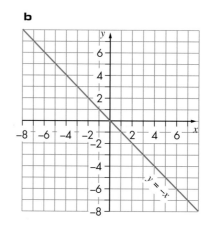

4 The line on grid **e** is horizontal. The lines on grids **a** to **d** get nearer and nearer to the horizontal.

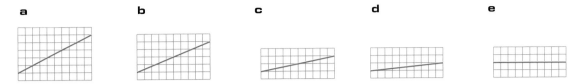

Find the gradient of each line in grids **a** to **d**. By looking at the values you obtain, what do you think the gradient of a horizontal line is?

5 The line on grid **e** is vertical. The lines on grids **a** to **d** get nearer and nearer to the vertical.

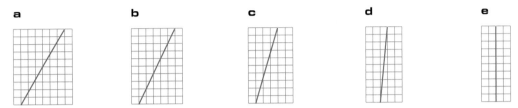

Find the gradient of each line in grids **a** to **d**. By looking at the values you obtain, what do you think the gradient of a vertical line is?

Gradient-intercept method for drawing graphs

The ideas that you have discovered in the last activity lead to another way of plotting lines, known as the **gradient-intercept** method.

EXAMPLE 4

Draw the graph of $y = 3x - 1$, using the gradient-intercept method.

- Because the constant term is –1, we know that the graph goes through the *y*-axis at –1. We mark this point with a dot or a cross (**A** on diagram **i**).

- The number in front of *x* (called the **coefficient** of *x*) gives the relationship between *y* and *x*. Because the coefficient of *x* is 3, this tells us that *y* is 3 times the *x* value, so the gradient of the line is 3. For an *x*-step of one unit, there is a *y*-step of three. Starting at –1 on the *y*-axis, we move one square across and three squares up and mark this point with a dot or a cross (**B** on diagram **i**).

Repeat this from every new point. You can also move one square back and three squares down. When enough points have been marked, join the dots (or crosses) to make the graph (diagram **ii**). Note that if the points are not in a straight line, a mistake has been made.

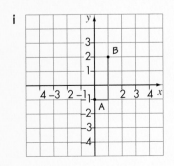 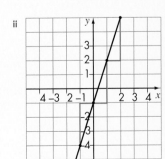

C

1 Draw these lines using the gradient-intercept method. Use the same grid, taking x from -10 to 10 and y from -10 to 10. If the grid gets too "crowded", draw another one.

a $y = 2x + 6$ **b** $y = 3x - 4$ **c** $y = \frac{1}{2}x + 5$

d $y = x + 7$ **e** $y = 4x - 3$ **f** $y = 2x - 7$

g $y = \frac{1}{4}x - 3$ **h** $y = \frac{2}{3}x + 4$ **i** $y = 6x - 5$

j $y = x + 8$ **k** $y = \frac{4}{5}x - 2$ **l** $y = 3x - 9$

2 a Using the gradient-intercept method, draw the following lines on the same grid. Use axes with ranges $-6 \leqslant x \leqslant 6$ and $-8 \leqslant y \leqslant 8$.

   i $y = 3x + 1$ **ii** $y = 2x + 3$

b Where do the lines cross?

3 a Using the gradient-intercept method, draw the following lines on the same grid. Use axes with ranges $-14 \leqslant x \leqslant 4$ and $-2 \leqslant y \leqslant 6$.

   i $y = \dfrac{x}{3} + 3$ **ii** $y = \dfrac{x}{4} + 2$

b Where do the lines cross?

4 a Using the gradient-intercept method draw the following lines on the same grid. Use axes with ranges $-4 \leqslant x \leqslant 6$ and $-6 \leqslant y \leqslant 8$.

   i $y = x + 3$ **ii** $y = 2x$

b Where do the lines cross?

Cover-up method for drawing graphs

The x-axis has the equation $y = 0$. This means that all points on the x-axis have a y-value of 0.

The y-axis has the equation $x = 0$. This means that all points on the y-axis have an x-value of 0.

We can use these facts to draw any line that has an equation of the form:

$$ax + by = c.$$

EXAMPLE 5

Draw the graph of $4x + 5y = 20$.

Because the value of x is 0 on the y-axis, we can solve the equation for y:

$$4(0) + 5y = 20$$
$$5y = 20$$
$$\Rightarrow \quad y = 4$$

Hence, the line passes through the point $(0, 4)$ on the y-axis (diagram **A**).

Because the value of y is 0 on the x-axis, we can also solve the equation for x:

$$4x + 5(0) = 20$$
$$4x = 20$$
$$\Rightarrow \quad x = 5$$

Hence, the line passes through the point $(5, 0)$ on the x-axis (diagram **B**). We need only two points to draw a line. (Normally, we would like a third point but in this case we can accept two.) The graph is drawn by joining the points $(0, 4)$ and $(5, 0)$ (diagram **C**).

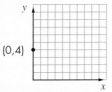

A

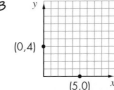

B

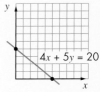

C

This type of equation can be drawn very easily, without much working at all, using the cover-up method.

Start with the equation	$4x + 5y = 20$
Cover up the x-term:	$\boxed{} + 5y = 20$
Solve the equation (when $x = 0$):	$y = 4$
Now cover up the y-term:	$4x + \boxed{} = 20$
Solve the equation (when $y = 0$):	$x = 5$

This gives the points $(0, 4)$ on the y-axis and $(5, 0)$ on the x-axis.

EXAMPLE 6

Draw the graph of $2x - 3y = 12$.

Start with the equation	$2x - 3y = 12$
Cover up the x-term:	$\boxed{} - 3y = 12$
Solve the equation (when $x = 0$):	$y = -4$
Now cover up the y-term:	$2x + \boxed{} = 12$
Solve the equation (when $y = 0$):	$x = 6$

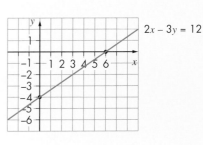

This gives the points $(0, -4)$ on the y-axis and $(6, 0)$ on the x-axis.

EXERCISE 16D

 Draw these lines using the cover-up method. Use the same grid, taking x from -10 to 10 and y from -10 to 10. If the grid gets too "crowded", draw another.

a $3x + 2y = 6$ **b** $4x + 3y = 12$ **c** $4x - 5y = 20$

d $x + y = 10$ **e** $3x - 2y = 18$ **f** $x - y = 4$

g $5x - 2y = 15$ **h** $2x - 3y = 15$ **i** $6x + 5y = 30$

j $x + y = -5$ **k** $x + y = 3$ **l** $x - y = -4$

 a Using the cover-up method, draw the following lines on the same grid. Use axes with ranges $-2 \leqslant x \leqslant 6$ and $-2 \leqslant y \leqslant 6$.

i $2x + y = 4$ **ii** $x - 2y = 2$

b Where do the lines cross?

 a Using the cover-up method, draw the following lines on the same grid. Use axes with ranges $-2 \leqslant x \leqslant 6$ and $-3 \leqslant y \leqslant 6$.

i $x + 2y = 6$ **ii** $2x - y = 2$

b Where do the lines cross?

4 **a** Using the cover-up method, draw the following lines on the same grid. Use axes with ranges $-6 \leqslant x \leqslant 8$ and $-2 \leqslant y \leqslant 8$.

i $x + y = 6$ **ii** $x - y = 2$

b Where do the lines cross?

16.2 Finding the equation of a line from its graph

In this section you will learn how to:	Key words
• find the equation of a line using its gradient and intercept	coefficient gradient intercept

The equation $y = mx + c$

When a graph can be expressed in the form $y = mx + c$, the **coefficient** of x, m, is the **gradient**, and the constant term, c, is the **intercept** on the y-axis.

This means that if we know the gradient, m, of a line and its intercept, c, on the y-axis, we can write down the equation of the line immediately.

For example, if $m = 3$ and $c = -5$, the equation of the line is $y = 3x - 5$.

All linear graphs can be expressed in the form $y = mx + c$.

This gives us a method of finding the equation of any line drawn on a pair of coordinate axes.

EXAMPLE 7

Find the equation of the line shown in diagram **A**.

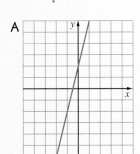 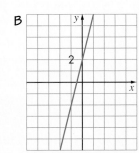 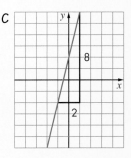

First, we find where the graph crosses the y-axis (diagram **B**).

So $c = 2$.

Next, we measure the gradient of the line (diagram **C**).

y-step = 8
x-step = 2
gradient = 8 ÷ 2 = 4

So $m = 4$.

Finally, we write down the equation of the line: $y = 4x + 2$.

EXERCISE 16E

1 Give the equation of each of these lines, all of which have positive gradients. (Each square represents 1 unit.)

a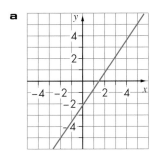

b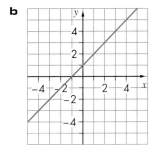

c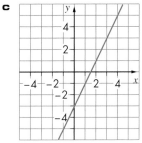

d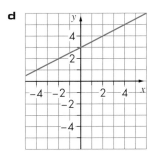

e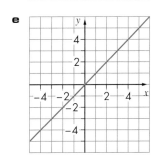

f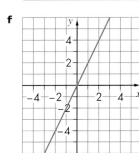

2 In each of these grids, there are two lines. (Each square represents 1 unit.)

a 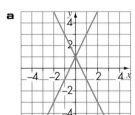 **b** 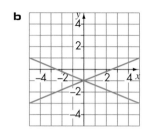 **c**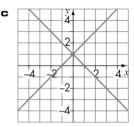

For each grid:

i find the equation of each of the lines,

ii describe any symmetries that you can see,

iii what connection is there between the gradients of each pair of lines?

3 Give the equation of each of these lines, all of which have negative gradients. (Each square represents 1 unit.)

a 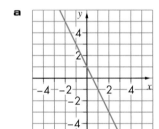 **b** 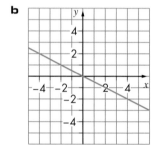 **c**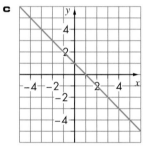

d 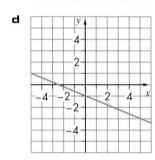 **e**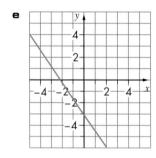

4 In each of these grids, there are three lines. One of them is $y = x$. (Each square represents one unit.)

a 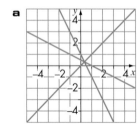 **b** 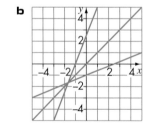 **c**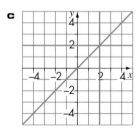

For each grid:

i find the equation of each of the other two lines,

ii describe any symmetries that you can see,

iii what connection is there between the gradients of each group of lines?

In this section you will learn how to:
- use straight-line graphs to find formulae
- solve simultaneous linear equations using graphs

Key words

formula
(pl: formulae)
rule

In the Year 10 book on pages 310 and 311, you met two uses of graphs in kinematics, and the use of graphs to represent mortgage repayment and the rate of change of depth as a container is filled with water. Two other uses of graphs which we will now consider are finding formulae and solving simultaneous equations. Solving quadratic and other equations by graphical methods is covered in Chapter 17.

Finding formulae or rules

EXAMPLE 8

A taxi fare will cost more the further you go. The graph on the right illustrates the fares in one part of England.

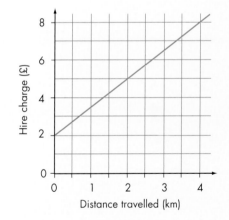

The taxi company charges a basic hire fee to start with of £2.00. This is shown on the graph as the point where the line cuts through the hire-charge axis (when distance travelled is 0).

The gradient of the line is:

$$\frac{8-2}{4} = \frac{6}{4} = 1.5$$

This represents the hire charge per kilometre travelled.

So the total hire charge is made up of two parts: a basic hire charge of £2.00 and an additional charge of £1.50 per kilometre travelled. This can be put in a formula as

Hire charge = £2.00 + £1.50 per kilometre.

In this example, £2.00 is the constant term in the formula (the equation of the graph).

EXERCISE 16F

1 This graph is a conversion graph between °C and °F.

    a How many °F are equivalent to a temperature of 0 °C?

    b What is the gradient of the line?

    c From your answers to parts **a** and **b**, write down a rule which can be used to convert °C to °F.

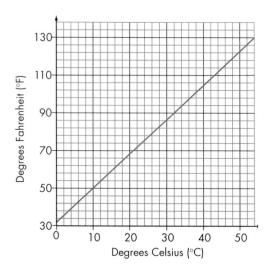

2 This graph illustrates charges for fuel.

    a What is the gradient of the line?

    b The standing charge is the basic charge before the cost per unit is added. What is the standing charge?

    c Write down the rule used to work out the total charge for different amounts of units used.

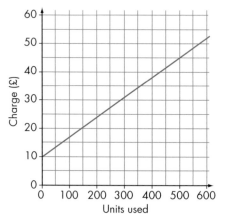

3 This graph shows the hire charge for heaters over so many days.

    a Calculate the gradient of the line.

    b What is the basic charge before the daily hire charge is added on?

    c Write down the rule used to work out the total hire charge.

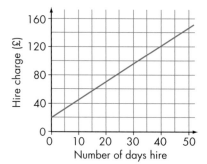

4 This graph shows the hire charge for a conference centre depending on the number of people at the conference.

    a Calculate the gradient of the line.

    b What is the basic fee for hiring the conference centre?

    c Write down the rule used to work out the total hire charge for the centre.

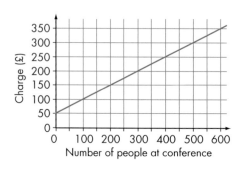

5 This graph shows the length of a spring when different weights are attached to it.

a Calculate the gradient of the line.

b How long is the spring when no weight is attached to it?

c By how much does the spring extend per kilogram?

d Write down the rule for finding the length of the spring for different weights.

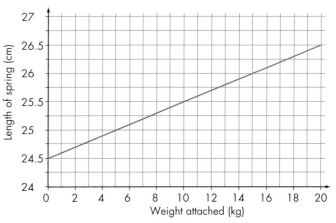

Solving simultaneous equations

EXAMPLE 9

By drawing their graphs on the same grid, find the solution of these simultaneous equations.

a $3x + y = 6$ **b** $y = 4x - 1$

a The first graph is drawn using the cover-up method. It crosses the x-axis at $(2, 0)$ and the y-axis at $(0, 6)$.

b This graph can be drawn by finding some points or by the gradient-intercept method. If you use the gradient-intercept method, you find the graph crosses the y-axis at -1 and has a gradient of 4.

The point where the graphs intersect is $(1, 3)$. So the solution to the simultaneous equations is $x = 1$, $y = 3$.

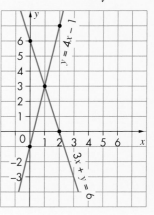

EXERCISE 16G

By drawing their graphs, find the solution of each of these pairs of simultaneous equations.

1 $x + 4y = 8$
$x - y = 3$

2 $y = 2x - 1$
$3x + 2y = 12$

3 $y = 2x + 4$
$y = x + 7$

4 $y = x$
$x + y = 10$

5 $y = 2x + 3$
$5x + y = 10$

6 $y = 5x + 1$
$y = 2x + 10$

7 $y = x + 8$
$x + y = 4$

8 $y - 3x = 9$
$y = x - 3$

9 $y = -x$
$y = 4x - 5$

10 $3x + 2y = 18$
$y = 3x$

11 $y = 3x + 2$
$y + x = 10$

12 $y = \dfrac{x}{3} + 1$
$x + y = 11$

Parallel and perpendicular lines

This section will show you how to:

- draw linear graphs parallel or perpendicular to other lines and passing through a specific point

Key words

negative reciprocal
parallel
perpendicular

EXAMPLE 10

In each of these grids, there are two lines.

a 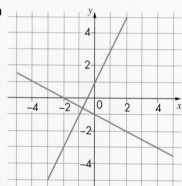 b 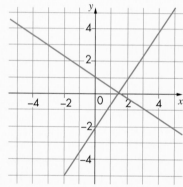 c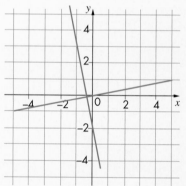

For each grid:

i find the equation of each line,

ii describe the geometrical relationship between the lines,

iii describe the numerical relationships between their gradients.

  i Grid a: the lines have equations $y = 2x + 1$, $y = -\frac{1}{2}x - 1$

     Grid b: the lines have equations $y = \frac{3}{2}x - 2$, $y = -\frac{2}{3}x + 1$

     Grid c: the lines have equations $y = \frac{1}{5}x$, $y = -5x - 2$

  ii In each case the lines are perpendicular (at right angles)

  iii In each case the gradients are reciprocals of each other but with different signs.

Note: If two lines are **parallel**, then their gradients are equal.

If two lines are **perpendicular**, their gradients are **negative reciprocals** of each other.

EXAMPLE 11

Find the line that is perpendicular to the line $y = \frac{1}{2}x - 3$ and passes through $(0, 5)$.

The gradient of the new line will be the negative reciprocal of $\frac{1}{2}$ which is -2.

The point $(0, 5)$ is the intercept on the y-axis so the equation of the line is $y = -2x + 5$.

EXAMPLE 12

The point A is $(2, -1)$ and the point B is $(4, 5)$.

a Find the equation of the line parallel to AB and passing through $(2, 8)$.

b Find the equation of the line perpendicular to the midpoint of AB.

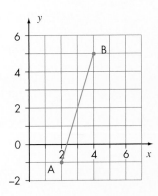

a The gradient of AB is 3, so the new equation is of the form

$$y = 3x + c.$$

The new line passes through $(2, 8)$, so $8 = 3 \times 2 + c$
$$\Rightarrow \quad c = 2$$

Hence the line is $y = 3x + 2$.

b The midpoint of AB is $(3, 2)$.

The gradient of the perpendicular line is the negative reciprocal of 3, which is $-\frac{1}{3}$.

We could find c as in part **a** but we can also do a sketch on the grid. This will show that the perpendicular line passes through $(0, 3)$.

Hence the equation of the line is $y = -\frac{1}{3}x + 3$.

EXERCISE 16H

1 Write down the negative reciprocals of the following numbers.

a 2

b -3

c 5

d -1

e $\frac{1}{2}$

f $\frac{1}{4}$

g $-\frac{1}{3}$

h $-\frac{2}{3}$

i 1.5

j 10

k -6

l $\frac{4}{3}$

2 Write down the equation of the line perpendicular to each of the following lines and which passes through the same point on the y-axis.

a $y = 2x - 1$

b $y = -3x + 1$

c $y = x + 2$

d $y = -x + 2$

e $y = \frac{1}{2}x + 3$

f $y = \frac{1}{4}x - 3$

g $y = -\frac{1}{3}x$

h $y = -\frac{2}{3}x - 5$

A

A*

3 Write down the equations of these lines.

a parallel to $y = 4x - 5$ and passes through $(0, 1)$

b parallel to $y = \frac{1}{2}x + 3$ and passes through $(0, -2)$

c parallel to $y = -x + 2$ and passes through $(0, 3)$

4 Write down the equations of these lines.

a perpendicular to $y = 3x + 2$ and passes through $(0, -1)$

b perpendicular to $y = -\frac{1}{3}x - 2$ and passes through $(0, 5)$

c perpendicular to $y = x - 5$ and passes through $(0, 1)$

5 A is the point $(1, 5)$. B is the point $(3, 3)$.

a Find the equation of the line parallel to AB and passing through $(5, 9)$.

b Find the equation of the line perpendicular to AB and passing through the midpoint of AB.

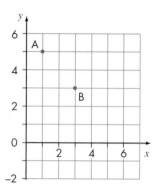

6 Find the equation of the line that passes through the midpoint of AB, where A is $(-5, -3)$ and B is $(-1, 3)$, and has a gradient of 2.

7 Find the equation of the line perpendicular to $y = 4x - 3$, passing though $(-4, 3)$.

8 A is the point $(0, 6)$, B is the point $(5, 5)$ and C is the point $(4, 0)$.

a Write down the point where the line BC intercepts the y-axis.

b Work out the equation of the line AB.

c Write down the equation of the line BC.

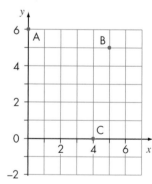

9 Find the equation of the perpendicular bisector of the points A $(1, 2)$ and B $(3, 6)$.

10 A is the point $(0, 4)$, B is the point $(4, 6)$ and C is the point $(2, 0)$.

a Find the equation of the line BC.

b Show that the point of intersection of the perpendicular bisectors of AB and AC is $(3, 3)$.

c Show algebraically that this point lies on the line BC.

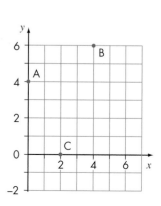

1 **a** Draw the graph of $y = 2x + 3$ for values of x from 0 to 5. Use a grid with axes covering $0 \leqslant x \leqslant 6$ and $0 \leqslant y \leqslant 14$.

b Use your graph to solve $6.5 = 2x + 3$.

2 The diagram shows a sketch of the graph of $y = 3x + 1$.

Copy the diagram, and draw and label sketch graphs of these.

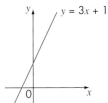

a $y = 1$

b $y = x + 1$

3 Here are five graphs labelled A, B, C, D and E.

Each of the equations in the table represents one of the graphs A to E.

Copy the table. Write the letter of each graph in the correct place in the table.

Equation	Graph
$x + y = 5$	
$y = x - 5$	
$y = -5 - x$	
$y = -5$	
$x = -5$	

Edexcel, Question 3, Paper 10B Higher, March 2005

4 Here are the equations of six lines.

i $y = 2x + 1$ **ii** $y = -\frac{1}{3}x - 3$ **iii** $y = \frac{1}{3}x - 1$

iv $y = 2x - 2$ **v** $y = 3x + 2$ **vi** $y = \frac{1}{2}x - 2$

a Which two lines are parallel?

b Which pairs of lines are perpendicular?

c Which two lines intersect on the y-axis?

5 The diagram shows three points A$(-1, 5)$, B$(2, -1)$ and C$(0, 5)$. The line L is parallel to AB and passes through C.

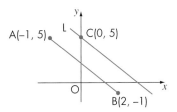

a Find the equation of the line L.

The line M is perpendicular to AB and passes through $(0, 0)$.

b Find the equation of the line M.

Edexcel, Question 6, Paper 18 Higher, June 2005

6 **a** Find the equation of the straight line which passes through the point $(0, 3)$ and is perpendicular to the straight line with equation $y = 2x$.

The graphs of $y = 2x^2$ and $y = mx - 2$ intersect at the points A and B. The point B has coordinates $(2, 8)$.

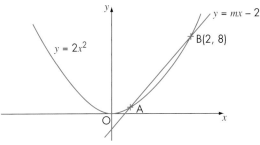

b Find the coordinates of the point A.

Edexcel, Question 13, Paper 18 Higher, June 2003

7 A is the point $(5, 5)$. B is the point $(3, 1)$. Find the equation of the line perpendicular to AB and passing through the midpoint of AB.

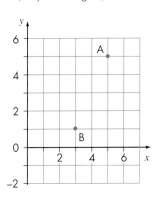

8 Find the equation of the line parallel to the line $y = 3x + 5$ passing through the point $(2, 9)$.

9 Find the equation of the perpendicular bisector of the line joining the two points A$(4, 3)$ and B$(8, 5)$.

10 A is the point $(6, 3)$, B is the point $(0, 5)$. Find algebraically, the point of intersection of the line perpendicular to AB passing through the midpoint and the line $2y + x = 4$.

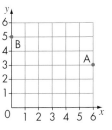

WORKED EXAM QUESTION

a   Find the equation of the line shown.

b   Find the equation of the line perpendicular to the line shown and passing through $(0, -5)$.

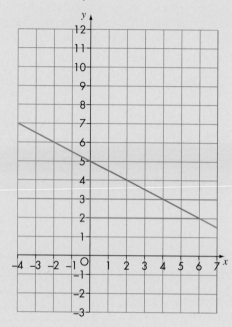

Solution

a   Intercept is at $(0, 5)$ ————— First identify the point where the line crosses the y-axis. This is the intercept, c.

Gradient $= -\dfrac{3}{6} = -\dfrac{1}{2}$ ————— Draw a right-angled triangle using grid lines as two sides of the triangle and part of the line as the hypotenuse. (Shown in red on diagram.)

Measure the y-step and the x-step of the triangle and divide the y-step by the x-step to get the gradient, m.

Equation of the line is $y = -\dfrac{1}{2}x + 5$ ————— As the line slopes down from left to right the gradient is negative.

Put the two numbers into the equation $y = mx + c$ to get the equation of the line.

b   Gradient is 2 ————— Gradient of y a perpendicular line is the negative reciprocal of $-\frac{1}{2}$.

Intercept is $(0, -5)$ ————— Intercept is given.

Equation is $y = 2x - 5$ ————— Give equation in the form $y = mx + c$.

GRADE YOURSELF

D Able to draw straight lines by plotting points

C Able to draw straight lines using the gradient-intercept method

Able to solve a pair of linear simultaneous equations from their graphs

A Able to find the equations of linear graphs parallel and perpendicular to other linear graphs, that pass through specific points

What you should know now

- How to draw linear graphs

- How to solve simultaneous linear equations by finding the intersection point of the graphs of the equations or other related equations

- How to use gradients to find equations of parallel and perpendicular graphs

More graphs and equations

1 Quadratic graphs

2 Other graphs

3 Solving equations by the method of intersection

This chapter will show you ...

- how to draw quadratic, cubic, reciprocal and exponential graphs
- how to use graphs to find exact or approximate solutions to equations

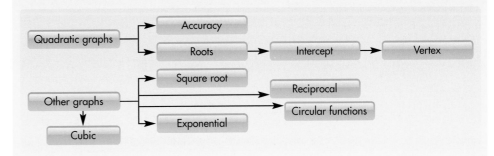

What you should already know

- How to draw linear graphs
- How to find the equation of a graph using the gradient-intercept method

Quick check

1 Draw the graph of $y = 3x - 1$ for values of x from -2 to $+3$.

2 Give the equation of the graph shown.

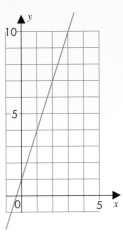

Quadratic graphs

This section will show you how to:
- draw and read values from quadratic graphs

A **quadratic** graph has a term in x^2 in its equation. All of the following are quadratic equations and each would produce a quadratic graph.

$y = x^2$ $\qquad\qquad$ $y = x^2 + 5$ $\qquad\qquad$ $y = x^2 - 3x$

$y = x^2 + 5x + 6$ $\qquad$ $y = 3x^2 - 5x + 4$

EXAMPLE 1

Draw the graph of $y = x^2 + 5x + 6$ for $-5 \leqslant x \leqslant 3$.

Make a table, as shown below. Work out each row (x^2, $5x$, 6) separately, adding them together to obtain the values of y. Then plot the points from the table.

x	−5	−4	−3	−2	−1	0	1	2	3
x^2	25	16	9	4	1	0	1	4	9
$5x$	−25	−20	−15	−10	−5	0	5	10	15
6	6	6	6	6	6	6	6	6	6
y	6	2	0	0	2	6	12	20	30

Note that in an examination paper you may be given only the first and last rows, with some values filled in. For example,

x	−5	−4	−3	−2	−1	0	1	2	3
y	6		0		2				30

In this case, you would either construct your own table, or work out the remaining y-values with a calculator.

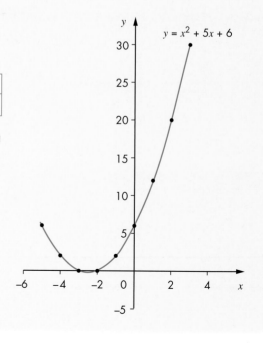

EXAMPLE 2

a Complete the table for $y = 3x^2 - 5x + 4$ for $-1 \leqslant x \leqslant 3$, then draw the graph.

x	−1	−0.5	0	0.5	1	1.5	2	2.5	3
y	12			2.25	2			10.25	16

b Use your graph to find the value of y when $x = 2.2$.

c Use your graph to find the values of x that give a y-value of 9.

a The table gives only some values. So you either set up your own table with $3x^2$, $-5x$ and $+4$, or calculate each y-value. For example, on the majority of scientific calculators, the value for -0.5 will be worked out as

Check that you get an answer of 7.25.

If you want to make sure that you are doing the correct arithmetic with your calculator, try some values for x for which you know the answer. For example, try $x = 0.5$, and see whether your answer is 2.25.

The complete table should be:

x	−1	−0.5	0	0.5	1	1.5	2	2.5	3
y	12	7.25	4	2.25	2	3.25	6	10.25	16

The graph is shown on the right.

b To find the corresponding y-value for any value of x, you start on the x-axis at that x-value, go up to the curve, across to the y-axis and read off the y-value. This procedure is marked on the graph with arrows.

Always show these arrows because even if you make a mistake and misread the scales, you may still get a mark.

When $x = 2.2$, $y = 7.5$.

c This time start at 9 on the y-axis and read off the two x-values that correspond to a y-value of 9. Again, this procedure is marked on the graph with arrows.

When $y = 9$, $x = -0.7$ or $x = 2.4$.

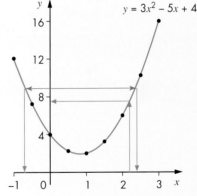

Drawing accurate graphs

Note that although it is difficult to draw accurate curves, examiners work to a *tolerance of only 1 mm.*

Here are some of the more common ways in which marks are lost in an examination (see also diagrams on the following page).

- When the points are too far apart, a curve tends to "wobble".

- Drawing curves in small sections leads to "feathering".

- The place where a curve should turn smoothly is drawn "flat".

- A line is drawn through a point which, clearly, has been incorrectly plotted.

A quadratic curve drawn correctly will always give a smooth curve.

Here are some tips which will make it easier for you to draw smooth, curved lines.

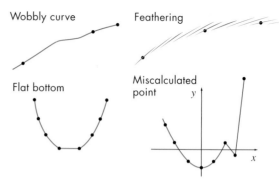

- If you are *right-handed*, turn your piece of paper or your exercise book round so that you draw from left to right. Your hand is steadier this way than trying to draw from right to left or away from your body.
  If you are *left-handed*, you should find drawing from right to left the more accurate way.

- Move your pencil over the points as a practice run without drawing the curve.

- Do one continuous curve and only stop at a plotted point.

- Use a *sharp* pencil and do not press too heavily, so that you may easily rub out mistakes.

Normally in an examination, grids are provided with the axes clearly marked. This is so that the examiner can place a transparent master over a graph and see immediately whether any lines are badly drawn or points are misplotted. Remember that a tolerance of 1 mm is all that you are allowed. In the exercises below, suitable ranges are suggested for the axes. You can use any type of graph paper to draw the graphs.

Also you do not need to work out all values in a table. If you use a calculator, you need only to work out the y-value. The other rows in the table are just working lines to break down the calculation.

EXERCISE 17A

1 **a** Copy and complete the table for the graph of $y = 3x^2$ for values of x from -3 to 3.

x	-3	-2	-1	0	1	2	3
y	27		3			12	

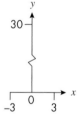

b Use your graph to find the value of y when $x = -1.5$.

c Use your graph to find the values of x that give a y-value of 10.

2 **a** Copy and complete the table for the graph of $y = x^2 + 2$ for values of x from -5 to 5.

x	-5	-4	-3	-2	-1	0	1	2	3	4	5
$y = x^2 + 2$	27		11					6			

b Use your graph to find the value of y when $x = -2.5$.

c Use your graph to find the values of x that give a y-value of 14.

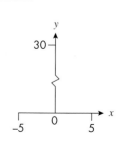

3 **a** Copy and complete the table for the graph of $y = x^2 - 2x - 8$ for values of x from –5 to 5.

x	–5	–4	–3	–2	–1	0	1	2	3	4	5
x^2	25		9					4			
$-2x$	10							–4			
-8	–8							–8			
y	27							–8			

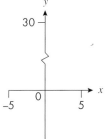

b Use your graph to find the value of y when $x = 0.5$.

c Use your graph to find the values of x that give a y-value of –3.

4 **a** Copy and complete the table for the graph of $y = x^2 + 2x - 1$ for values of x from –3 to 3.

x	–3	–2	–1	0	1	2	3
x^2	9				1	4	
$+2x$	–6		–2			4	
-1	–1	–1				–1	
y	2					7	

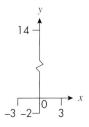

b Use your graph to find the y-value when $x = -2.5$.

c Use your graph to find the values of x that give a y-value of 1.

d On the same axes, draw the graph of $y = \dfrac{x}{2} + 2$.

e Where do the graphs $y = x^2 + 2x - 1$ and $y = \dfrac{x}{2} + 2$ cross?

5 **a** Copy and complete the table for the graph of $y = x^2 - x + 6$ for values of x from –3 to 3.

x	–3	–2	–1	0	1	2	3
x^2	9				1	4	
$-x$	3					–2	
$+6$	6					6	
y	18					8	

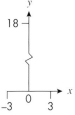

b Use your graph to find the y-value when $x = 2.5$.

c Use your graph to find the values of x that give a y-value of 8.

d Copy and complete the table to draw the graph of $y = x^2 + 5$ on the same axes.

x	–3	–2	–1	0	1	2	3
y	14		6				14

e Where do the graphs $y = x^2 - x + 6$ and $y = x^2 + 5$ cross?

27

a Copy and complete the table for the graph of $y = x^2 + 2x + 1$ for values of x from -3 to 3.

x	-3	-2	-1	0	1	2	3
x^2	9				1	4	
$+2x$	-6					4	
$+1$	1					1	
y	4						

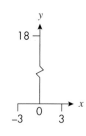

b Use your graph to find the y-value when $x = 1.7$.

c Use your graph to find the values of x that give a y-value of 2.

d On the same axes, draw the graph of $y = 2x + 2$.

e Where do the graphs $y = x^2 + 2x + 1$ and $y = 2x + 2$ cross?

 a Copy and complete the table for the graph of $y = 2x^2 - 5x - 3$ for values of x from -2 to 4.

x	-2	-1.5	-1	-0.5	0	0.5	1	1.5	2	2.5	3	3.5	4
y	15	9			-3	-5				-3			9

b Where does the graph cross the x-axis?

The significant points of a quadratic graph

A quadratic graph has four points that are of interest to a mathematician. These are the points A, B, C and D on the diagram. A and B are called the **roots**, and are where the graph crosses the x-axis, C is the point where the graph crosses the y-axis (the **intercept**) and D is the **vertex**, and is the lowest or highest point of the graph.

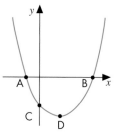 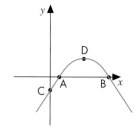

The roots

If you look at your answer to question **7** in Exercise 17A, you will see that the graph crosses the x-axis at $x = -0.5$ and $x = 3$. Since the x-axis is the line $y = 0$, the y-value at any point on the x-axis is zero. So, you have found the solution to the equation

$$0 = 2x^2 - 5x - 3 \quad \text{that is} \quad 2x^2 - 5x - 3 = 0$$

You met equations of this type in Chapter 12. They are known as quadratic equations.

You solved them either by factorisation or by using the quadratic formula. That is, you found the values of x that made them true. Such values are called the roots of an equation. So in the case of the quadratic equation $2x^2 - 5x - 3 = 0$, its roots are -0.5 and 3.

Let's check these values:

For $x = 3.0$ $2(3)^2 - 5(3) - 3 = 18 - 15 - 3 = 0$

For $x = 0.5$ $2(-0.5)^2 - 5(-0.5) - 3 = 0.5 + 2.5 - 3 = 0$

We can find the roots of a quadratic equation by drawing its graph and finding where the graph crosses the x-axis.

EXAMPLE 3

a Draw the graph of $y = x^2 - 3x - 4$ for $-2 \leqslant x \leqslant 5$.

b Use your graph to find the roots of the equation $x^2 - 3x - 4 = 0$.

a Set up a table.

x	-2	-1	0	1	2	3	4	5
x^2	4	1	0	1	4	9	16	25
$-3x$	6	3	0	-3	-6	-9	-12	-15
-4	-4	-4	-4	-4	-4	-4	-4	-4
y	6	0	-4	-6	-6	-4	0	6

Draw the graph.

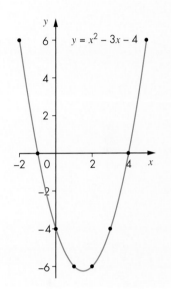

b The points where the graph crosses the x-axis are -1 and 4.

So, the roots of $x^2 - 3x - 4 = 0$ are $x = -1$ and $x = 4$.

Note that sometimes the quadratic graph may not cross the x-axis. In this case there are no roots. This was dealt with in section 12.6.

The y-intercept

If you look at all the quadratic graphs we have drawn so far you will see a connection between the equation and the point where the graph crosses the y-axis. Very simply, the constant term of the equation $y = ax^2 + bx + c$ (that is, the value c) is where the graph crosses the y-axis. The intercept is at $(0, c)$.

The vertex

The lowest (or highest) point of a quadratic graph is called the vertex.

If it is the highest point, it is called the **maximum**.

If it is the lowest point, it is called the **minimum**.

It is difficult to find a general rule for the point, but the x-coordinate is always half-way between the roots.

The easiest way to find the y-value is to substitute the x-value into the original equation.

Another way to find the vertex is to use completing the square (see Year 10 book, section 12.5, page 293).

EXAMPLE 4

a Write the equation $x^2 - 3x - 4 = 0$ in the form $(x - p)^2 - q = 0$

b What is the least value of the graph $y = x^2 - 3x - 4$?

a $x^2 - 3x - 4 = (x - 1\frac{1}{2})^2 - 2\frac{1}{4} - 4$

$\qquad\qquad\quad = (x - 1\frac{1}{2})^2 - 6\frac{1}{4}$

b Looking at the graph drawn in Example 3 you can see that the minimum point is at $(1\frac{1}{2}, -6\frac{1}{4})$, so the least value is $-6\frac{1}{4}$.

You should be able to see the connection between the vertex point and the equation written in completing the square form.

As a general rule when a quadratic is written in the form $(x - p)^2 + q$ then the minimum point is (p, q). Note the sign change of p.

Note: If the x^2 term is negative then the graph will be inverted and the vertex will be a maximum.

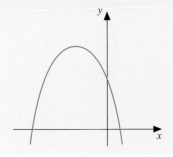

EXERCISE 17B

1 **a** Copy and complete the table to draw the graph of $y = x^2 - 4$ for $-4 \leqslant x \leqslant 4$.

x	−4	−3	−2	−1	0	1	2	3	4
y	12			−3				5	

b Use your graph to find the roots of $x^2 - 4 = 0$.

2 **a** Copy and complete the table to draw the graph of $y = x^2 - 9$ for $-4 \leqslant x \leqslant 4$.

x	−4	−3	−2	−1	0	1	2	3	4
y	7				−9			0	

b Use your graph to find the roots of $x^2 - 9 = 0$.

3 **a** Look at the equations of the graphs you drew in questions **1** and **2**. Is there a connection between the numbers in each equation and its roots?

b Before you draw the graphs in parts **c** and **d**, try to predict what their roots will be ($\sqrt{5} \approx 2.2$).

c Copy and complete the table to draw the graph of $y = x^2 - 1$ for $-4 \leqslant x \leqslant 4$.

x	−4	−3	−2	−1	0	1	2	3	4
y	15				−1			8	

d Copy and complete the table to draw the graph of $y = x^2 - 5$ for $-4 \leqslant x \leqslant 4$.

x	-4	-3	-2	-1	0	1	2	3	4
y	11		-1					4	

e Were your predictions correct?

4 **a** Copy and complete the table to draw the graph of $y = x^2 + 4x$ for $-5 \leqslant x \leqslant 2$.

x	-5	-4	-3	-2	-1	0	1	2
x^2	25			4			1	
$+4x$	-20			-8			4	
y	5			-4			5	

b Use your graph to find the roots of the equation $x^2 + 4x = 0$.

5 **a** Copy and complete the table to draw the graph of $y = x^2 - 6x$ for $-2 \leqslant x \leqslant 8$.

x	-2	-1	0	1	2	3	4	5	6	7	8
x^2	4			1			16				
$-6x$	12			-6			-24				
y	16			-5			-8				

b Use your graph to find the roots of the equation $x^2 - 6x = 0$.

6 **a** Copy and complete the table to draw the graph of $y = x^2 + 3x$ for $-5 \leqslant x \leqslant 3$.

x	-5	-4	-3	-2	-1	0	1	2	3
y	10			-2				10	

b Use your graph to find the roots of the equation $x^2 + 3x = 0$.

7 **a** Look at the equations of the graphs you drew in questions **4**, **5** and **6**. Is there a connection between the numbers in each equation and the roots?

b Before you draw the graphs in parts **c** and **d**, try to predict what their roots will be.

c Copy and complete the table to draw the graph of $y = x^2 - 3x$ for $-2 \leqslant x \leqslant 5$.

x	-2	-1	0	1	2	3	4	5
y	10			-2				10

d Copy and complete the table to draw the graph of $y = x^2 + 5x$ for $-6 \leqslant x \leqslant 2$.

x	-6	-5	-4	-3	-2	-1	0	1	2
y	6			-6				6	

e Were your predictions correct?

8 **a** Copy and complete the table to draw the graph of $y = x^2 - 4x + 4$ for $-1 \leqslant x \leqslant 5$.

x	−1	0	1	2	3	4	5
y	9				1		

b Use your graph to find the roots of the equation $x^2 - 4x + 4 = 0$.

c What happens with the roots?

9 **a** Copy and complete the table to draw the graph of $y = x^2 - 6x + 3$ for $-1 \leqslant x \leqslant 7$.

x	−1	0	1	2	3	4	5	6	7
y	10			−5			−2		

b Use your graph to find the roots of the equation $x^2 - 6x + 3 = 0$.

10 **a** Copy and complete the table to draw the graph of $y = 2x^2 + 5x - 6$ for $-5 \leqslant x \leqslant 2$.

x	−5	−4	−3	−2	−1	0	1	2
y								

b Use your graph to find the roots of the equation $2x^2 + 5x - 6 = 0$.

11 For questions **1** to **7** write down the following.

a the point of intersection of the graph with the y-axis

b the coordinates of the minimum point (vertex) of each graph

c Explain the connection between these points and the original equation.

12 **a** Write the equation $y = x^2 - 4x + 4$ in the form $y = (x - p)^2 + q$.

b Write down the minimum value of the equation $y = x^2 - 4x + 4$.

13 **a** Write the equation $y = x^2 - 6x + 3$ in the form $y = (x - p)^2 + q$.

b Write down the minimum value of the equation $y = x^2 - 6x + 3$.

14 **a** Write the equation $y = x^2 - 8x + 2$ in the form $y = (x - p)^2 + q$.

b Write down the minimum value of the equation $y = x^2 - 8x + 2$.

15 **a** Write the equation $y = -x^2 + 2x - 6$ in the form $y = -(x - p)^2 + q$.

b Write down the minimum value of the equation $y = -x^2 + 2x - 6$.

This section will show you how to:

- recognise important graphs that you will meet in higher GCSE

Key words

asymptote
cosine
cubic
exponential
    functions
reciprocal
sine
square root

Square-root graphs

The graph of $y^2 = x$ is one you should be able to recognise and draw.

When you are working out coordinates in order to plot $y = \sqrt{x}$, remember that for every value of x (except $x = 0$) there are two **square roots**, one positive and the other negative, which give pairs of coordinates. For example,

when $x = 1$, $y = \pm 1$ giving coordinates $(1, -1)$ and $(1, 1)$

when $x = 4$, $y = \pm 2$ giving coordinates $(4, -2)$ and $(4, 2)$

In the case of $x = 0$, $y = 0$ and so there is only one coordinate: $(0, 0)$.

Using these five points, you can draw the graph.

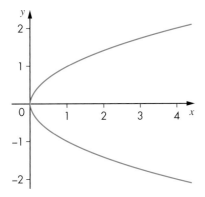

Reciprocal graphs

A **reciprocal** equation has the form $y = \dfrac{a}{x}$.

Examples of reciprocal equations are:

$$y = \frac{1}{x} \qquad y = \frac{4}{x} \qquad y = -\frac{3}{x}$$

All reciprocal graphs have a similar shape and some symmetry properties.

EXAMPLE 5

Complete the table to draw the graph of $y = \dfrac{1}{x}$ for $-4 \leqslant x \leqslant 4$.

x	−4	−3	−2	−1	1	2	3	4
y								

Values are rounded off to two decimal places, as it is unlikely that you could plot a value more accurately than this. The completed table is

x	−4	−3	−2	−1	1	2	3	4
y	−0.25	−0.33	−0.5	−1	1	0.5	0.33	0.25

The graph plotted from these values is shown in **A**. This is not much of a graph and does not show the properties of the reciprocal function. If we take *x*-values from −0.8 to 0.8 in steps of 0.2, we get the next table.

Note that we cannot use $x = 0$ since $\dfrac{1}{0}$ is infinity.

x	−0.8	−0.6	−0.4	−0.2	0.2	0.4	0.6	0.8
y	−1.25	−1.67	−2.5	−5	5	2.5	1.67	1.25

Plotting these points as well gives the graph in **B**.

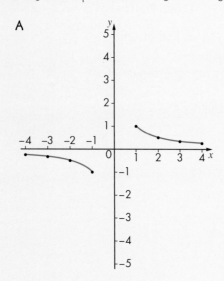
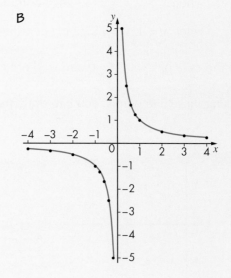

From the graph in **B**, the following properties can be seen.

- The lines $y = x$ and $y = -x$ are lines of symmetry.

- The closer *x* gets to zero, the nearer the graph gets to the *y*-axis.

- As *x* increases, the graph gets closer to the *x*-axis.

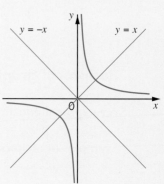

The graph never actually touches the axes, it just gets closer and closer to them. A line to which a graph gets closer but never touches or crosses is called an **asymptote**.

These properties are true for *all reciprocal graphs*.

EXERCISE 17C

1 **a** Copy and complete the table to draw the graph of $y = \dfrac{2}{x}$ for $-4 \leqslant x \leqslant 4$.

x	0.2	0.4	0.5	0.8	1	1.5	2	3	4
y	10		4	2.5			1		0.5

b Use your graph to find the following.

   i the y-value when $x = 2.5$ **ii** the x-value when $y = -1.25$

2 **a** Copy and complete the table to draw the graph of $y^2 = 25x$ for $0 \leqslant x \leqslant 5$.

x	0	1	2	3	4	5
$\sqrt{x}$					2 and −2	
$y = 5\sqrt{x}$					10 and −10	

b Use your graph to find the following.

   i the values of y when $x = 3.5$ **ii** the value of x when $y = 8$

3 **a** Copy and complete the table to draw the graph of $4y^2 = x$ for $0 \leqslant x \leqslant 5$.

x	0	1	2	3	4	5
$\sqrt{x}$					2 and −2	
$y = \frac{1}{2}\sqrt{x}$					1 and −1	

b Use your graph to find the following.

   i the values of y when $x = 2.5$ **ii** the value of x when $y = 0.75$

4 **a** Copy and complete the table to draw the graph of $y = \dfrac{1}{x}$ for $-5 \leqslant x \leqslant 5$.

x	0.1	0.2	0.4	0.5	1	2	2.5	4	5
y	10		2.5		1				0.2

b On the same axes, draw the line $x + y = 5$.

c Use your graph to find the x-values of the points where the graphs cross.

5 **a** Copy and complete the table to draw the graph of $y = \dfrac{5}{x}$ for $-20 \leqslant x \leqslant 20$.

x	0.2	0.4	0.5	1	2	5	10	15	20
y	25		10						0.25

b On the same axes, draw the line $y = x + 10$.

c Use your graph to find the x-values of the points where the graphs cross.

Cubic graphs

A **cubic** function or graph is one which contains a term in x^3. The following are examples of cubic graphs:

$$y = x^3 \qquad y = x^3 - 2x^2 - 3x - 4 \qquad y = x^3 - x^2 - 4x + 4 \qquad y = x^3 + 3x$$

The techniques used to draw them are exactly the same as those for quadratic and reciprocal graphs.

EXAMPLE 6

a Complete the table to draw the graph of $y = x^3 - x^2 - 4x + 4$ for $-3 \leqslant x \leqslant 3$.

x	-3	-2.5	-2	-1.5	-1	-0.5	0	0.5	1	1.5	2	2.5	3
y	-20.00		0.00		6.00		4.00	1.88				3.38	10.00

b By drawing a suitable line on the graph find the solution of the equation $x^3 - x^2 - 4x - 1 = 0$.

a The completed table (to 2 decimal places) is given below and the graph is shown below right.

x	-3	-2.5	-2	-1.5	-1	-0.5	0	0.5	1	1.5	2	2.5	3
y	-20.00	-7.88	0.00	4.38	6.00	5.63	4.00	1.88	0.00	-0.88	0.00	3.38	10.00

b Can you see the similarity between the equation of the graph, $y = x^3 - x^2 - 4x + 4$, and the equation to be solved, $x^3 - x^2 - 4x - 1 = 0$?

Rearrange the equation to be solved as $x^3 - x^2 - 4x + 4 = $ something.

That is, make the left-hand side of the equation to be solved the same as the right-hand side of the equation of the graph. You can do this by adding 5 to the -1 to make $+4$. So add 5 to both sides of the equation to be solved

$$x^3 - x^2 - 4x - 1 + 5 = 0 + 5$$
$$x^3 - x^2 - 4x + 4 = 5$$

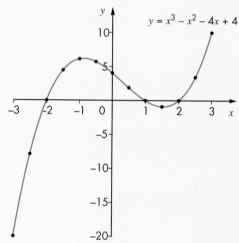

Hence, you simply need to draw the straight line $y = 5$ and find the x-coordinates of the points where it crosses

$$y = x^3 - x^2 - 4x + 4.$$

The solutions can now be read from the graph as

$$x = -1.4, -0.3 \text{ and } 2.7.$$

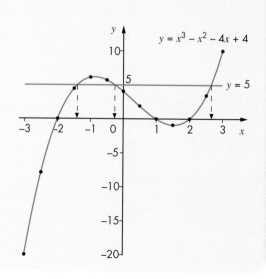

EXERCISE 17D

1 **a** Copy and complete the table to draw the graph of $y = x^3 + 3$ for $-3 \leqslant x \leqslant 3$.

x	−3	−2.5	−2	−1.5	−1	−0.5	0	0.5	1	1.5	2	2.5	3
y	−24.00	−12.63			2.00		3.00	3.13			11.00		30.00

b Use your graph to find the *y*-value for an *x*-value of 1.2.

2 **a** Copy and complete the table to draw the graph of $y = 2x^3$ for $-3 \leqslant x \leqslant 3$.

x	−3	−2.5	−2	−1.5	−1	−0.5	0	0.5	1	1.5	2	2.5	3
y		−31.25		−6.75			0.00	0.25			16.00		

b Use your graph to find the *y*-value for an *x*-value of 2.7.

3 **a** Copy and complete the table to draw the graph of $y = -x^3$ for $-3 \leqslant x \leqslant 3$.

x	−3	−2.5	−2	−1.5	−1	−0.5	0	0.5	1	1.5	2	2.5	3
y	27.00		8.00	3.38			0.00	−0.13			−8.00	−15.63	

b Use your graph to find the *y*-value for an *x*-value of −0.6.

4 **a** Copy and complete the table to draw the graph of $y = x^3 + 3x$ for $-3 \leqslant x \leqslant 3$.

x	−3	−2.5	−2	−1.5	−1	−0.5	0	0.5	1	1.5	2	2.5	3
y	−36.00		−14.00	−7.88			0.00	1.63				23.13	

b Use your graph to find the *x*-value for a *y*-value of 2.

5 **a** Copy and complete the table to draw the graph of $y = x^3 - 3x^2 - 3x$ for $-3 \leqslant x \leqslant 3$.

x	−3	−2.5	−2	−1.5	−1	−0.5	0	0.5	1	1.5	2	2.5	3
y	−45.00		−14.00	−5.63			0.00	−0.63				−10.63	

b Use your graph to find the *y*-value for an *x*-value of 1.8.

6 **a** Copy and complete the table to draw the graph of $y = x^3 - 2x + 5$ for $-3 \leqslant x \leqslant 3$.

x	−3	−2.5	−2	−1.5	−1	−0.5	0	0.5	1	1.5	2	2.5	3
y	−16.00		1.00	4.63			5.00	4.13				15.63	

b On the same axes, draw the graph of $y = x + 6$.

c Use your graph to find the *x*-values of the points where the graphs cross.

7 **a** Complete the table to draw the graph of $y = x^3 - 2x + 1$ for $-3 \leqslant x \leqslant 3$.

x	−3	−2.5	−2	−1.5	−1	−0.5	0	0.5	1	1.5	2	2.5	3
y	−20.00		−3.00	0.63			1.00	0.13				11.63	

b On the same axes, draw the graph of $y = x$.

c Use your graph to find the x-values of the points where the graphs cross.

8 Write down whether each of these graphs are "linear", "quadratic", "reciprocal", "cubic" or "none of these".

a
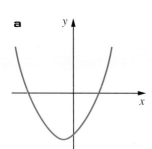

b
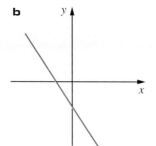

c
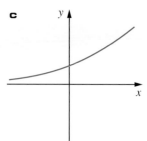

d
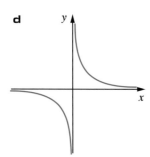

e
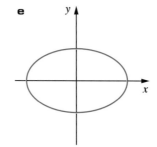

f
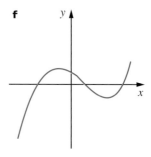

g
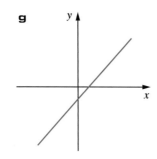

h
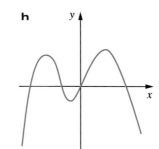

i
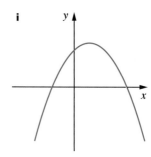

Exponential graphs

Equations which have the form $y = k^x$, where k is a positive number, are called **exponential functions**.

Exponential functions share the following properties.

- When k is greater than 1, the value of y increases steeply as x increases, which you can see from the graph on the right.

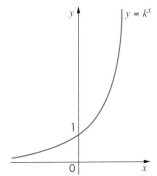

- Also when k is greater than 1, as x takes on increasingly large negative values, the closer y gets to zero, and so the graph gets nearer and nearer to the negative x-axis. y never actually becomes zero and so the graph never actually touches the negative x-axis. That is, the negative x-axis is an asymptote to the graph. (See also page 34.)

- Whatever the value of k, the graph always intercepts the y-axis at 1, because here $y = k^0$.

- The reciprocal graph, $y = k^{-x}$, is the reflection in the y-axis of the graph of $y = k^x$, as you can see from the graph (on the right).

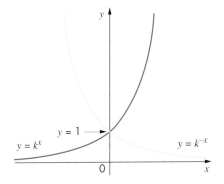

EXAMPLE 7

a Complete the table below for $y = 2^x$ for values of x from -5 to $+5$. (Values are rounded to 2 decimal places.)

x	-5	-4	-3	-2	-1	0	1	2	3	4	5
$y = 2^x$	0.03	0.06	0.13			1	2	4			32

b Plot the graph of $y = 2^x$ for $-5 \leqslant x \leqslant 5$.

c Use your graph to estimate the value of y when $x = 2.5$.

d Use your graph to estimate the value of x when $y = 0.75$.

a The values missing from the table are: 0.25, 0.5, 8 and 16.

b Part of the graph (drawn to scale) is shown on the next page.

c Draw a line vertically from $x = 2.5$ until it meets the graph and then read across. The y-value is 5.7.

d Draw a line horizontally from $y = 0.75$, the *x*-value is −0.4.

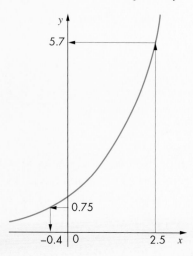

EXERCISE 17E

1 **a** Complete the table below for $y = 3^x$ for values of *x* from −4 to +3. (Values are rounded to 2 decimal places.)

x	−4	−3	−2	−1	0	1	2	3
$y = 3^x$	0.01	0.04			1	3		

b Plot the graph of $y = 3^x$ for $-4 \leqslant x \leqslant 3$. (Take the *y*-axis from 0 to 30.)

c Use your graph to estimate the value of *y* when $x = 2.5$.

d Use your graph to estimate the value of *x* when $y = 0.5$.

2 **a** Complete the table below for $y = (\frac{1}{2})^x$ for values of *x* from −5 to +5. (Values are rounded to 2 decimal places.)

x	−5	−4	−3	−2	−1	0	1	2	3	4	5
$y = (\frac{1}{2})^x$			8			1				0.06	0.03

b Plot the graph of $y = (\frac{1}{2})^x$ for $-5 \leqslant x \leqslant 5$. (Take the *y*-axis from 0 to 35.)

c Use your graph to estimate the value of *y* when $x = 2.5$.

d Use your graph to estimate the value of *x* when $y = 0.75$.

3 One grain of rice is placed on the first square of a chess board. Two grains of rice are placed on the second square, four grains on the third square and so on.

a Explain why $y = 2^{(n-1)}$ gives the number of grains of rice on the *n*th square.

b Complete the table for the number of grains of rice on the first 10 squares

Square	1	2	3	4	5	6	7	8	9	10
Grains	1	2	4							

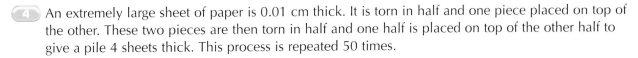

    c Use the rule to work out how many grains of rice there are on the 64th square.

    d If 1000 grains of rice are worth 5p, how much is the rice on the 64th square worth?

4 An extremely large sheet of paper is 0.01 cm thick. It is torn in half and one piece placed on top of the other. These two pieces are then torn in half and one half is placed on top of the other half to give a pile 4 sheets thick. This process is repeated 50 times.

    a Complete the table to show how many pieces there are in the pile after each tear.

Tears	1	2	3	4	5	6	7	8
Pieces	2	4						

    b Write down a rule for the number of pieces after *n* tears.

    c How many pieces will there be piled up after 50 tears?

    d How thick is this pile?

The circular function graphs

You saw the graphs of $y = \sin x$ and $y = \cos x$ in Chapter 15.

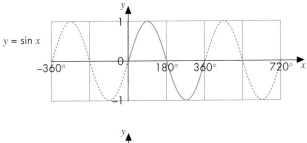

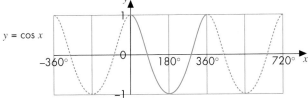

These graphs have some special properties.

- They are cyclic. This means that they repeat indefinitely in both directions.

- For every value of **sine** or **cosine** between –1 and 1 there are 2 angles between 0° and 360°, and an infinite number of angles altogether.

- The sine graph has rotational symmetry about (180°, 0) and has line symmetry between 0° and 180° about $x = 90°$, and between 180° and 360° about $x = 270°$.

- The cosine graph has line symmetry about $x = 180°$, and has rotational symmetry between 0° and 180° about (90°, 0) and between 180° and 360° about (270°, 0).

The graphs can be used to find angles with certain values of sine and cosine.

EXAMPLE 8

Given that sin 42° = 0.669, find another angle between 0° and 360° that also has a sine of 0.669.

Plot the approximate value 0.669 on the sine graph and use the symmetry to work out the other value.

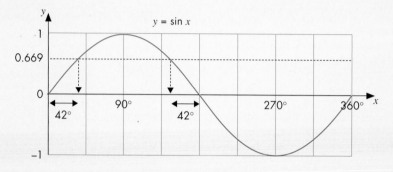

The other value is 180° − 42° = 138°.

EXAMPLE 9

Given that cos 110° = −0.342, find two angles between 0° and 360° that have a cosine of +0.342.

Plot the approximate values −0.342 and 0.342 on the cosine graph and use the symmetry to work out the values.

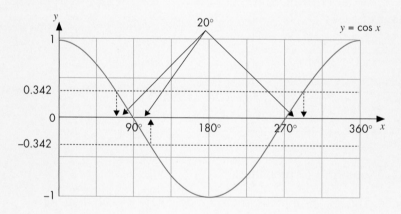

The required values are 90° − 20° = 70° and 270° + 20° = 290°.

EXERCISE 17F

1 Given that sin 65° = 0.906, find another angle between 0° and 360° that also has a sine of 0.906.

2 Given that sin 213° = –0.545, find another angle between 0° and 360° that also has a sine of –0.545.

3 Given that cos 36° = 0.809, find another angle between 0° and 360° that also has a cosine of 0.809.

4 Given that cos 165° = –0.966, find another angle between 0° and 360° that also has a cosine of –0.966.

5 Given that sin 30° = 0.5, find two angles between 0° and 360° that have a sine of –0.5.

6 Given that cos 45° = 0.707, find two angles between 0° and 360° that have a cosine of –0.707.

7 Given that sin 26° = 0.438

    a write down an angle between 0° and 90° that has a cosine of 0.438,

    b find two angles between 0° and 360° that have a sine of –0.438,

    c find two angles between 0° and 360° that have a cosine of –0.438.

17.3 Solving equations by the method of intersection

This section will show you how to:

- solve equations by the method of intersecting graphs

Many equations can be solved by drawing two intersecting graphs on the same axes and using the x-value(s) of their point(s) of intersection. (In the GCSE examination, you are very likely to be presented with one drawn graph and asked to draw a straight line to solve a new equation.)

EXAMPLE 10

Show how each equation given below can be solved using the graph of $y = x^3 - 2x - 2$ and its intersection with another graph. In each case, give the equation of the other graph and the solution(s).

    a $x^3 - 2x - 4 = 0$ **b** $x^3 - 3x - 1 = 0$

    a This method will give the required graph.

Step 1: Write down the original (given) equation.	$y = x^3 - 2x - 2$
Step 2: Write down the (new) equation to be solved in reverse.	$0 = x^3 - 2x - 4$
Step 3: Subtract these equations.	$y = \qquad\qquad + 2$

        Step 4: Draw this line on the original graph to solve the new equation.

The graphs of $y = x^3 - 2x - 2$ and $y = 2$ are drawn on the same axes.

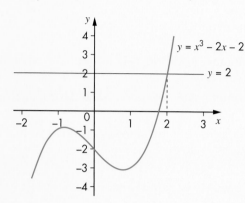

The intersection of these two graphs is the solution of $x^3 - 2x - 4 = 0$.

The solution is $x = 2$.

This works because you are drawing a straight line along with the original graph, and solving where they intersect.

At the points of intersection you can say:
    original equation = straight line

Rearranging this gives:
    (original equation) − (straight line) = 0

You have been asked to solve:
    (new equation) = 0

So (original equation) − (straight line) = (new equation)

Rearranging this again gives:
    (original equation) − (new equation) = straight line

Note: In GCSE exams the curve is always drawn already and you will only have to draw the straight line.

b Write down given graph:

Write down new equation:

Subtract:

$$y = x^3 - 2x - 2$$
$$0 = x^3 - 3x - 1$$
$$\overline{}$$
$$y = + x - 1$$

The graphs of $y = x^3 - 2x - 2$ and $y = x - 1$ are then drawn on the same axes.

The intersection of the two graphs is the solution of $x^3 - 3x - 1 = 0$.

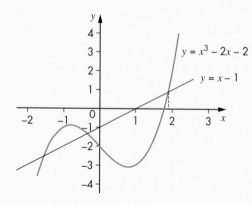

The solutions are $x = -1.5, -0.3$ and 1.9.

EXAMPLE 11

The graph shows the curve $y = x^2 + 3x - 2$.

By drawing a suitable straight line, solve these equations.

a $x^2 + 3x - 1 = 0$

b $x^2 + 2x - 3 = 0$

a	Given graph:	$y = x^2 + 3x - 2$
	New equation:	$0 = x^2 + 3x - 1$
	Subtract:	$y = \qquad -1$
	Draw:	$y = -1$
	Solutions:	$x = 0.3, -3.3$

b	Given graph:	$y = x^2 + 3x - 2$
	New equation:	$0 = x^2 + 2x - 3$
	Subtract:	$y = \quad + x \ + 1$
	Draw:	$y = x + 1$
	Solutions:	$x = 1, -3$

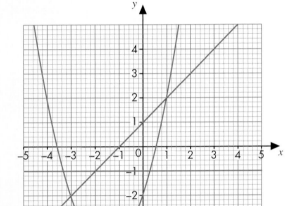

EXERCISE 17G

In questions **1** to **5**, use the graphs given here. Trace the graphs or place a ruler over them in the position of the line. Solution values only need to be given to 1 decimal place. In questions **6** to **10**, either draw the graphs yourself or use a graphics calculator to draw them.

 On the following page is the graph of $y = x^2 - 3x - 6$.

a Solve these equations.

i $x^2 - 3x - 6 = 0$

ii $x^2 - 3x - 6 = 4$

iii $x^2 - 3x - 2 = 0$

b By drawing a suitable straight line solve $2x^2 - 6x + 2 = 0$.

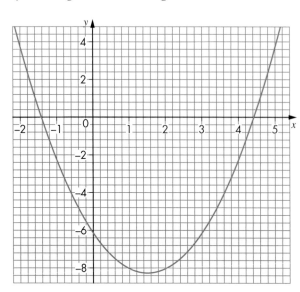

2 Below is the graph of $y = x^2 + 4x - 5$.

a Solve $x^2 + 4x - 5 = 0$.

b By drawing suitable straight lines solve these equations.

  i $x^2 + 4x - 5 = 2$

  ii $x^2 + 4x - 4 = 0$

  iii $3x^2 + 12x + 6 = 0$

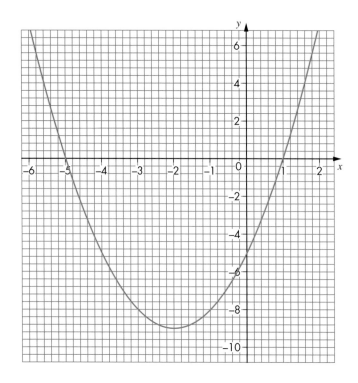

3 Below are the graphs of $y = x^2 - 5x + 3$ and $y = x + 3$.

   a Solve these equations.   **i** $x^2 - 6x = 0$ **ii** $x^2 - 5x + 3 = 0$

   b By drawing suitable straight lines solve these equations.

   i $x^2 - 5x + 3 = 2$ **ii** $x^2 - 5x - 2 = 0$

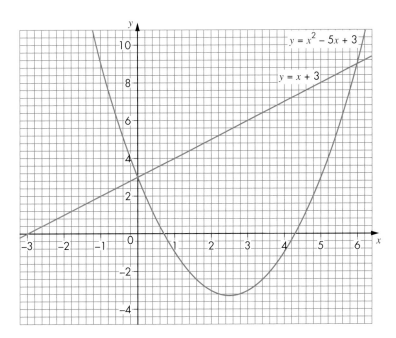

4 Below are the graphs of $y = x^2 - 2$ and $y = x + 2$.

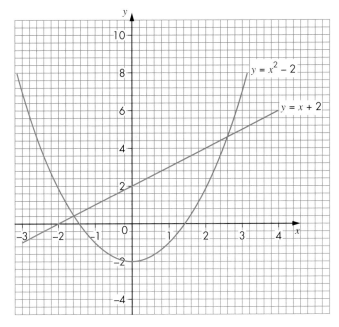

   a Solve these equations.   **i** $x^2 - x - 4 = 0$ **ii** $x^2 - 2 = 0$

   b By drawing suitable straight lines solve these equations.

   i $x^2 - 2 = 3$ **ii** $x^2 - 4 = 0$

⑤ Below are the graphs of $y = x^3 - 2x^2$, $y = 2x + 1$ and $y = x - 1$.

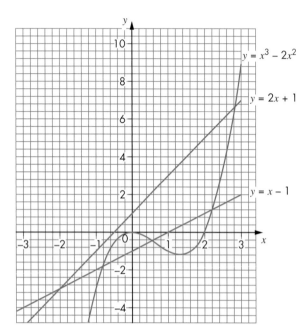

Solve these equations.

a $x^3 - 2x^2 = 0$ **b** $x^3 - 2x^2 = 3$ **c** $x^3 - 2x^2 + 1 = 0$

d $x^3 - 2x^2 - 2x - 1 = 0$ **e** $x^3 - 2x^2 - x + 1 = 0$

⑥ Draw the graph of $y = x^2 - 4x - 2$.

    a Solve $x^2 - 4x - 2 = 0$.

    b By drawing a suitable straight line solve $x^2 - 4x - 5 = 0$.

⑦ Draw the graph of $y = 2x^2 - 5$.

    a Solve $2x^2 - 5 = 0$.

    b By drawing a suitable straight line solve $2x^2 - 3 = 0$.

⑧ Draw the graphs of $y = x^2 - 3$ and $y = x + 2$ on the same axes. Use the graphs to solve these equations.

    a $x^2 - 5 = 0$ **b** $x^2 - x - 5 = 0$

⑨ Draw the graphs of $y = x^2 - 3x - 2$ and $y = 2x - 3$ on the same axes. Use the graphs to solve these equations.

    a $x^2 - 3x - 1 = 0$ **b** $x^2 - 5x + 1 = 0$

⑩ Draw the graphs of $y = x^3 - 2x^2 + 3x - 4$ and $y = 3x - 1$ on the same axes. Use the graphs to solve these equations.

    a $x^3 - 2x^2 + 3x - 6 = 0$ **b** $x^3 - 2x^2 - 3 = 0$

1 a Complete the table of values for $y = x^2 - 3x - 1$.

x	−2	−1	0	1	2	3	4
y		3	−1	−3			3

b Draw the graph on a grid labelling the x-axis from −2 to 4 and the y-axis from −4 to 10.

c Use your graph to state the minimum value of y.

Edexcel, Question 2, Paper 10A Higher, March 2003

2 a Copy and complete the table of values for $y = (x + 3)(2 - x)$.

x	−3	−2	−1	0	1	2	3
y		4	6	6	4		

b Draw the graph of $y = (x + 3)(2 - x)$ for values of x from −3 to +3. Use a grid with an x-axis from −4 to 4 and a y-axis from −8 to 8.

c Use the graph to solve the equation $(x + 3)(2 - x) = 2$.

3 a Four graphs are sketched.

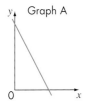
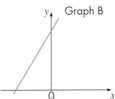

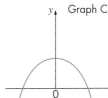
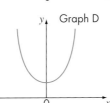

Complete the following statements.

$y = 3x + 5$ matches graph ....

$y = x^2 + 5$ matches graph ....

$y + 3x = 5$ matches graph ....

b Sketch the graph of $y = x^3$

4 a Complete the table of values for $y = (0.7)^x$

x	0	1	2	3	4
y	1	0.7	0.49		0.24

b Draw the graph of $y = (0.7)^x$ for values of x from 0 to 4. Use a grid with an x-axis from 0 to 5 and a y-axis from 0 to 1, marked off every 0.1 units.

c Use your graph to solve the equation $(0.7)^x = 0.6$

5 a Complete the table of values for the graph of $y = 4x(11 - 2x)$.

x	0	1	2	3	4	5	6
y	0			60			−24

b On a copy of the grid, draw the graph of $y = 4x(11 - 2x)$

c Use your graph to find the maximum value of y.

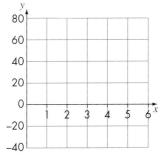

Edexcel, Question 5, Paper 10B Higher, January 2004

6 Here is a sketch of the graph of $y = 25 - \dfrac{(x - 8)^2}{4}$ for $0 \leqslant x \leqslant 12$

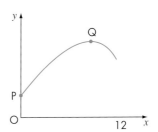

P and Q are points on the graph.
P is the point at which the graph meets the y-axis.
Q is the point at which y has its maximum value.

a Find the coordinates of

  i P

  ii Q

b Show that $25 - \dfrac{(x - 8)^2}{4} = \dfrac{(2 + x)(18 - x)}{4}$

Edexcel, Question 10, Paper 18 Higher, June 2005

WORKED EXAM QUESTION

The diagram right shows the graph of

$$y = x^3 - 12x$$

for values of x from -4 to 4.

a Use the graph to find estimates of the three
   solutions of the equation

   $$x^3 - 12x = 0$$

b By drawing a suitable straight line on the grid,
   find estimates of the solutions of the equation

   $$x^3 - 12x - 5 = 0$$

   Label clearly the straight line that you have drawn.

c By drawing a suitable straight line on the grid,
   find estimates of the solutions of the equation

   $$x^3 - 14x + 5 = 0$$

   Label clearly the straight line that you have drawn.

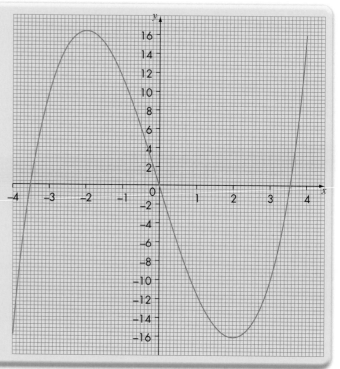

Solution

a -3.5, 0 and 3.5

> To find the values where the given graph
> is equal to zero read from the x-axis.
> These are the roots of the equation.

b -3.3, -0.5, 3.7

> To find the straight line subtract the
> required curve from the given curve.
> Given curve $y = x^3 - 12x$
> New curve $0 = x^3 - 12x - 5$
> Subtract $y = + 5$
> Draw $y = 5$

c -3.9, 0.4, 3.5

> To find the straight line subtract the
> required curve from the given curve.
> Given curve $y = x^3 - 12x$
> New curve $0 = x^3 - 14x + 5$
> Subtract $y = + 2x - 5$
> Draw $y = 2x - 5$

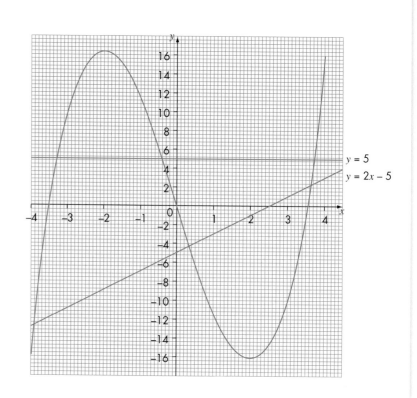

GRADE YOURSELF

Able to draw quadratic graphs using a table of values

B Able to solve quadratic equations from their graphs

B Plot cubic graphs using a table of values

B Recognise the shapes of the graphs $y = x^3$ and $y = \dfrac{1}{x}$

Able to draw a variety of graphs such as exponential graphs and reciprocal graphs using a table of values

A* Able to solve equations using the intersection of two graphs

A* Use trigonometric graphs to solve sine and cosine problems

What you should know now

- How to draw non-linear graphs
- How to solve equations by finding the intersection points of the graphs of the equations with the x-axis or other related equations

Statistics 2

1 Line graphs

2 Stem-and-leaf diagrams

3 Scatter diagrams

4 Cumulative frequency diagrams

5 Box plots

6 Measures of dispersion

This chapter will show you ...

- how to interpret and draw line graphs and stem-and-leaf diagrams
- how to draw scatter diagrams and lines of best fit
- how to interpret scatter diagrams and the different types of correlation
- how to draw and interpret cumulative frequency diagrams
- how to draw and interpret box plots
- how to calculate the standard deviation of a set of data

Visual overview

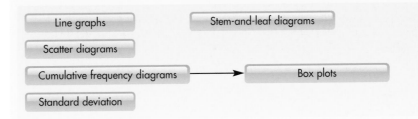

What you should already know

- How to plot coordinate points
- How to read information from charts and tables
- How to calculate the mean of a set of data from a frequency table
- How to recognise a positive or negative gradient

Quick check

1 The table shows the number of children in 10 classes in a primary school.

Calculate the mean number of children in each class.

Number of children	27	28	29	30	31
Frequency	1	2	4	2	1

Line graphs

In this section you will learn how to:
- draw a line graph to show trends in data

Key words
line graphs
trends

Line graphs are usually used in statistics to show how data changes over a period of time. One use is to indicate **trends**: for example, line graphs can be used to show whether the Earth's temperature is increasing as the concentration of carbon dioxide builds up in the atmosphere, or whether a firm's profit margin is falling year on year.

Line graphs are best drawn on graph paper.

EXAMPLE 1

This line graph shows the profit made each year by a company over a five-year period.

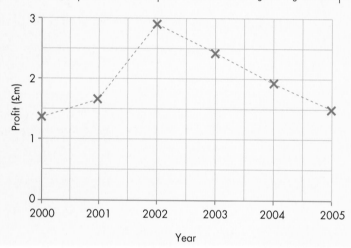

For this graph, the values between the plotted points have no meaning because the profit of the company would have been calculated at the end of every year. In cases like this, the lines are often dashed. Although the trend appears to be that profits have fallen after 2002, it would not be sensible to try to predict what will happen after 2005.

EXERCISE 18A

1. The table shows the estimated number of tourists world wide.

Year	1970	1975	1980	1985	1990	1995	2000	2005
No. of tourists (millions)	60	100	150	220	280	290	320	340

a Draw a line graph for the data.

b From your graph estimate the number of tourists in 2002.

c In which five-year period did world tourism increase the most?

d Explain the trend in world tourism. What reasons can you give to explain this trend?

The table shows the maximum and minimum daily temperatures for London over a week.

Day	Sunday	Monday	Tuesday	Wednesday	Thursday	Friday	Saturday
Maximum (°C)	12	14	16	15	16	14	10
Minimum (°C)	4	5	7	8	7	4	3

a Draw line graphs on the *same axes* to show the maximum and minimum temperatures.

b Find the smallest and greatest difference between the maximum and minimum temperatures.

 ## Stem-and-leaf diagrams

In this section you will learn how to:
- draw and read information from an ordered stem-and-leaf diagram

Key words
discrete data
ordered
raw data
unordered

Raw data

If you are recording the ages of the first 20 people who line up at a bus stop in the morning, the **raw data** might look like this.

23, 13, 34, 44, 26, 12, 41, 31, 20, 18, 19, 31, 48, 32, 45, 14, 12, 27, 31, 19

This data is **unordered** and is difficult to read and analyse. When the data is **ordered**, it looks like this.

12, 12, 13, 14, 18, 19, 19, 20, 23, 26, 27, 31, 31, 31, 32, 34, 41, 44, 45, 48

This is easier to read and analyse.

Another method for displaying **discrete data** such as this, is a stem-and-leaf diagram. The tens values will be the "stem" and the units values will be the "leaves".

Key: 1 | 2 represents 12

1	2	2	3	4	8	9	9
2	0	3	6	7			
3	1	1	1	2	4		
4	1	4	5	8			

This is called an ordered stem-and-leaf diagram and gives a better idea of how the data is distributed.

A stem-and-leaf diagram should always have a key.

EXAMPLE 2

Put the following data into an ordered stem-and-leaf diagram.

45, 62, 58, 58, 61, 49, 61, 47, 52, 58, 48, 56, 65, 46, 54

a What is the modal value?

b What is the median value?

c What is the range of the values?

First decide on the stem and leaf.

In this case, the tens digit will be the stem and the units digit will be the leaf.

Key: 4 5 represents 45

4	5	6	7	8	9	
5	2	4	6	8	8	8
6	1	1	2	5		

a The modal value is the most common, which is 58.

b There are 15 values, so the median will be the (15 + 1) ÷ 2th value, or 8th value. Counting from either the top or the bottom, the median is 56.

c The range is the difference between the largest and the smallest value, which is 65 − 45 = 20.

EXERCISE 18B

1 The heights of 15 tulips are measured.

43 cm, 39 cm, 41 cm, 29 cm, 36 cm,

34 cm, 43 cm, 48 cm, 38 cm, 35 cm,

41 cm, 38 cm, 43 cm, 28 cm, 48 cm

a Show the results in an ordered stem-and-leaf diagram, using this key.

Key: 4 3 represents 43 cm

b What is the modal height?

c What is the median height?

d What is the range of the heights?

2 A student records the number of text messages she receives each day for two weeks.

12, 18, 21, 9, 17, 23, 8, 2, 20, 13, 17, 22, 9, 9

a Show the results in an ordered stem-and-leaf diagram, using this key.

Key: 1 2 represents 12 messages

b What was the modal number of text messages received in a day?

c What was the median number of text messages received in a day?

In this section you will learn how to:
- draw, interpret and use scatter diagrams

Key words

line of best fit
negative
    correlation
no correlation
positive
    correlation
scatter
    diagram
variable

A **scatter diagram** (also called a scattergraph or scattergram) is a method of comparing two **variables** by plotting on a graph their corresponding values (usually taken from a table). In other words, the variables are treated just like a set of (*x*, *y*) coordinates.

In the scatter diagram below, the marks scored by pupils in an English test are plotted against the marks they scored in a mathematics test. This graph shows positive **correlation**. This means that the pupils who got high marks in the mathematics test also tended to get high marks in the English test.

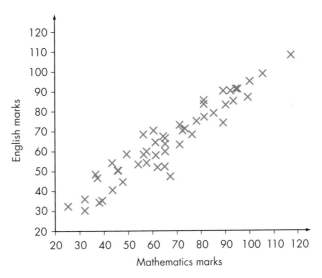

Correlation

This section will explain the different types of correlation.

Here are three statements that may or may not be true.

> The taller people are, the wider their arm span is likely to be.

> The older a car is, the lower its value will be.

> The distance you live from your place of work will affect how much you earn.

These relationships could be tested by collecting data and plotting the data on a scatter diagram.

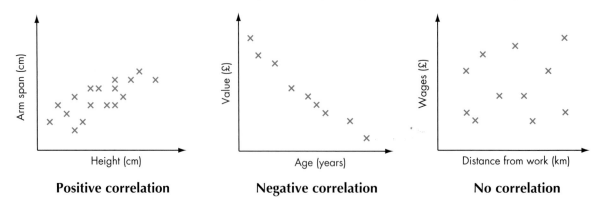

Positive correlation   **Negative correlation**   **No correlation**

For example, the first statement may give a scatter diagram like the first diagram above. This diagram has positive correlation because as one quantity increases so does the other. From such a scatter diagram we could say that the taller someone is, the wider the arm span.

Testing the second statement may give a scatter diagram like the second one. This diagram has **negative correlation** because as one quantity increases, the other quantity decreases. From such a scatter diagram we could say that as a car gets older, its value decreases.

Testing the third statement may give a scatter diagram like the third one. This scatter diagram has **no correlation**. There is no relationship between the distance a person lives from his or her work and how much the person earns.

EXAMPLE 3

The graphs show the relationship between the temperature and the amount of ice cream sold, and that between the age of people and the amount of ice cream they eat.

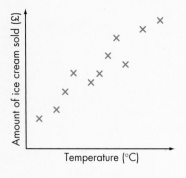   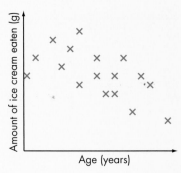

a Comment on the correlation of each graph.

b What does each graph tell you?

The first graph has positive correlation and tells us that as the temperature increases, the amount of ice cream sold increases.

The second graph has negative correlation and tells us that as people get older, they eat less ice cream.

Line of best fit

This section will explain how to draw and use a line of best fit.

The **line of best fit** is a straight line that goes between all the points on a scatter diagram, passing as close as possible to all of them. You should try to have the same number of points on both sides of the line. Because you are drawing this line by eye, examiners make a generous allowance around the correct answer. The line of best fit for the scatter diagram on page 57 is shown below.

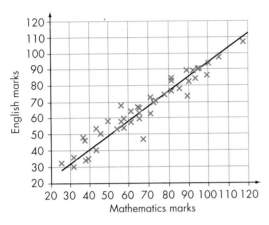 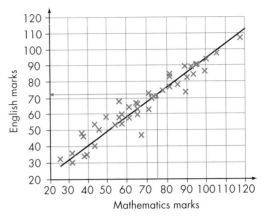

The line of best fit can be used to answer the following type of question: A girl took the mathematics test and scored 75 marks, but was ill for the English test. How many marks was she likely to have scored?

The answer is found by drawing a line up from 75 on the mathematics axis to the line of best fit and then drawing a line across to the English axis. This gives 73, which is the mark she is likely to have scored in the English test.

EXERCISE 18C

1 Describe the correlation of each of these four graphs and write in words what each graph tells you.

a
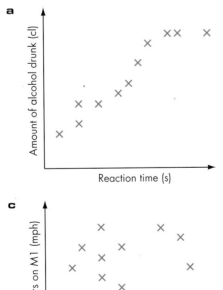

b
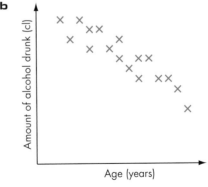

c
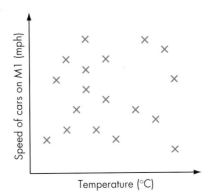

d
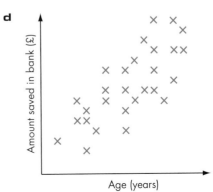

2 The table shows the results of a science experiment in which a ball is rolled along a desk top. The speed of the ball is measured at various points.

Distance from start (cm)	10	20	30	40	50	60	70	80
Speed (cm/s)	18	16	13	10	7	5	3	0

a Plot the data on a scatter diagram.

b Draw the line of best fit.

c If the ball's speed had been measured at 5 cm from the start, what is it likely to have been?

d How far from the start was the ball when its speed was 12 cm/s?

> **HINTS AND TIPS**
>
> Usually in exams axes are given and most, if not all, of the points are plotted.

3 The table shows the marks for ten pupils in their mathematics and geography examinations.

Pupil	Anna	Beryl	Cath	Dema	Ethel	Fatima	Greta	Hannah	Imogen	Joan
Maths	57	65	34	87	42	35	59	61	25	35
Geog	45	61	30	78	41	36	35	57	23	34

a Plot the data on a scatter diagram. Take the *x*-axis for the mathematics scores and mark it from 20 to 100. Take the *y*-axis for the geography scores and mark it from 20 to 100.

b Draw the line of best fit.

c One of the pupils was ill when she took the geography examination. Which pupil was it most likely to be?

d If another pupil, Kate, was absent for the geography examination but scored 75 in mathematics, what mark would you expect her to have got in geography?

e If another pupil, Lynne, was absent for the mathematics examination but scored 65 in geography, what mark would you expect her to have got in mathematics?

4 The heights, in centimetres, of twenty mothers and their 15-year-old daughters were measured. These are the results.

Mother	153	162	147	183	174	169	152	164	186	178
Daughter	145	155	142	167	167	151	145	152	163	168
Mother	175	173	158	168	181	173	166	162	180	156
Daughter	172	167	160	154	170	164	156	150	160	152

a Plot these results on a scatter diagram. Take the *x*-axis for the mothers' heights from 140 to 200. Take the *y*-axis for the daughters' heights from 140 to 200.

b Is it true that the tall mothers have tall daughters?

5 A form teacher carried out a survey of his class. He asked pupils to say how many hours per week they spent playing sport and how many hours per week they spent watching TV. This table shows the results of the survey.

Pupil	1	2	3	4	5	6	7	8	9	10
Hours playing sport	12	3	5	15	11	0	9	7	6	12
Hours watching TV	18	26	24	16	19	27	12	13	17	14

Pupil	11	12	13	14	15	16	17	18	19	20
Hours playing sport	12	10	7	6	7	3	1	2	0	12
Hours watching TV	22	16	18	22	12	28	18	20	25	13

a Plot these results on a scatter diagram. Take the *x*-axis as the number of hours playing sport and mark it from 0 to 20. Take the *y*-axis as the number of hours watching TV and mark it from 0 to 30.

b If you knew that another pupil from the form watched 8 hours of TV a week, would you be able to predict how long she or he spent playing sport? Explain why.

Cumulative frequency diagrams

In this section you will learn how to:

● find a measure of dispersion (the interquartile range) and a measure of location (the median) using a graph

Key words

cumulative frequency diagram
dispersion
interquartile range
lower quartile
median
upper quartile

The **interquartile range** is a measure of the **dispersion** of a set of data. The advantage of the interquartile range is that it eliminates extreme values, and bases the measure of spread on the middle 50% of the data. This section will show how to find the interquartile range, and the median, of a set of data by drawing a **cumulative frequency diagram**.

Look back at the marks of the 50 pupils in the mathematics test (see page 57). These can be put into a grouped table, as shown on the next page. Note that it includes a column for the cumulative frequency, which is found by adding each frequency to the sum of all preceding frequencies.

Mark	Number of pupils	Cumulative frequency
21 to 30	1	1
31 to 40	6	7
41 to 50	6	13
51 to 60	8	21
61 to 70	8	29
71 to 80	6	35
81 to 90	7	42
91 to 100	6	48
101 to 110	1	49
111 to 120	1	50

This data can then be used to plot a graph of the top value of each group against its cumulative frequency. The points to be plotted are (30, 1), (40, 7), (50, 13), (60, 21), etc., which will give the graph shown below. Note that the cumulative frequency is *always* the vertical (*y*) axis.

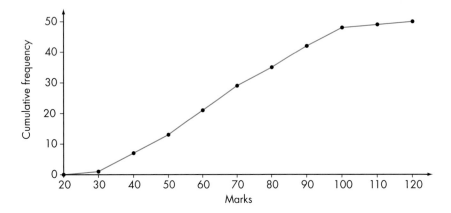

Also note that the scales on both axes are labelled at each graduation mark, in the usual way. Do not label the scales as shown here – it is wrong.

21–30	31–40	41–50

The plotted points can be joined in two different ways:

- by straight lines, to give a cumulative frequency polygon

- by a freehand curve, to give a cumulative frequency curve or ogive.

They are both called cumulative frequency diagrams.

In an examination you are most likely to be asked to draw a cumulative frequency diagram, and the type (polygon or curve) is up to you. Both will give similar results. The cumulative frequency diagram can be used in several ways, as you will now see.

The median

The **median** is the middle item of data once all the items have been put in order of size, from lowest to highest. So, if you have *n* items of data plotted as a cumulative frequency diagram, the median can be found from the middle value of the cumulative frequency, that is the $\frac{n}{2}$th value.

But remember, if you want to find the median from a simple list of discrete data, you *must* use the $(\frac{n+1}{2})$th value. The reason for the difference is that the cumulative frequency diagram treats the data as continuous, even when using data such as examination marks which are discrete. The reason you can use the $\frac{n}{2}$th value when working with cumulative frequency diagrams is that you are only looking for an estimate of the median.

There are 50 values in the table on page 62. The middle value will be the 25th value. Draw a horizontal line from the 25th value to meet the graph then go down to the horizontal axis. This will give an estimate of the median. In this example, the median is about 65 marks.

The interquartile range

By dividing the cumulative frequency into four parts, we obtain quartiles and the interquartile range.

The **lower quartile** is the item one quarter of the way up the cumulative frequency axis and is found by looking at the $\frac{n}{4}$th value.

The **upper quartile** is the item three-quarters of the way up the cumulative frequency axis and is found by looking at the $\frac{3n}{4}$th value.

The **interquartile range** is the difference between the lower and upper quartiles.

These are illustrated on the graph below.

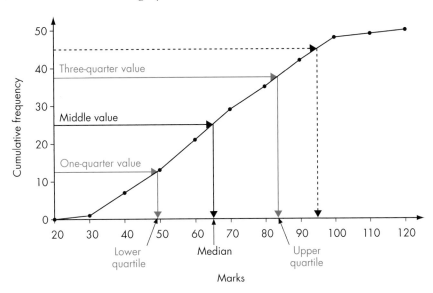

The quarter and three-quarter values out of 50 values are the 12.5th value and the 37.5th value. Draw lines across to the cumulative frequency curve from these values and down to the horizontal axis. These give the lower and upper quartiles. In this example, the lower quartile is 49 marks, the upper quartile is 83 marks, and the interquartile range is 83 − 49 = 34 marks.

Note that problems like these are often followed up with an extra question such as: The Head of Mathematics decides to give a special award to the top 10% of pupils. What would the cut-off mark be?

The top 10% would be the top 5 pupils (10% of 50 is 5). Draw a line across from the 45th pupil to the graph and down to the horizontal axis. This gives a cut-off mark of 95.

EXAMPLE 4

The table below shows the marks of 100 pupils in a mathematics SAT.

a   Draw a cumulative frequency curve.

b   Use your graph to find the median and the interquartile range.

c   Pupils who score less than 44 do not get a SAT level awarded. How many pupils will not get a SAT level?

Mark	Number of pupils	Cumulative frequency
$21 \leqslant x \leqslant 30$	3	3
$31 \leqslant x \leqslant 40$	9	12
$41 \leqslant x \leqslant 50$	12	24
$51 \leqslant x \leqslant 60$	15	39
$61 \leqslant x \leqslant 70$	22	61
$71 \leqslant x \leqslant 80$	16	77
$81 \leqslant x \leqslant 90$	10	87
$91 \leqslant x \leqslant 100$	8	95
$101 \leqslant x \leqslant 110$	3	98
$111 \leqslant x \leqslant 120$	2	100

The groups are given in a different way to those in the table on page 62. You will meet several ways of giving groups (for example, 21–30, $20 < x \leqslant 30$, $21 < x < 30$) but the important thing to remember is to plot the top point of each group against the corresponding cumulative frequency.

a and **b** Draw the graph and put on the lines for the median (50th value), lower and upper quartiles (25th and 75th values).

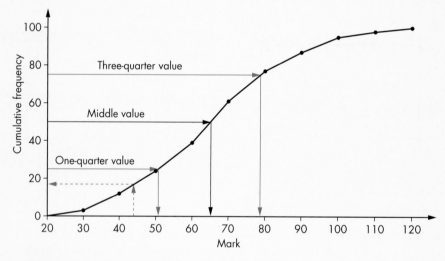

The required answers are read from the graph.

Median = 65 marks
Lower quartile = 51 marks
Upper quartile = 79 marks
Interquartile range = 79 − 51 = 28 marks

c   At 44 on the mark axis draw a perpendicular line to intersect the graph, and at the point of intersection draw a horizontal line across to the cumulative frequency axis, as shown. Number of pupils without a SAT level = 18

Note, an alternative way in which the table in Example 4 could have been set out is shown below. This arrangement has the advantage that the points to be plotted are taken straight from the last two columns. You have to decide which method you prefer. In examination papers, the columns of tables are sometimes given without headings, so you will need to be familiar with all the different ways in which the data can be set out.

Mark	Number of pupils	Less than	Cumulative frequency
$21 \leqslant x \leqslant 30$	3	30	3
$31 \leqslant x \leqslant 40$	9	40	12
$41 \leqslant x \leqslant 50$	12	50	24
$51 \leqslant x \leqslant 60$	15	60	39
$61 \leqslant x \leqslant 70$	22	70	61
$71 \leqslant x \leqslant 80$	16	80	77
$81 \leqslant x \leqslant 90$	10	90	87
$91 \leqslant x \leqslant 100$	8	100	95
$101 \leqslant x \leqslant 110$	3	110	98
$111 \leqslant x \leqslant 120$	2	120	100

EXERCISE 18D

1 A class of 30 children was asked to estimate one minute. The teacher recorded the times the pupils actually said. The table on the right shows the results.

a Copy the table and complete a cumulative frequency column.

b Draw a cumulative frequency diagram.

c Use your diagram to estimate the median time and the interquartile range.

Time (seconds)	Number of pupils
$20 < x \leqslant 30$	1
$30 < x \leqslant 40$	3
$40 < x \leqslant 50$	6
$50 < x \leqslant 60$	12
$60 < x \leqslant 70$	3
$70 < x \leqslant 80$	3
$80 < x \leqslant 90$	2

2 A group of 50 pensioners was given the same task as the children in question 1. The results are shown in the table on the right.

a Copy the table and complete a cumulative frequency column.

b Draw a cumulative frequency diagram.

c Use your diagram to estimate the median time and the interquartile range.

d Which group, the children or the pensioners, would you say was better at estimating time? Give a reason for your answer.

Time (seconds)	Number of pensioners
$10 < x \leqslant 20$	1
$20 < x \leqslant 30$	2
$30 < x \leqslant 40$	2
$40 < x \leqslant 50$	9
$50 < x \leqslant 60$	17
$60 < x \leqslant 70$	13
$70 < x \leqslant 80$	3
$80 < x \leqslant 90$	2
$90 < x \leqslant 100$	1

3 The sizes of 360 secondary schools in South Yorkshire are recorded in the table on the right.

Number of pupils	Number of schools
100–199	12
200–299	18
300–399	33
400–499	50
500–599	63
600–699	74
700–799	64
800–899	35
900–999	11

a Copy the table and complete a cumulative frequency column.

b Draw a cumulative frequency diagram.

c Use your diagram to estimate the median size of the schools and the interquartile range.

d Schools with less than 350 pupils are threatened with closure. About how many schools are threatened with closure?

4 The temperature at a seaside resort was recorded over a period of 50 days. The temperature was recorded to the nearest degree. The table on the right shows the results.

Temperature (°C)	Number of days
5–7	2
8–10	3
11–13	5
14–16	6
17–19	6
20–22	9
23–25	8
26–28	6
29–31	5

a Copy the table and complete a cumulative frequency column.

b Draw a cumulative frequency diagram. Note that as the temperature is to the nearest degree the top values of the groups are 7.5°C, 10.5°C, 13.5°C, 16.5°C, etc.

c Use your diagram to estimate the median temperature and the interquartile range.

5 At the school charity fête, a game consists of throwing three darts and recording the total score. The results of the first 80 people to throw are recorded in the table on the right.

Total score	Number of players
$1 \leqslant x \leqslant 20$	9
$21 \leqslant x \leqslant 40$	13
$41 \leqslant x \leqslant 60$	23
$61 \leqslant x \leqslant 80$	15
$81 \leqslant x \leqslant 100$	11
$101 \leqslant x \leqslant 120$	7
$121 \leqslant x \leqslant 140$	2

a Draw a cumulative frequency diagram to show the data.

b Use your diagram to estimate the median score and the interquartile range.

c People who score over 90 get a prize. About what percentage of the people get a prize?

6 One hundred pupils in a primary school were asked to say how much pocket money they each get in a week. The results are in the table on the right.

Amount of pocket money (p)	No. of pupils
51–100	6
101–150	10
151–200	20
201–250	28
251–300	18
301–350	11
351–400	5
401–450	2

a Copy the table and complete a cumulative frequency column.

b Draw a cumulative frequency diagram.

c Use your diagram to estimate the median amount of pocket money and the interquartile range.

Box plots

In this section you will learn how to:

● draw and read box plots

Another way of displaying data for comparison is by means of a box-and-whisker plot (or just **box plot**). This requires five pieces of data. These are the **lowest value**, the **lower quartile** (Q_1), the **median** (Q_2), the **upper quartile** (Q_3) and the **highest value**. They are drawn in the following way.

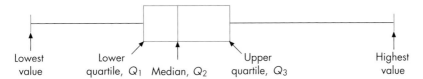

These data are always placed against a scale so that their values are accurately plotted.

The following diagrams show how the cumulative frequency curve, the frequency curve and the box plot are connected for three common types of distribution.

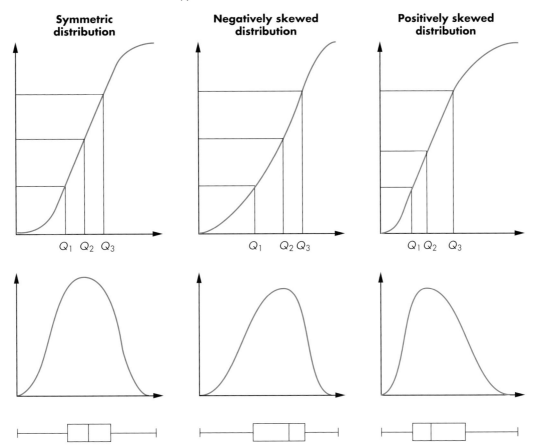

EXAMPLE 5

The box plot for the girls' marks in last year's SATs is shown on the grid below.

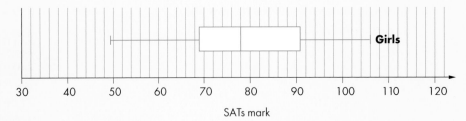

SATs mark

The boys' results for the same SATs are: lowest mark 39; lower quartile 65; median 78; upper quartile 87; highest mark 112.

a On the same grid, plot the box plot for the boys' marks.

b Comment on the differences between the two distributions of marks.

a The data for boys and girls is plotted on the grid below.

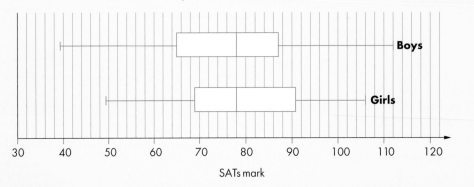

SATs mark

b The girls and boys have the same median mark but both the lower and upper quartiles for the girls are higher than those for the boys, and the girls' range is slightly smaller than the boys'. This suggests that the girls did better than the boys overall, even though a boy got the highest mark.

EXERCISE 18E

1 The box plot shows the times taken for a group of pensioners to do a set of ten long-division calculations.

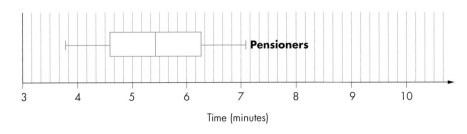

Time (minutes)

The same set of calculations was given to some students in Year 11. Their results are: shortest time 3 minutes 20 seconds; lower quartile 6 minutes 10 seconds; median 7 minutes; upper quartile 7 minutes 50 seconds; longest time 9 minutes 40 seconds.

a Copy the diagram and draw a box plot for the students' times.

b Comment on the differences between the two distributions.

2 The box plots for the noon temperature at two resorts, recorded over a year, are shown on the grid below.

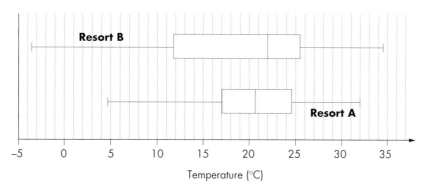

a Comment on the differences in the two distributions.

b Mary wants to go on holiday in July. Which resort would you recommend and why?

3 The following table shows some data on the annual salary for 100 men and 100 women.

	Lowest salary	Lower quartile	Median salary	Upper quartile	Highest salary
Men	£6500	£16 000	£20 000	£22 000	£44 500
Women	£7000	£14 000	£16 000	£21 500	£33 500

a Draw box plots to compare both sets of data.

b Comment on the differences between the distributions.

4 The table shows the monthly salaries of 100 families.

Monthly salary (£)	No. of families
1451–1500	8
1501–1550	14
1551–1600	25
1601–1650	35
1651–1700	14
1701–1750	4

a Draw a cumulative frequency diagram to show the data.

b Estimate the median monthly salary and the interquartile range.

c The lowest monthly salary was £1480 and the highest was £1740.

    i Draw a box plot to show the distribution of salaries.

    ii Is the distribution symmetric, negatively skewed or positively skewed?

5 Indicate whether the following sets of data are likely to be symmetric, negatively skewed or positively skewed.

a heights of adult males

b annual salaries of adult males

c shoe sizes of adult males

d weights of babies born in Britain

e speeds of cars on a motorway in the middle of the night

f speeds of cars on a motorway in the rush hour

g shopping bills in a supermarket the week before Christmas

1 Some students took a test. The table shows information about their marks.

Minimum mark	10
Lower quartile	33
Interquartile range	35
Median mark	43
Range	65

Use this information to draw a box plot using the guide below.

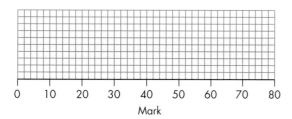

Edexcel, Question 2, Paper 10A Higher, March 2004

2 60 office workers recorded the number of words per minute they could type.

The grouped frequency table gives information about the number of words per minute they could type.

Number of words, (w) per minute	Frequency
$0 \leqslant w < 20$	6
$20 \leqslant w < 40$	18
$40 \leqslant w < 60$	16
$60 \leqslant w < 80$	15
$80 \leqslant w < 100$	3
$100 \leqslant w < 120$	2

a Find the class interval in which the median lies.

The cumulative frequency graph for this information has been drawn on the grid.

b Use this graph to work out an estimate for the interquartile range of the number of words per minute.

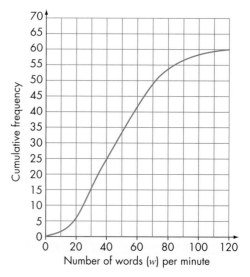

c Use this graph to work out an estimate for the number of workers who could type *more* than 70 words per minute.

Edexcel, Question 3, Paper 10A Higher, January 2005

3 90 students took an examination. The grouped frequency table shows information about their results.

Mark (x)	Frequency
$0 < x \leqslant 10$	3
$10 < x \leqslant 20$	10
$20 < x \leqslant 30$	17
$30 < x \leqslant 40$	30
$40 < x \leqslant 50$	21
$50 < x \leqslant 60$	7
$60 < x \leqslant 70$	2

a Copy and complete the cumulative frequency table.

Mark (x)	Frequency
$0 < x \leqslant 10$	3
$10 < x \leqslant 20$	
$20 < x \leqslant 30$	
$30 < x \leqslant 40$	
$40 < x \leqslant 50$	
$50 < x \leqslant 60$	
$60 < x \leqslant 70$	

b Draw a cumulative frequency graph for your table. Use a grid with an *x*-axis from 0 to 60 and a *y*-axis from 0 to 100.

c Use your graph to find an estimate for the median mark.

The pass mark for the examination was 28.

d Use your graph to find an estimate for the number of students who passed the examination.

Edexcel, Question 3, Paper 10A Higher, January 2004

WORKED EXAM QUESTION

Derek makes men's and women's shirts. He needs to know the range of collar sizes so he measures 100 men's necks.
The results are shown in the table.

a Draw a cumulative frequency diagram to show this information
b Use the diagram to find
  i the median
  ii the interquartile range
c The box plot shows the neck sizes of 100 women.

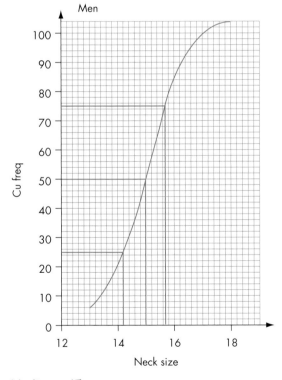

11 12 13 14 15 16 17   Neck size, cm

Comment on the differences in the distribution of neck sizes for men and women.

Neck size, n (cm)	Frequency
$12 < n \leq 13$	5
$13 < n \leq 14$	16
$14 < n \leq 15$	28
$15 < n \leq 16$	37
$16 < n \leq 17$	10
$17 < n \leq 18$	4

Solution

a Cumulative Frequencies: 5, 21, 49, 86, 96, 100

First work out the cumulative frequencies. The easiest way to do this is with another column on the table.

b

Plot the points (13, 5), (14, 21), etc.
i.e the top value of each group against the cumulative frequency.

Draw lines from 50 (median), 25 (lower quartile) and 75 (upper quartile) from the vertical axis across to the graph and down to the horizontal axis. Subtract lower quartile from upper quartile for the inter-quartile range.

Median = 15 cm
IQR = 15.7 − 14.2 = 1.5 cm

c The men have a higher median (about 1.5 cm higher) and the women have a larger interquartile range
(About 2.5 cm compared to 1.5 cm)

Comment on the differences between the medians and the interquartile ranges. Use numerical values to show you know how to read the box plot.

Michael Jones is a journalist. He writes articles for a monthly magazine.

He is asked to write a report on the changes in the population of the UK over the 25 years from 1976 to 2001.

Michael does some research, and finds the following figures for 1976 and 2001.

He calculates the percentage change for each age group to the nearest percent. Help him to complete the table.

Age distribution in the UK (numbers in millions)			
Age (a) in years	1976	2001	% change
$0 \le a < 15$	12.9	11.1	–14%
$15 \le a < 25$	8.1	7.2	
$25 \le a < 35$	7.9	8.4	
$35 \le a < 45$	6.4	8.8	
$45 \le a < 55$	9.8	7.8	
$55 \le a < 65$	3.1	6.2	
$65 \le a < 75$	5.1	4.9	
$75 \le a < 85$	2.3	3.3	
$85 \le a < 105$	0.5	1.1	

He also decides to find an estimate of the mean in 1976 and 2001.

He uses this table to help. Complete the calculations for him.

Midpoint of ages	1976 frequency (millions)	midpoint x frequency	2001 frequency (millions)	midpoint x frequency
7.5	12.9	96.75	11.1	83.25
20	8.1		7.2	
	7.9		8.4	
	6.4		8.8	
	9.8		7.8	
	3.1		6.2	
	5.1		4.9	
	2.3		3.3	
	0.5		1.1	
Totals				
Mean age				

Finally he wants to find the median ages and interquartile ranges (IQR).

Complete the cumulative frequencies below, then draw cumulative frequency graphs and use them to find the median and IQR for both years.

Cumulative frequencies for age distributions (in millions)									
	< 15	< 25	< 35	< 45	< 55	< 65	< 75	< 85	<105
1976	12.9	21	28.9						
2001	11.1	18.3							

Michael summarises the statistical data in a table. He rounds every answer to the nearest whole number of years.

Complete the table for him.

	1976	2001
mean		
median		
upper quartile		
lower quartile		
IQR		

He writes the following article. Write down the words that should go in the spaces.

Are we living longer?

Michael Jones reports on the change in the population of the UK from 1976 to 2001.

The total population for the UK in 1976 was approximately 56.1 million, which increased to 58.8 million in 2001. This means that over 25 years, the population has grown by _____ million people. During this time period, the largest percentage increase occurred in the age group _____ with a staggering _____% increase.

However the largest percentage decrease of _____% occurred in the age group _____. The reasons for this could possibly be due to rationing and a shortage of men in the decade following the second world war.

The mean age of the population has increased from _____ years old to _____ years old (both values are given to the nearest whole year).

This increase of _____ years appears to reinforce the claim made by politicians that as medical science advances and our standard of living and diet improve, it means that we are living longer.

The median age for the two years shows a slightly larger increase than the mean, going from _____ years up to _____ years. The lower and upper quartiles also increase by _____years, thus showing a shift upwards by _____ years of the central 50% of the population.

So, does this show a healthier, happier Britain?

Well, it certainly appears that we are on average living longer. The mean and median both show the average age increasing. But, will the trend continue? Certainly our standard of living has improved, and the treatment of illnesses is improving at a rapid rate, but what about our eating habits? These too are changing.

Fast food + less exercise = obesity. Is this the maths equation that will reverse the trend in the age of the population?

Read next months article, **We are what we eat – true or false?** which looks more closely at the UK's expanding waistlines.

Do you think this article is well written? Is it misleading in any way? Can you write a better article for him?

GRADE YOURSELF

D Able to draw an ordered stem-and-leaf diagram

D Able to draw a line of best fit on a scatter diagram

C Recognise the different types of correlation

C Able to interpret a line of best fit

B Able to draw a cumulative frequency diagram

B Able to find medians and quartiles from cumulative frequency diagrams

B Able to draw and interpret box plots

What you should know now

- How to read information from statistical diagrams including stem-and-leaf diagrams
- How to plot scatter diagrams, recognise correlation, draw lines of best fit and use them to predict values
- How to construct a cumulative frequency diagram
- How to draw and interpret box plots

Probability

This chapter will show you ...

- how to work out the probability of events, either using theoretical models or experimental models
- how to predict outcomes using theoretical models and compare experimental and theoretical data
- how to calculate probabilities for combined events

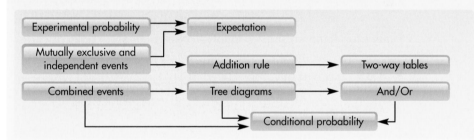

What you should already know

- That the probability scale goes from 0 to 1
- How to use the probability scale and to assess the likelihood of events depending on their position on the scale
- How to cancel, add and subtract factors

Quick check

1 Draw a probability scale and put an arrow to show approximately the probability of each of the following events happening.

a The next TV programme you watch will have been made in Britain.

b A person in your class will have been born in April.

c It will snow in July in Spain.

d In the next Olympic Games, a man will run the 100 m race in less than 20 seconds.

e During this week, you will drink some water or pop.

Terminology

The topic of probability has its own special terminology, which will be explained as it arises. For example, a **trial** is one go at performing something, such as throwing a dice or tossing a coin. So, if we throw a dice 10 times, we perform 10 trials.

Two other probability terms are **event** and **outcome**. An event is anything whose probability we want to measure. An outcome is any way in which an event can happen.

Another probability term is **at random**. This means "without looking" or "not knowing what the outcome is in advance".

Note: "Dice" is used in this book in preference to "die" for the singular form of the noun, as well as for the plural. This is in keeping with growing common usage, including in examination papers.

Probability facts

The probability of a *certain* event is 1 and the probability of an *impossible* event is 0.

Probability is never greater than 1 or less than 0.

Many probability examples involve coins, dice and packs of cards. Here is a reminder of their outcomes.

- A coin has two outcomes: head or tail.

- An ordinary six-sided dice has six outcomes: 1, 2, 3, 4, 5, 6.

- A pack of cards consists of 52 cards divided into four suits: Hearts (red), Spades (black), Diamonds (red), and Clubs (black). Each suit consists of 13 cards bearing the following values: 2, 3, 4, 5, 6, 7, 8, 9, 10, Jack, Queen, King and Ace. The Jack, Queen and King are called "picture cards". (The Ace is sometimes also called a picture card.) So the total number of outcomes is 52.

Probability is defined as

$$P(\text{event}) = \frac{\text{Number of ways the event can happen}}{\text{Total number of all possible outcomes}}$$

This definition always leads to a fraction which should be cancelled down to its simplest form. Make sure that you know how to cancel down fractions with or without a calculator. It is acceptable to give a probability as a decimal or a percentage but a fraction is better.

This definition can be used to work out the probability of events, as the following example shows.

EXAMPLE 1

A card is drawn from a pack of cards. What is the probability that it is one of the following?

a a red card   b a Spade   c a seven

d a picture card   e a number less than 5   f a red King

a There are 26 red cards, so P(red card) = $\frac{26}{52}$ = $\frac{1}{2}$

b There are 13 Spades, so P(Spade) = $\frac{13}{52}$ = $\frac{1}{4}$

c There are four sevens, so P(seven) = $\frac{4}{52}$ = $\frac{1}{13}$

d There are 12 picture cards, so P(picture card) = $\frac{12}{52}$ = $\frac{3}{13}$

e If you count the value of an Ace as 1, there are 16 cards with a value less than 5.
So, P(number less than 5) = $\frac{16}{52}$ = $\frac{4}{13}$

f There are 2 red Kings, so P(red King) = $\frac{2}{52}$ = $\frac{1}{26}$

19.1   Experimental probability

In this section you will learn how to:

- calculate experimental probabilities and relative frequencies
- estimate probabilities from experiments
- use different methods to estimate probabilities

Key words

experimental probability
relative frequency
trials

The value of number of heads ÷ number of tosses is called an **experimental probability**. As the number of **trials** or experiments increases, the value of the experimental probability gets closer to the true or theoretical probability.

Experimental probability is also known as the **relative frequency** of an event. The relative frequency of an event is an estimate for the theoretical probability. It is given by

$$\text{Relative frequency of an event} = \frac{\text{Frequency of the event}}{\text{Total number of trials}}$$

EXAMPLE 2

The frequency table shows the speeds of 160 vehicles which pass a radar speed check on a dual carriageway.

Speed (mph)	20–29	30–39	40–49	50–59	60–69	70+
Frequency	14	23	28	35	52	8

a What is the experimental probability that a vehicle is travelling faster than 70 mph?

b If 500 vehicles pass the speed check, estimate how many will be travelling faster than 70 mph.

a The experimental probability is the relative frequency, which is $\frac{8}{160} = \frac{1}{20}$

b The number of vehicles travelling faster than 70 mph will be $\frac{1}{20}$ of 500.

That is, $500 \div 20 = 25$ vehicles

Finding probabilities

There are three ways in which the probability of an event can be found.

- If we can work out the theoretical probability of an event – for example, drawing a King from a pack of cards – this is called using equally likely outcomes.

- Some events, such as buying a certain brand of dog food, cannot be calculated using equally likely outcomes. To find the probability of such an event, we can perform an experiment or conduct a survey. This is called collecting experimental data. The more data we collect, the better the estimate is.

- The probability of some events, such as an earthquake occurring in Japan, cannot be found by either of the above methods. One of the things we can do is to look at data collected over a long period of time and make an estimate (sometimes called a best guess) at the chance of the event happening. This is called looking at historical data.

EXAMPLE 3

Which method (A, B or C) would you use to estimate the probabilities of the events a to e?

    A: Use equally likely outcomes

    B: Conduct a survey/collect data

    C: Look at historical data

a Someone in your class will go abroad for a holiday this year.

b You will win the National Lottery.

c Your bus home will be late.

d It will snow on Christmas Day.

e You will pick a red seven from a pack of cards.

a You would have to ask all the members of your class what they intended to do for their holidays this year. You would therefore conduct a survey, method B.

b The odds on winning are about 14 million to 1. This is an equally likely outcome, method A.

c If you catch the bus every day, you can collect data over several weeks. This would be method C.

d If you check whether it snowed on Christmas Day for the last few years you would be able to make a good estimate of the probability. This would be method C.

e There are two red sevens out of 52 cards, so the probability of picking one can be calculated: P(red seven) $= \frac{2}{52} = \frac{1}{26}$

This is method A.

EXERCISE 19A

1 Naseer throws a dice and records the number of sixes that he gets after various numbers of throws. The table shows his results.

Number of throws	10	50	100	200	500	1000	2000
Number of sixes	2	4	10	21	74	163	329

a Calculate the experimental probability of a six at each stage that Naseer recorded his results.

b How many ways can a dice land?

c How many of these ways give a six?

d What is the theoretical probability of throwing a six with a dice?

e If Naseer threw the dice a total of 6000 times, how many sixes would you expect him to get?

2 Marie made a five-sided spinner, like the one shown in the diagram. She used it to play a board game with her friend Sarah. The girls thought that the spinner wasn't very fair as it seemed to land on some numbers more than others. They spun the spinner 200 times and recorded the results. The results are shown in the table.

Side spinner lands on	1	2	3	4	5
Number of times	19	27	32	53	69

a Work out the experimental probability of each number.

b How many times would you expect each number to occur if the spinner is fair?

c Do you think that the spinner is fair? Give a reason for your answer.

3 Sarah thought she could make a much more accurate spinner. After she had made it, she tested it and recorded how many times she scored a 5. Her results are shown in the table.

Number of spins	10	50	100	500
Number of fives	3	12	32	107

a Sarah made a mistake in recording the number of fives. Which number in the second row above is wrong? Give a reason for your answer.

b These are the full results for 500 spins.

Side spinner lands on	1	2	3	4	5
Number of times	96	112	87	98	107

Do you think the spinner is fair? Give a reason for your answer.

 4 A sampling bottle contains 20 balls. The balls are either black or white. (A sampling bottle is a sealed bottle with a clear plastic tube at one end into which one of the balls can be tipped.) Kenny conducts an experiment to see how many black balls are in the bottle. He takes various numbers of samples and records how many of them showed a black ball. The results are shown in the table.

Number of samples	Number of black balls	Experimental probability
10	2	
100	25	
200	76	
500	210	
1000	385	
5000	1987	

a Copy the table and calculate the experimental probability of getting a black ball at each stage.

b Using this information, how many black balls do you think are in the bottle?

5 Another sampling bottle contains red, white and blue balls. It is known that there are 20 balls in the bottle altogether. Carrie performs an experiment to see how many of each colour are in the bottle. She starts off putting down a tally each time a colour shows in the clear plastic tube.

Red	White	Blue
ЖЖ ЖЖ ЖЖ ЖЖ II	ЖЖ ЖЖ ЖЖ III	ЖЖ ЖЖ II

Unfortunately, she forgets to count how many times she performs the experiment, so every now and again she counts up the tallies and records them in a table (see below).

Red	White	Blue	Total
22	18	12	52
48	31	16	95
65	37	24	126
107	61	32	200
152	93	62	307
206	128	84	418

The relative frequency of the red balls is calculated by dividing the frequency of red by the total number of trials, so at each stage these are

0.423   0.505   0.516   0.535   0.495   0.493

These answers are rounded off to three significant figures.

a Calculate the relative frequencies of the white balls at each stage to three significant figures.

b Calculate the relative frequencies of the blue balls at each stage to three significant figures.

c Round off the final relative frequencies for Carrie's 418 trials to one decimal place.

d What is the total of the answers in part **c**?

e How many balls of each colour do you think are in the bottle? Explain your answer.

 6 Using card and a cocktail stick, make a six-sided spinner, as shown below.

 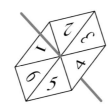

When you have made the spinner, spin it 120 times and record your results in a table like the one below.

Number	Tally	Total
1	ЖЖ ll	
2	llll	

a Which number occurred the most?

b How many times would you expect to get each number?

c Is your spinner fair?

d Explain your answer to part **c**.

 7 Use a set of number cards from 1 to 10 (or make your own set) and work with a partner. Take it in turns to choose a card and keep a record each time of what card you get. Shuffle the cards each time and repeat the experiment 60 times. Put your results in a copy of this table.

Score	1	2	3	4	5	6	7	8	9	10
Total										

a How many times would you expect to get each number?

b Do you think you and your partner conducted this experiment fairly?

c Explain your answer to part **b**.

8 A four-sided dice has faces numbered 1, 2, 3 and 4. The score is the face on which it lands. Five pupils throw the dice to see if it is biased. They each throw it a different number of times. Their results are shown in the table.

Pupil	Total number of throws	Score			
		1	2	3	4
Alfred	20	7	6	3	4
Brian	50	19	16	8	7
Caryl	250	102	76	42	30
Deema	80	25	25	12	18
Emma	150	61	46	26	17

a Which pupil will have the most reliable set of results? Why?

b Add up all the score columns and work out the relative frequency of each score. Give your answers to two decimal places.

c Is the dice biased? Explain your answer.

9 Which of these methods would you use to estimate or state the probability of each of the events **a** to **h**?

Method A: Equally likely outcomes

Method B: Survey or experiment

Method C: Look at historical data

a How people will vote in the next election.

b A drawing pin dropped on a desk will land point up.

c A Premiership football team will win the FA Cup.

d You will win a school raffle.

e The next car to drive down the road will be red.

f You will throw a "double six" with two dice.

g Someone in your class likes classical music.

h A person picked at random from your school will be a vegetarian.

10 If you were about to choose a card from a pack of yellow cards numbered from 1 to 10, what would be the chance of each of the events **a** to **i** occurring? Copy and complete each of these statements with a word or phrase chosen from "impossible", "not likely", "50–50 chance", "quite likely", or "certain".

a The likelihood that the next card chosen will be a four is ......

b The likelihood that the next card chosen will be pink is ......

c The likelihood that the next card chosen will be a seven is ......

d The likelihood that the next card chosen will be a number less than 11 is ......

e The likelihood that the next card chosen will be a number bigger than 11 is ......

f The likelihood that the next card chosen will be an even number is ......

g The likelihood that the next card chosen will be a number more than 5 is ......

h The likelihood that the next card chosen will be a multiple of 1 is ......

i The likelihood that the next card chosen will be a prime number is ......

C

19.2 Mutually exclusive and exhaustive events

In this section you will learn how to:
- recognise mutually exclusive, complementary and exhaustive events

Key words
complementary
exhaustive
mutually
    exclusive

If a bag contains three black, two yellow and five white balls and only one ball is allowed to be taken at random from the bag, then by the basic definition of probability

$$P(\text{black ball}) = \frac{3}{10}$$

$$P(\text{yellow ball}) = \frac{2}{10} = \frac{1}{5}$$

$$P(\text{white ball}) = \frac{5}{10} = \frac{1}{2}$$

We can also say that the probability of choosing a black ball or a yellow ball is $= \frac{5}{10} = \frac{1}{2}$

The events "picking a yellow ball" and "picking a black ball" can never happen at the same time when only one ball is taken out: that is, a ball can be either black or yellow. Such events are called **mutually exclusive**. Other examples of mutually exclusive events are tossing a head or a tail with a coin, drawing a King or an Ace from a pack of cards and throwing an even or an odd number with a dice.

An example of events that are not mutually exclusive would be drawing a red card and a King from a pack of cards. There are two red Kings, so these events could be true at the same time.

EXAMPLE 4

An ordinary dice is thrown.

a What is the probability of throwing

   i an even number?   **ii** an odd number?

b What is the total of the answers to part **a**?

c Is it possible to get a score on a dice that is both odd and even?

a i $P(\text{even}) = \dfrac{1}{2}$ **ii** $P(\text{odd}) = \dfrac{1}{2}$ **b** $\dfrac{1}{2} + \dfrac{1}{2} = 1$ **c** No

Events such as those in Example 4 are mutually exclusive because they can never happen at the same time. Because there are no other possibilities, they are also called **exhaustive** events. The probabilities of exhaustive events add up to 1.

EXAMPLE 5

A bag contains only black and white balls. The probability of picking at random a black ball from the bag is $\frac{7}{10}$.

a What is the probability of picking a white ball from the bag?

b Can you say how many black and white balls are in the bag?

a As the event "picking a white ball" and the event "picking a black ball" are mutually exclusive and exhaustive then

$$P(\text{white}) = 1 - P(\text{black}) = 1 - \frac{7}{10} = \frac{3}{10}$$

b You cannot say precisely what the number of balls is although you can say that there could be seven black and three white, fourteen black and six white, or any combination of black and white balls in the ratio 7 : 3.

Complementary event

If there is an event A, the **complementary** event of A is

   Event A *not* happening

Any event is mutually exclusive and exhaustive to its complementary event. That is,

   P(event A not happening) = 1 – P(event A happening)

which can be stated as

   P(event) + P(complementary event) = 1

For example, the probability of getting a King from a pack of cards is $\frac{4}{52} = \frac{1}{13}$, so the probability of *not* getting a King is

$$1 - \frac{1}{13} = \frac{12}{13}$$

EXERCISE 19B

1 Say whether these pairs of events are mutually exclusive or not.

a tossing a head with a coin/tossing a tail with a coin

b throwing a number less than 3 with a dice/throwing a number greater than 3 with a dice

c drawing a Spade from a pack of cards/drawing an Ace from a pack of cards

d drawing a Spade from a pack of cards/drawing a red card from a pack of cards

e if two people are to be chosen from three girls and two boys: choosing two girls/choosing two boys

f drawing a red card from a pack of cards/drawing a black card from a pack of cards

2 Which of the pairs of mutually exclusive events in question **1** are also exhaustive?

3 Each morning I run to work or get a lift. The probability that I run to work is $\frac{2}{5}$.
What is the probability that I get a lift?

4 A letter is to be chosen at random from this set of letter-cards.

a What is the probability the letter is

  i an S?   **ii** a T?   **iii** a vowel?

b Which of these pairs of events are mutually exclusive?

  i picking an S / picking a T   **ii** picking an S / picking a vowel

  iii picking an S / picking another consonant   **iv** picking a vowel / picking a consonant

c Which pair of mutually exclusive events in part **b** is also exhaustive?

5 Two people are to be chosen for a job from this set of five people.

a List all of the possible pairs (there are 10 altogether).

b What is the probability that the pair of people chosen will

  i both be female?   **ii** both be male?

  iii both have the same initial?   **iv** have different initials?

Jane Dave Anne Jack John

c Which of these pairs of events are mutually exclusive?

  i picking two women/picking two men

  ii picking two people of the same sex/picking two people of opposite sex

  iii picking two people with the same initial/picking two men

  iv picking two people with the same initial/picking two women

d Which pair of mutually exclusive events in part **c** is also exhaustive?

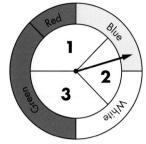

6 A spinner consists of an outer ring of coloured sectors and an inner circle of numbered sectors, as shown.

a The probability of getting 2 is $\frac{1}{4}$. The probabilities of getting 1 or 3 are equal. What is the probability of getting 3?

b The probability of getting blue is $\frac{1}{4}$. The probability of getting white $\frac{1}{4}$. The probability of getting green is $\frac{3}{8}$. What is the probability of getting red?

c Which of these pairs of events are mutually exclusive?

   i getting 3/getting 2   **ii** getting 3/getting green

   iii getting 3/getting blue   **iv** getting blue/getting red

d Explain why it is not possible to get a colour that is mutually exclusive to the event "getting an odd number".

7 At the morning break, I have the choice of coffee, tea or hot chocolate. If the probability I choose coffee is $\frac{3}{5}$, the probability I choose tea is $\frac{1}{4}$, what is the probability I choose hot chocolate?

8 Assemblies at school are always taken by the head, the deputy head or the senior teacher. If the head takes the assembly, the probability that she goes over time is $\frac{1}{2}$. If the deputy takes the assembly, the probability that he goes over time is $\frac{1}{4}$. Explain why it is not necessarily true to say that the probability that the senior teacher goes over time is $\frac{1}{4}$.

9 A hotelier conducted a survey of guests staying at her hotel. The table shows some of the results of her survey.

Type of guest	Probability
Man	0.7
Woman	0.3
American man	0.2
American woman	0.05
Vegetarian	0.3
Married	0.6

a A guest was chosen at random. From the table, work out these probabilities.

   i the guest was American

   ii the guest was single

   iii the guest was not a vegetarian

b Explain why it is not possible to work out from the table the probability of a guest being a married vegetarian.

c From the table, give two examples of pairs of types of guest that would form a pair of mutually exclusive events.

d From the table, give one example of a pair of types of guest that would form a pair of exhaustive events.

Expectation

In this section you will learn how to:

- predict the likely number of successful events given the number of trials and the probability of any one event

Key word

expectation

When we know the probability of an event, we can predict how many times we would expect that event to happen in a certain number of trials.

Note that this is what we *expect*. It is not what is going to happen. If what we expected always happened, life would be very dull and boring and the National Lottery would be a waste of time.

EXAMPLE 6

A bag contains 20 balls, nine of which are black, six white and five yellow. A ball is drawn at random from the bag, its colour noted and then it is put back in the bag. This is repeated 500 times.

a How many times would you expect a black ball to be drawn?

b How many times would you expect a yellow ball to be drawn?

c How many times would you expect a black or a yellow ball to be drawn?

a P(black ball) = $\frac{9}{20}$

Expected number of black balls = $\frac{9}{20} \times 500 = 225$

b P(yellow ball) = $\frac{5}{20} = \frac{1}{4}$

Expected number of yellow balls = $\frac{1}{4} \times 500 = 125$

c Expected number of black or yellow balls = 225 + 125 = 350

EXAMPLE 7

Four in 10 cars sold in Britain are made by Japanese companies.

a What is the probability that the next car to drive down your road will be Japanese?

b If there are 2000 cars in a multistorey car park, how many of them would you expect to be Japanese?

a P(Japanese car) = $\frac{4}{10} = \frac{2}{5} = 0.4$

b Expected number of Japanese cars in 2000 cars = 0.4 × 2000 = 800 cars

EXERCISE 19C

 1 I throw an ordinary dice 150 times. How many times can I expect to get a score of 6?

 2 I toss a coin 2000 times. How many times can I expect to get a head?

 3 I draw a card from a pack of cards and replace it. I do this 520 times. How many times would I expect to get these?

    a a black card   **b** a King

    c a Heart   **d** the King of Hearts

 4 The ball in a roulette wheel can land in 37 spaces which are the numbers between 0 and 36 inclusive. I always bet on the same number, 13. If I play all evening and there is a total of 185 spins of the wheel in that time, how many times could I expect to win?

 5 In a bag there are 30 balls, 15 of which are red, 5 yellow, 5 green, and 5 blue. A ball is taken out at random and then replaced. This is repeated 300 times. How many times would I expect to get these outcomes?

    a a red ball   **b** a yellow or blue ball

    c a ball that is not blue   **d** a pink ball

 6 The same experiment described in question **5** is carried out 1000 times. Approximately how many times would you expect to get **a** a green ball, **b** a ball that is not blue?

 7 A sampling bottle (as described in question **4** of Exercise 19A) contains red and white balls. It is known that the probability of getting a red ball is 0.3. 1500 samples are taken. How many of them would you expect to give a white ball?

 8 Josie said: "When I throw a dice, I expect to get a score of 3.5."

"Impossible," said Paul, "you can't score 3.5 with a dice."

"Do this and I'll prove it," said Josie.

    a An ordinary dice is thrown 60 times. Fill in the table for the expected number of times each score will occur.

Score						
Expected occurrences						

    b Now work out the average score that is expected over 60 throws.

    c There is an easy way to get an answer of 3.5 for the expected average score. Can you see what it is?

 9 I have 20 tickets for a raffle and I know that the probability of my winning the prize is 0.05. How many tickets were sold altogether in the raffle?

Two-way tables

In this section you will learn how to:

- read a two-way table and use them to work out probabilities and interpret data

Key word

two-way tables

A **two-way table** is a table that links together two variables. For example, the following table shows how many boys and girls are in a form and whether they are left- or right-handed.

	Boys	Girls
Left-handed	2	4
Right-handed	10	13

This table shows the colour and make of cars in the school car park.

	Red	Blue	White
Ford	2	4	1
Vauxhall	0	1	2
Toyota	3	3	4
Peugeot	2	0	3

One variable is written in the rows of the table and the other variable is written in the columns of the table.

EXAMPLE 8

Using the first two-way table above, answer these questions.

a If a pupil is selected at random from the form what is the probability that the pupil is a left-handed boy?

b It is known that a pupil selected at random is a girl. What is the probability that she is right-handed?

a $\frac{2}{29}$

b $\frac{13}{17}$

EXAMPLE 9

Using the second two-way table above, answer these questions.

a What percentage of the cars in the car park are red?

b What percentage of the white cars are Vauxhalls?

a 28%. Seven out of 25 is the same as 28 out of 100.

b 20%. Two out of 10 is 20%.

EXERCISE 19D

D

1 The two-way table shows the age and sex of a sample of 50 pupils in a school.

	Age (years)					
	11	**12**	**13**	**14**	**15**	**16**
Number of boys	4	3	6	2	5	4
Number of girls	2	5	3	6	4	6

a How many pupils are aged 13 years or less?

b What percentage of the pupils in the table are 16?

c A pupil from the table is selected at random. What is the probability that the pupil will be 14 years of age. Give your answer as a fraction in its lowest form.

d There are 1000 pupils in the school. Use the table to estimate how many boys are in the school altogether.

2 The two-way table shows the number of adults and the number of cars in 50 houses in one street.

		Number of adults			
		1	**2**	**3**	**4**
Number of cars	**0**	2	1	0	0
	1	3	13	3	1
	2	0	10	6	4
	3	0	1	4	2

a How many houses have exactly two adults and two cars?

b How many houses altogether have three cars?

c What percentage of the houses have three cars?

d What percentage of the houses with just one car have three adults living in the house?

3 Jane has two four-sided spinners. One has the numbers 1 to 4 and the other has the numbers 5 to 8.

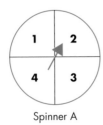

Spinner A

Spinner B

Both spinners are spun together.

The two-way table (on the next page) shows all the ways the two spinners can land.

Some of the total scores are filled in.

		Score on spinner A			
		1	**2**	**3**	**4**
	5	6	7		
Score on spinner B	**6**	7			
	7				
	8				

a Complete the table to show all the possible total scores.

b How many of the total scores are 9?

c When the two spinners are spun together what is the probability that the total score will be

   i 9?

   ii 8?

   iii a prime number?

4 The table shows information about the number of items in Flossy's music collection.

		Type of music		
		Pop	**Folk**	**Classical**
	Tape	16	5	2
Format	**CD**	51	9	13
	Mini disc	9	2	0

a How many pop tapes does Flossy have?

b How many items of folk music does Flossy have?

c How many CDs does Flossy have?

d If a CD is chosen at random from all the CDs, what is the probability that it will be a pop CD?

5 Zoe throws a fair coin and rolls a fair dice.

If the coin shows a head she records the score on the dice.

If the coin shows tails she doubles the number on the dice.

a Complete the two-way table to show Zoe's possible scores.

		Number on dice					
		1	**2**	**3**	**4**	**5**	**6**
Coin	**Head**	1	2				
	Tail	2	4				

b How many of the scores are square numbers?

c What is the probability of getting a score that is a square number?

6 A gardener plants some sunflower seeds in a greenhouse and plants some in the garden. After they have fully grown, he measures the diameter of the sunflower heads. The table shows his results.

	Greenhouse	Garden
Mean diameter	16.8 cm	14.5 cm
Range of diameter	3.2 cm	1.8 cm

a The gardener who wants to enter competitions says "the sunflowers from the greenhouse are better".

Using the data in the table, give a reason to justify this statement.

b The gardener's wife, who does flower arranging says "the sunflowers from the garden are better".

Using the data in the table, give a reason to justify this statement.

7 The two-way table shows the wages for the men and women in a factory.

Wage, w, (£) per week	Men	Women
£100 < w ≤ £150	3	4
£150 < w ≤ £200	7	5
£200 < w ≤ £250	23	12
£250 < w ≤ £300	48	27
£300 < w ≤ £350	32	11
More than £350	7	1

a What percentage of the men earn between £250 and £300 per week?

b What percentage of the women earn between £250 and £300 per week?

c Is it possible to work out the mean wage of the men and women? Explain your answer.

19.5 Addition rule for events

In this section you will learn how to:
● work out the probability of two events such as
P(event A) or P(event B)

Key word
either

We have used the addition rule already but it has not yet been formally defined.

When two events are mutually exclusive, we can work out the probability of **either** of them occurring by adding up the separate probabilities.

EXAMPLE 10

A bag contains twelve red balls, eight green balls, five blue balls and fifteen black balls. A ball is drawn at random. What is the probability of it being each of these?

a red   **b** black   **c** red or black

d not green   **e** neither green nor blue

a $P(\text{red}) = \dfrac{12}{40} = \dfrac{3}{10}$ **b** $P(\text{black}) = \dfrac{15}{40} = \dfrac{3}{8}$

c $P(\text{red or black}) = P(\text{red}) + P(\text{black}) = \dfrac{3}{10} + \dfrac{3}{8} = \dfrac{27}{40}$

d $P(\text{not green}) = \dfrac{32}{40} = \dfrac{4}{5}$

e $P(\text{neither green nor blue}) = P(\text{red or black}) = \dfrac{27}{40}$

The last part of Example 10 is another illustration of how confusing probability can be. You might think

$$P(\text{neither green nor blue}) = P(\text{not green}) + P(\text{not blue}) = \frac{32}{40} + \frac{35}{40} = \frac{67}{40}$$

This cannot be correct, as the answer is greater than 1. In fact, the events "not green" and "not blue" are not mutually exclusive, as there are lots of balls that are true for both events.

 **EXERCISE 19E**

1 Iqbal throws an ordinary dice. What is the probability that he throws these scores?

     a 2   **b** 5   **c** 2 or 5

2 Jennifer draws a card from a pack of cards. What is the probability that she draws these?

     a a Heart   **b** a Club   **c** a Heart or a Club

3 Jasper draws a card from a pack of cards. What is the probability that he draws one of the following numbers?

     a 2   **b** 6   **c** 2 or 6

4 A letter is chosen at random from the letters on these cards. What is the probability of choosing each of these?

     a a B   **b** a vowel   **c** a B or a vowel

D

5 A bag contains 10 white balls, 12 black balls and 8 red balls. A ball is drawn at random from the bag. What is the probability of each of these outcomes?

a white

b black

c black or white

d not red

e not red or black

HINTS AND TIPS

You can only add fractions with the same denominator.

C

6 At the School Fayre the tombola stall gives out a prize if you draw from the drum a numbered ticket that ends in 0 or 5. There are 300 tickets in the drum altogether and the probability of getting a winning ticket is 0.4.

a What is the probability of getting a losing ticket?

b How many winning tickets are there in the drum?

7 John needs his calculator for his mathematics lesson. It is either in his pocket, bag or locker. The probability it is in his pocket is 0.35; the probability it is in his bag is 0.45. What is the probability that

a he will have the calculator for the lesson?

b it is in his locker?

8 A spinner has numbers and colours on it, as shown in the diagram. Their probabilities are given in the tables.

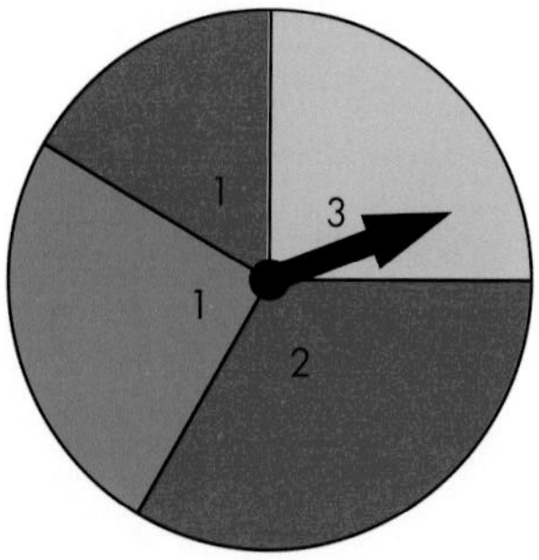

When the spinner is spun what is the probability of each of the following?

a red or green

b 2 or 3

c 3 or green

d 2 or green

e **i** Explain why the answer to P(1 or red) is not 0.9.

ii What is the answer to P(1 or red)?

Red	0.5
Green	0.25
Blue	0.25

1	0.4
2	0.35
3	0.25

9 Debbie has 20 unlabelled pirate CDs, 12 of which are rock, 5 are pop and 3 are classical. She picks a CD at random. What is the probability of these outcomes?

a rock or pop

b pop or classical

c not pop

10 The probability that it rains on Monday is 0.5. The probability that it rains on Tuesday is 0.5 and the probability that it rains on Wednesday is 0.5. Kelly argues that it is certain to rain on Monday, Tuesday or Wednesday because 0.5 + 0.5 + 0.5 = 1.5, which is bigger than 1 so that it is a certain event. Explain why she is wrong.

Combined events

In this section you will learn how to:
- work out the probability of two events occurring at the same time

Key words
probability
space
diagram
sample space
diagram

There are many situations where two events occur together. Some examples are given below. Note that in each case all the possible outcomes of the events are shown in diagrams. These are called **probability space diagrams** or **sample space diagrams**.

Throwing two dice

Imagine that two dice, one red and one blue, are thrown. The red dice can land with any one of six scores: 1, 2, 3, 4, 5 or 6. The blue dice can also land with any one of six scores. This gives a total of 36 possible combinations. These are shown in the left-hand diagram, where each combination is given as (2, 3), etc. The first number is the score on the blue dice and the second number is the score on the red dice.

The combination (2, 3) gives a total score of 5. The total scores for all the combinations are shown in the right-hand diagram.

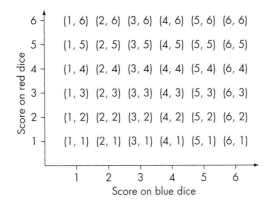
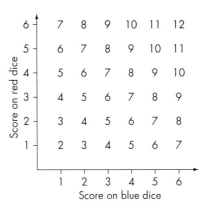

From the diagram on the right, we can see that there are two ways to get a score of 3. This gives a probability of

$$P(3) = \frac{2}{36} = \frac{1}{18}$$

From the diagram on the left, we can see that there are six ways to get a "double". This gives a probability of

$$P(double) = \frac{6}{36} = \frac{1}{6}$$

Throwing coins

Throwing one coin

There are two equally likely outcomes, head or tail

Throwing two coins together

There are four equally likely outcomes

$$P(2 \text{ heads}) = \frac{1}{4}$$

$$P(\text{head and tail}) = 2 \text{ ways out of } 4 = \frac{2}{4} = \frac{1}{2}$$

Dice and coins

Throwing a dice and a coin

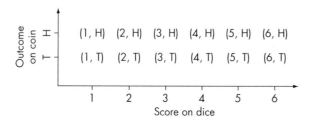

$$P(\text{head and an even number}) = 3 \text{ ways out of } 12 = \frac{3}{12} = \frac{1}{4}$$

 EXERCISE 19F

1 To answer these questions, use the right-hand diagram on page 95 for the total scores when two dice are thrown together.

    a What is the most likely score?

    b Which two scores are least likely?

    c Write down the probabilities of all scores from 2 to 12.

    d What is the probability of each of these scores?

        i bigger than 10   **ii** between 3 and 7   **iii** even

        iv a square number   **v** a prime number   **vi** a triangular number

2 Using the left-hand diagram on page 95 that shows, as coordinates, the outcomes when two dice are thrown together, what is the probability of each of these?

    a the score is an even "double"

    b at least one of the dice shows 2

    c the score on one dice is twice the score on the other dice

    d at least one of the dice shows a multiple of 3

3 Using the left-hand diagram on page 95 that shows, as coordinates, the outcomes when two dice are thrown together, what is the probability of each of these?

a both dice show a 6

b at least one of the dice shows a six

c exactly one dice shows a six

4 The diagram shows the score for the event "the difference between the scores when two dice are thrown". Copy and complete the diagram.

For the event described above, what is the probability of a difference of each of these?

a 1   **b** 0   **c** 4

d 6   **e** an odd number

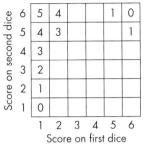

5 When two coins are thrown together, what is the probability of each of these outcomes?

a 2 heads   **b** a head and a tail

c at least 1 tail   **d** no tails

Use the diagram of the outcomes when two coins are thrown together, on page 96.

6 Two five-sided spinners are spun together and the total score of the faces that they land on is worked out. Copy and complete this probability space diagram.

a What is the most likely score?

b When two five-sided spinners are spun together, what is the probability of each of these?

     i the total score is 5   **ii** the total score is an even number

     iii the score is a "double"   **iv** the score is less than 7

7 When three coins are tossed together, what is the probability of each of these outcomes?

a three heads   **b** two heads and one tail

c at least one tail   **d** no tails

8 When one coin is tossed there are two outcomes. When two coins are tossed, there are four outcomes. When three coins are tossed, there are eight outcomes.

a How many outcomes will there be when four coins are tossed?

b How many outcomes will there be when five coins are tossed?

c How many outcomes will there be when ten coins are tossed?

d How many outcomes will there be when n coins are tossed?

C

9 When a dice and a coin are thrown together, what is the probability of each of the following outcomes?

a You get a head on the coin and a 6 on the dice.

b You get a tail on the coin and an even number on the dice.

c You get a head on the coin and a square number on the dice.

Use the diagram on page 96 that shows the outcomes when a dice and a coin are thrown together.

19.7 Tree diagrams

In this section you will learn how to:
- use sample space diagrams and tree diagrams to work out the probability of combined events

Key words
combined events
space diagram
tree diagram

Imagine we have to draw two cards from this pack of six cards, but we must replace the first card before we select the second card.

One way we could show all the outcomes of this experiment is to construct a **probability space diagram**. For example, this could be an array set in a pair of axes, like those used for the two dice (see page 95), or a pictogram, like those used for the coins, or simply a list of all the outcomes. By showing all the outcomes of our experiment as an array, we obtain the diagram below.

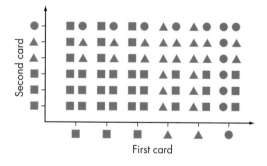

From the diagram, we can see immediately that the probability of picking, say, two squares is 9 out of 36 pairs of cards. So,

$$P(2 \text{ squares}) = \frac{9}{36} = \frac{1}{4}$$

EXAMPLE 11

Using the probability space diagram on page 98, what is the probability of getting each of these outcomes?

a a square and a triangle (in any order)

b two circles

c two shapes the same

a There are 12 combinations which give a square and a triangle together. There are six when a square is chosen first and six when a triangle is chosen first. So,

$$P(\text{square and triangle, in any order}) = \frac{12}{36} = \frac{1}{3}$$

b There is only one combination which gives two circles. So,

$$P(\text{two circles}) = \frac{1}{36}$$

c There are nine combinations of two squares together, four combinations of two triangles together, and one combination of two circles together. These give a total of 14 combinations with two shapes the same. So,

$$P(\text{two shapes the same}) = \frac{14}{36} = \frac{7}{18}$$

An alternative method to tackling problems involving **combined events** is to use a **tree diagram**.

When we pick the first card, there are three possible outcomes: a square, a triangle or a circle. For a single event,

$$P(\text{square}) = \frac{1}{2} \qquad P(\text{triangle}) = \frac{1}{3} \qquad P(\text{circle}) = \frac{1}{6}$$

We can show this by depicting each event as a branch and writing its probability on the branch.

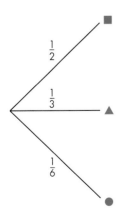

The diagram can then be extended to take into account a second choice. Because the first card has been replaced, we can still pick a square, a triangle or a circle. This is true no matter what is chosen the first time. We can demonstrate this by adding three more branches to the "squares" branch in the diagram.

Here is the complete tree diagram.

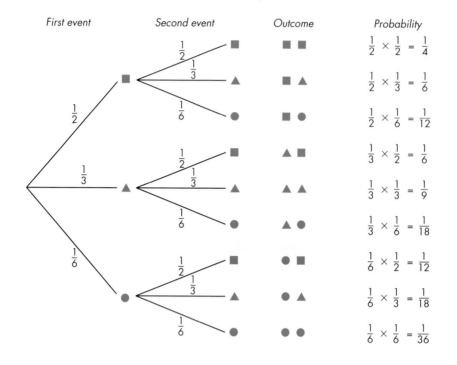

The probability of any outcome is calculated by multiplying together the probabilities on its branches. For instance,

$$P(\text{two squares}) = \frac{1}{2} \times \frac{1}{2} = \frac{1}{4}$$

$$P(\text{triangle followed by circle}) = \frac{1}{3} \times \frac{1}{6} = \frac{1}{18}$$

EXAMPLE 12

Using the tree diagram above, what is the probability of obtaining each of the following?

a two triangles

b a circle followed by a triangle

c a square and a triangle, in any order

d two circles

e two shapes the same

a $P(\text{two triangles}) = \dfrac{1}{9}$

b $P(\text{circle followed by triangle}) = \dfrac{1}{18}$

c There are two places in the outcome column which have a square and a triangle. These are the second and fourth rows. The probability of each is $\frac{1}{6}$. Their combined probability is given by the addition rule.

$$P(\text{square and triangle, in any order}) = \frac{1}{6} + \frac{1}{6} = \frac{1}{3}$$

d P(two circles) = $\frac{1}{36}$

e There are three places in the outcome column which have two shapes the same. These are the first, fifth and last rows. The probabilities are respectively $\frac{1}{4}, \frac{1}{9}$ and $\frac{1}{36}$. Their combined probability is given by the addition rule.

$$P(\text{two shapes the same}) = \frac{1}{4} + \frac{1}{9} + \frac{1}{36} = \frac{7}{18}$$

Note that the answers to parts **c**, **d** and **e** are the same as the answers obtained in Example 11.

EXERCISE 19G

1 A coin is tossed twice. Copy and complete the tree diagram below to show all the outcomes.

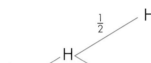

| First event | Second event | Outcome | Probability |

$\frac{1}{2}$ H   (H, H) $\frac{1}{2} \times \frac{1}{2} = \frac{1}{4}$

H

$\frac{1}{2}$ T

H

$\frac{1}{2}$ T

T

Use your tree diagram to work out the probability of each of these outcomes.

a getting two heads

b getting a head and a tail

c getting at least one tail

2 A card is drawn from a pack of cards. It is replaced, the pack is shuffled and another card is drawn.

a What is the probability that either card was an Ace?

b What is the probability that either card was not an Ace?

c Draw a tree diagram to show the outcomes of two cards being drawn as described. Use the tree diagram to work out the probability of each of these.

  i both cards will be Aces

  ii at least one of the cards will be an Ace

3 On my way to work, I drive through two sets of road works with traffic lights which only show green or red. I know that the probability of the first set being green is $\frac{1}{3}$ and the probability of the second set being green is $\frac{1}{2}$.

a What is the probability that the first set of lights will be red?

b What is the probability that the second set of lights will be red?

c Copy and complete the tree diagram below, showing the possible outcomes when passing through both sets of lights.

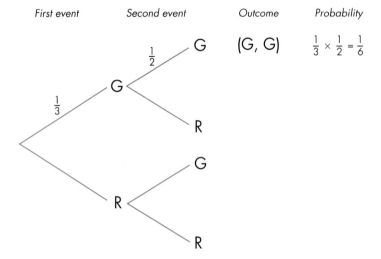

First event   Second event   Outcome   Probability

G   (G, G) $\frac{1}{3} \times \frac{1}{2} = \frac{1}{6}$

d Using the tree diagram, what is the probability of each of the following outcomes?

i I do not get held up at either set of lights

ii I get held up at exactly one set of lights

iii I get held up at least once

e Over a school term I make 90 journeys to work. On how many days can I expect to get two green lights?

4 Six out of every 10 cars in Britain are foreign made.

a What is the probability that any car will be British made?

b Two cars can be seen approaching in the distance. Draw a tree diagram to work out the probability of each of these outcomes.

i both cars will be British made

ii one car will be British and the other car will be foreign made

Three coins are tossed. Complete the tree diagram below and use it to answer the questions.

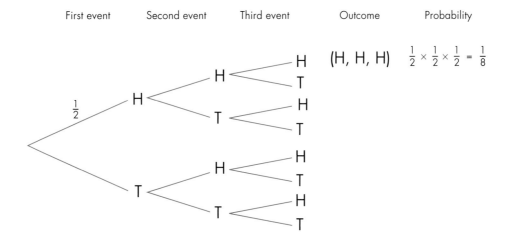

First event   Second event   Third event   Outcome   Probability

(H, H, H) $\frac{1}{2} \times \frac{1}{2} \times \frac{1}{2} = \frac{1}{8}$

If a coin is tossed three times, what is the probability that you get each of these outcomes?

a three heads

b two heads and a tail

c at least one tail

 Thomas has to take a three-part language examination paper. The first part is speaking. He has a 0.4 chance of passing this part. The second is listening. He has a 0.5 chance of passing this part. The third part is writing. He has a 0.7 chance of passing this part. Draw a tree diagram covering three events where the first event is passing or failing the speaking part of the examination, the second event is passing or failing the listening part, and the third event is passing or failing the writing part.

a If he passes all three parts, his father will give him £20. What is the probability that he gets the money?

b If he passes two parts only, he can resit the other part. What is the chance he will have to resit?

c If he fails all three parts, he will be thrown off the course. What is the chance he is thrown off the course?

 In a group of ten girls, six like the pop group Smudge and four like the pop group Mirage. Two girls are to be chosen for a pop quiz.

a What is the probability that the first girl chosen will be a Smudge fan?

b Draw a tree diagram to show the outcomes of choosing two girls and which pop groups they like. (Remember, once a girl has been chosen the first time she cannot be chosen again.)

c Use your tree diagram to work out the probability of each of these.

i both girls chosen will like Smudge

ii both girls chosen will like the same group

iii both girls chosen will like different groups

8 Look at all the tree diagrams that have been drawn so far.

a What do the probabilities across any set of branches (outlined in the diagram below) always add up to?

b What do the final probabilities (outlined in the diagram below) always add up to?

c You should now be able to fill in all of the missing values in the diagram.

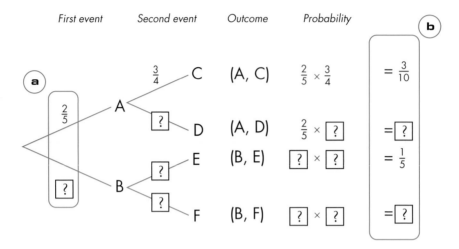

19.8 Independent events

In this section you will learn how to:	Key words
• use the connectors "and" and "or" to find the probability of combined events	and independent events or

If the outcome of event A does not effect the outcome of event B, then events A and B are called **independent events**. Most of the combined events we have looked at so far have been independent events.

It is possible to work out problems on combined events without using tree diagrams. The method explained in Example 13 is basically the same as that of a tree diagram but uses the words **and** and **or**.

EXAMPLE 13

The chance that Ashley hits a target with an arrow is $\frac{1}{4}$. He has two shots at the target. What is the probability of each of these?

a He hits the target both times.

b He hits the target once only.

c He hits the target at least once.

a P(hits both times) = P(first shot hits **and** second shot hits) = $\frac{1}{4} \times \frac{1}{4} = \frac{1}{16}$

b P(hits the target once only) = P (first hits **and** second misses **or** first misses **and** second hits) = $\left(\frac{1}{4} \times \frac{3}{4}\right) + \left(\frac{3}{4} \times \frac{1}{4}\right) = \frac{3}{8}$

c P(hits at least once) = P(both hit **or** one hits) = $\frac{1}{16} + \frac{3}{8} = \frac{7}{16}$

Note the connections between the word "and" and the operation "times", and the word "or" and the operation "add".

EXERCISE 19H

 1 Alf tosses a coin twice. The coin is biased so it has a probability of $\frac{2}{3}$ of landing on a head. What is the probability that he gets

    a two heads?   **b** a head and a tail (in any order)?

 2 Bernice draws a card from a pack of cards, replaces it, shuffles the pack and then draws another card. What is the probability that the cards are

    a both Aces?   **b** an Ace and a King (in any order)?

 3 A dice is thrown twice. What is the probability that both scores are

    a even?   **b** one even and one odd (in any order)?

 4 I throw a dice three times. What is the probability of getting three sixes?

 5 A bag contains 15 white beads and 10 black beads. I take out a bead at random, replace it and take out another bead. What is the probability of each of these?

    a both beads are black

    b one bead is black and the other white (in any order)

 6 The probability that I am late for work on Monday is 0.4. The probability that I am late on Tuesday is 0.2. What is the probability of each of the following outcomes?

    a I am late for work on Monday and Tuesday.

    b I am late for work on Monday and on time on Tuesday.

    c I am on time on both Monday and Tuesday.

7 Ronda has to take a three-part language examination paper. The first part is speaking. She has a 0.7 chance of passing this part. The second part is listening. She has a 0.6 chance of passing this part. The third part is writing. She has a 0.8 chance of passing this part.

   a If she passes all three parts, her father will give her £20. What is the probability that she gets the money?

   b If she passes two parts only, she can resit the other part. What is the chance she will have to resit?

   c If she fails all three parts, she will be thrown off the course. What is the chance she is thrown off the course?

"At least" problems

In examination questions concerning combined events, it is common to ask for the probability of at least one of the events occurring. There are two ways to solve such problems.

- All possibilities can be written out, which takes a long time.

- Use P(at least one) = 1 – P(none)

The second option is much easier to work out and there is less chance of making a mistake.

EXAMPLE 14

A bag contains seven red and three black balls. A ball is taken out and replaced. This is repeated three times. What is the probability of getting each of these?

a no red balls

b at least one red ball

a P(no reds) = P(black, black, black) = $\frac{7}{10} \times \frac{7}{10} \times \frac{7}{10}$ = 0.343

b P(at least one red) = 1 – P(no reds) = 1 – 0.343 = 0.657

Note that the answer to part **b** is 1 minus the answer to part **a**. Examination questions often build up answers in this manner.

EXERCISE 19I

1 A dice is thrown three times.

   a What is the probability of not getting a 2?

   b What is the probability of at least one 2?

 2 Four coins are thrown. What is the probability of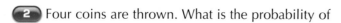

   a 4 tails?

   b at least 1 head?

3 Adam, Bashir and Clem take a mathematics test. The probability that Adam passes is 0.6, the probability that Bashir passes is 0.9, and the probability that Clem passes is 0.7. What is the probability of each of these outcomes?

    a all three pass

    b Bashir and Adam pass but Clem does not

    c all three fail

    d at least one passes

4 A bag contains 4 red and 6 blue balls. A ball is taken out and replaced. Another ball is taken out. What is the probability of each of these?

    a both balls are red   **b** both balls are blue   **c** at least one is red

5 a A dice is thrown three times. What is the probability of

    i 3 sixes?   **ii** no sixes?   **iii** at least one six?

    b A dice is thrown four times. What is the probability of

    i 4 sixes?   **ii** no sixes?   **iii** at least one six?

    c A dice is thrown five times. What is the probability of

    i 5 sixes?   **ii** no sixes?   **iii** at least one six?

    d A dice is thrown n times. What is the probability of

    i n sixes?   **ii** no sixes?   **iii** at least one six?

6 The probability that the school canteen serves chips on any day is $\frac{2}{3}$. In a week of five days, what is the probability of each of these?

    a chips are served every day

    b chips are not served on any day

    c chips are served on at least one day

7 The probability that Steve is late for work is $\frac{5}{6}$. The probability that Nigel is late for work is $\frac{9}{10}$. The probability that Gary is late for work is $\frac{1}{2}$. What is the probability that on a particular day

    a all three are late?   **b** none of them are late?   **c** at least one is late?

More advanced use of *and* and *or*

We have already seen how certain probability problems can be solved either by tree diagrams or by the use of the *and/or* method. Both methods are basically the same but the *and/or* method works better in the case of three events following one another or in situations where the number of outcomes of one event is greater than two. This is simply because the tree diagram would get too large and involved.

EXAMPLE 15

Three cards are to be drawn from a pack of cards. Each card is to be replaced before the next one is drawn. What is the probability of drawing each of these combinations?

a three Kings

b exactly two Kings and one other card

c no Kings

d at least one King

Let K be the event "Drawing a King". Let N be the event "Not drawing a King". Then you obtain

a $P(KKK) = \dfrac{1}{13} \times \dfrac{1}{13} \times \dfrac{1}{13} = \dfrac{1}{2197}$

b $P(\text{exactly two Kings}) = P(KKN) \text{ or } P(KNK) \text{ or } P(NKK)$

$$= \left(\dfrac{1}{13} \times \dfrac{1}{13} \times \dfrac{12}{13}\right) + \left(\dfrac{1}{13} \times \dfrac{12}{13} \times \dfrac{1}{13}\right) + \left(\dfrac{12}{13} \times \dfrac{1}{13} \times \dfrac{1}{13}\right) = \dfrac{36}{2197}$$

c $P(\text{no Kings}) = P(NNN) = \dfrac{12}{13} \times \dfrac{12}{13} \times \dfrac{12}{13} = \dfrac{1728}{2197}$

d $P(\text{at least one King}) = 1 - P(\text{no Kings}) = 1 - \dfrac{1728}{2197} = \dfrac{469}{2197}$

Note that in part **b** the notation stands for the probability that the first card is a King, the second is a King and the third is not a King; or the first is a King, the second is not a King and the third is a King; or the first is not a King, the second is a King and the third is a King.

Note also that the probability of each component of part **b** is exactly the same. So we could have done the calculation as

$$3 \times \dfrac{1}{13} \times \dfrac{1}{13} \times \dfrac{12}{13} = \dfrac{36}{2197}$$

Patterns of this kind often occur in probability.

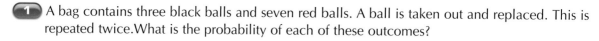

EXERCISE 19J

1 A bag contains three black balls and seven red balls. A ball is taken out and replaced. This is repeated twice. What is the probability of each of these outcomes?

a all three are black

b exactly two are black

c exactly one is black

d none are black

2 A dice is thrown four times. What is the probability of each of these?

a four sixes are thrown

b no sixes are thrown

c exactly one six is thrown

3 On my way to work I pass three sets of traffic lights. The probability that the first is green is $\frac{1}{2}$. The probability that the second is green is $\frac{1}{3}$. The probability that the third is green is $\frac{2}{3}$. What is the probability of each of these?

a all three are green

b exactly two are green

c exactly one is green

d none are green

e at least one is green

4 Alf is late for school with a probability of 0.9. Bert is late with a probability of 0.7. Chas is late with a probability of 0.6. On any particular day what is the probability of each of these?

   a exactly one of them being late   **b** exactly two of them being late

5 Daisy takes four A-levels. The probability that she will pass English is 0.7. The probability that she will pass history is 0.6. The probability she will pass geography is 0.8. The probability that she will pass general studies is 0.9. What is the probability of each of these?

   a she passes all four subjects

   b she passes exactly three subjects

   c she passes at least three subjects

6 The driving test is in two parts, a written test and a practical test. It is known that 90% of people who take the written test pass, and 60% of people who take the practical test pass. A person who passes the written test does not have to take it again. A person who fails the practical test does have to take it again.

   a What is the probability that someone passes the written test?

   b What is the probability that someone passes the practical test?

   c What is the probability that someone passes both tests?

   d What is the probability that someone passes the written test but takes two attempts to pass the practical test?

7 Six out of ten cars in Britain are made by foreign manufacturers. Three cars can be seen approaching in the distance.

   a What is the probability that the first one is foreign?

   b The first car is going so fast that its make could not be made out. What is the probability that the second car is foreign?

   c What is the probability that exactly two of the three cars are foreign?

   d Explain why, if the first car is foreign, the probability of the second car being foreign is still 6 out of 10.

8 Each day Mr Smith runs home. He has a choice of three routes: the road, the fields or the canal path. The road route is 4 miles, the fields route is 6 miles and the canal route is 5 miles. In a three-day period, what is the probability that Mr Smith runs a total distance of

   a exactly 17 miles   **b** exactly 13 miles

   c exactly 15 miles   **d** over 17 miles?

9 A rock climber attempts a difficult route. There are three hard moves at points A, B and C in the climb. The climber has a probability of 0.6, 0.3 and 0.7 respectively of completing each of these moves. What is the probability that the climber

   a completes the climb   **b** fails at move A

   c fails at move B   **d** fails at move C

In this section you will learn how to:
- work out the probability of combined events when the probabilities change after each event

Key word
conditional probability

The term **conditional probability** is used to describe the situation when the probability of an event is dependent on the outcome of another event. For instance, if a card is taken from a pack and not returned, then the probabilities for the next card drawn will be altered. The following example illustrates this situation.

EXAMPLE 16

A bag contains nine balls, of which five are white and four are black.

A ball is taken out and not replaced. Another is then taken out. If the first ball removed is black, what is the probability of each of these outcomes?

a the second ball will be black

b both balls will be black

When a black ball is removed, there are five white balls and three black balls left, reducing the total to eight.

Hence, when the second ball is taken out,

a P(second ball black) = $\dfrac{3}{8}$

b P(both balls black) = $\dfrac{4}{9} \times \dfrac{3}{8} = \dfrac{1}{6}$

EXERCISE 19K

 1 I put six CDs in my multi-player and put it on random play. Each CD has 10 tracks. Once a track is played, it is not played again.

    a What is the chance that track 5 on CD 6 is the first one played?

    b What is the maximum number of tracks that could be played before a track from CD 6 is played?

 2 There are five white and one brown eggs in an egg box. Kate decides to make a two-egg omelette. She takes each egg from the box without looking at its colour.

    a What is the probability that the first egg taken is brown?

    b If the first egg taken is brown, what is the probability that the second egg taken will be brown?

    c What is the probability that Kate gets an omelette made from each of these combinations?

        i two white eggs   **ii** one white and one brown egg   **iii** two brown eggs

 3 A box contains 10 red and 15 yellow balls. One is taken out and not replaced. Another is taken out.

    a If the first ball taken out is red, what is the probability that the second ball is

        i red?   **ii** yellow?

    b If the first ball taken out is yellow, what is the probability that the second ball is

        i red?   **ii** yellow?

 4 A fruit bowl contains six Granny Smith apples and eight Golden Delicious apples. Kevin takes two apples at random.

    a If the first apple is a Granny Smith, what is the probability that the second is

        i a Granny Smith?   **ii** a Golden Delicious?

    b What is the probability that

        i both are Granny Smiths?   **ii** both are Golden Delicious?

 5 Ann has a bargain box of tins. They are unlabelled but she knows that six tins contain soup and four contain peaches.

    a She opens two tins. What is the probability that

        i they are both soup?   **ii** they are both peaches?

    b What is the probability that she has to open two tins before she gets a tin of peaches?

    c What is the probability that she has to open three tins before she gets a tin of peaches?

    d What is the probability that she will get a tin of soup if she opens five tins?

 6 One in three cars on British roads is made in Britain. A car comes down the road. It is a British-made car. John says that the probability of the next car being British made is one in two because a British-made car has just gone past. Explain why he is wrong.

7 A bag contains three black balls and seven red balls. A ball is taken out and not replaced. This is repeated twice. What is the probability of each of these outcomes?

a all three are black

b exactly two are black

c exactly one is black

d none are black

8 One my way to work, I pass two sets of traffic lights. The probability that the first is green is $\frac{1}{3}$. If the first is green, the probability that the second is green is $\frac{1}{3}$. If the first is red, the probability that the second is green is $\frac{2}{3}$. What is the probability of each of these?

a both are green

b none are green

c exactly one is green

d at least one is green

9 A hand of five cards is dealt. What is the probability of each of these outcomes?

a all five are Spades

b all five are the same suit

c they are four Aces and any other card

d they are four of a kind and any other card

10 An engineering test is in two parts, a written test and a practical test. It is known that 90% who take the written test pass. When a person passes the written test, the probability that he/she will also pass the practical test is 60%. When a person fails the written test, the probability that he/she will pass the practical test is 20%.

a What is the probability that someone passes both tests?

b What is the probability that someone passes one test?

c What is the probability that someone fails both tests?

d What is the combined probability of the answers to parts a, b and c?

11 Each day Mr Smith runs home from work. He has a choice of three routes. The road, the fields or the canal path. On Monday, each route has an equal probability of being chosen. The route chosen on any day will not be picked the next day and so each of the other two routes has an equal probability of being chosen.

a Write down all the possible combinations so that Mr Smith runs home via the canal path on Wednesday (there are four of them).

b Calculate the probability that Mr Smith runs home via the canal path on Wednesday.

c Calculate the probability that Mr Smith runs home via the canal path on Tuesday.

d Using your results from parts b and c, write down the probability that Mr Smith runs home via the canal path on Thursday.

e Explain the answers to parts b, c and d.

1 Jacob has 2 bags of sweets.

Bag P contains 3 green sweets and 4 red sweets.
Bag Q contains 1 green sweet and 3 yellow sweets.

Jacob takes one sweet at random from each bag.

a Copy and complete the tree diagram.

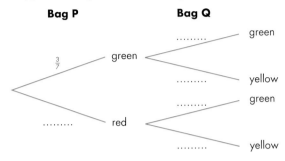

Bag P   **Bag Q**

b Calculate the probability that Jacob will take 2 green sweets.

Edexcel, Question 3, Paper 13B Higher, March 2004

2 a Jonathan has a bag containing 10 balls. The balls are red, green or blue. He takes a ball at random from the bag and notes its colour. He then replaces the ball in the bag and repeats the experiment 500 times.

The results are

Red	Green	Blue
235	168	97

i What is the relative frequency of picking a red ball?

ii How many of each coloured ball are in the bag?

b Matthew takes a ball at random from another bag and replaces it. He does this 10 times and gets 6 reds and 4 greens. He claims that there are no blue balls in the bag.

Explain why he could be wrong.

3 Julie and Pat are going to the cinema.

The probability that Julie will arrive late is 0.2.
The probability that Pat will arrive late is 0.6.
The two events are independent.

a Copy and complete the tree diagram.

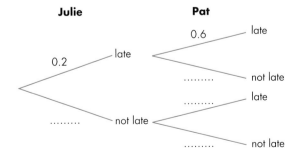

Julie   **Pat**

b What is the probability that Julie and Pat will both arrive late?

Edexcel, Question 6, Paper 13A Higher, January 2003

4 Arthur has a box of 10 unlabelled CDs. The CDs are pop, classical or dance. The table shows the probability of each type of music if a CD is taken out at random.

Type of music	Probability
Pop	0.6
Classical	0.1
Dance	

a What is the probability that a CD chosen at random is a dance CD?

b How many classical CDs are in the box?

c Arthur picks a CD at random and puts it in a 2-disc CD player. He then picks another CD at random and puts it in the player. Complete the tree diagram

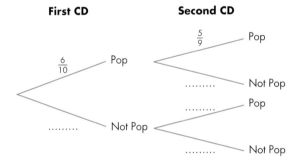

First CD   **Second CD**

d What is the probability that neither of the CDs is pop?

5 At the end of a course, army cadets have to pass an exam to gain a certificate. The probability of passing the exam at the first attempt is 0.65.
Those who fail are allowed to re-sit.
The probability of passing the re-sit is 0.7.
No further attempts are allowed.

a i Complete the tree diagram.

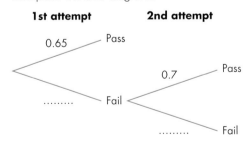

1st attempt   **2nd attempt**

ii What is the probability that a cadet fails to gain a certificate after two attempts?

b Five cadets take the exam.
What is the probability that all of them gain a certificate?

6 Jim spins a biased coin. The probability that it will land on heads is twice the probability that it will land on tails.

Jim spins the coin twice. Find the probability that it will land once on heads and once on tails.

Edexcel, Question 6, Paper 13B Higher, January 2004

7 A drinks machine uses cartridges to supply the drink. Billy has a job lot of eight cartridges which have lost their labels. He knows he has three teas and five coffees. He makes three drinks with the cartridges.

a What is the probability he gets three teas?

b What is the probability he gets exactly two coffees?

c What is the probability that he gets at least one coffee?

d Billy makes the three drinks and leaves the room. Betty comes in, tastes one of the drinks. She finds it is tea. What is the probability that the other two drinks are also tea?

WORKED EXAM QUESTION

The probability that Barney has a walk in the park on any day is $\frac{3}{4}$. The probability that Barney goes for a walk in the park and goes to the café $\frac{3}{16}$.

a One day Barney goes to the park. Calculate the probability that he goes to the café.

b Calculate the probability that Barney goes to the park and does not go to the café.

Solution

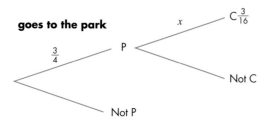

a P(Barney goes for a walk in the park) $\times x = \frac{3}{16}$

— Draw the part of the probability tree that you know about.

— Set up an equation.

$$\frac{3}{4} \times x = \frac{3}{16}$$

P(Barney goes to the café when he goes to the park) $= \frac{3}{16} \div \frac{3}{4}$

$$= \frac{3}{16} \times \frac{4}{3} = \frac{1}{4}$$

— Substitute in the probabilities and solve the equation. Remember to turn the fraction upside down and multiply by it when you divide.

b P(Barney does not go to the café) $= 1 - \frac{1}{4} = \frac{3}{4}$

P(Barney goes to the park and does not go to the café) $= \frac{3}{4} \times \frac{3}{4} = \frac{9}{16}$

— First work out the probability of the complementary event then use the 'and' rule for combined events.

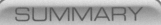

GRADE YOURSELF

D Able to calculate the probability of an event happening when you know the probability that the event does not happen and that the total probability of all possible outcomes is 1

D Able to predict the expected number of successes from a given number of trials if you know the probability of one success

C Able to calculate relative frequency from experimental evidence and compare this with the theoretical probability

B Able to draw a tree diagram to work out the probability of combined events

A Able to use *and/or* or a tree diagram to work out probabilities of specific outcomes of combined events

A* Able to work out the probabilities of combined events when the probability of each event changes depending on the outcome of the previous event

What you should know now

● How to calculate theoretical probabilities from different situations

Algebra 3

1 Algebraic fractions

2 Linear and non-linear simultaneous equations

3 Number sequences

4 General rules from given patterns

5 Quadratic sequences

6 Changing the subject of a formula

This chapter will show you ...

- how to combine fractions algebraically and solve equations with algebraic fractions
- how to solve linear and non-linear simultaneous equations
- some of the common sequences of numbers
- how to express a rule for a sequence in words and algebraically
- how to transpose a formula where the subject appears twice

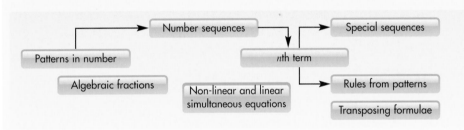

What you should already know

- How to state a rule for a simple linear sequence in words
- How to substitute numbers into an algebraic expression
- How to factorise simple linear expressions
- How to expand a pair of linear brackets to get a quadratic equation

Quick check

1 Write down the next three terms of these sequences.

a 2, 5, 8, 11, 14, ...　　　　**b** 1, 3, 6, 10, 15, 21, ...

c 40, 35, 30, 25, 20, ...　　　**d** 1, 4, 9, 16, 25, 36, ...

2 Work out the value of the expression $3n - 2$ for

a $n = 1$　　　　　**b** $n = 2$　　　　　**c** $n = 3$

3 Factorise

a $2x + 6$　　　　**b** $x^2 - x$　　　　**c** $10x^2 + 2x$

4 Expand

a $(x + 6)(x + 2)$　　**b** $(2x + 1)(x - 3)$　　**c** $(x - 2)^2$

5 Make x the subject of

a $2y + x = 3$　　**b** $x - 3y = 4$　　**c** $4y - x = 3$

In this section you will learn how to:
- simplify algebraic fractions
- solve equations containing algebraic fractions

Key words

brackets
cancel
cross-multiply
expression
factorise
identity

The following four **identities** are used to work out the value of fractions. An identity is a rule that is true for any values. The sign '≡' is used to show an identity.

Addition: $$\frac{a}{b} + \frac{c}{d} \equiv \frac{ad + bc}{bd}$$

Subtraction: $$\frac{a}{b} - \frac{c}{d} \equiv \frac{ad - bc}{bd}$$

Multiplication: $$\frac{a}{b} \times \frac{c}{d} \equiv \frac{ac}{bd}$$

Division: $$\frac{a}{b} \div \frac{c}{d} \equiv \frac{ad}{bc}$$

Note that a, b, c and d can be numbers, other letters or algebraic **expressions**. Remember:

- use **brackets**, if necessary

- **factorise** if you can

- **cancel** if you can.

EXAMPLE 1

Simplify   **a** $\dfrac{1}{x} + \dfrac{x}{2y}$ **b** $\dfrac{2}{b} - \dfrac{a}{2b}$

a Using the addition rule: $\dfrac{1}{x} + \dfrac{x}{2y} = \dfrac{(1)(2y) + (x)(x)}{(x)(2y)} = \dfrac{2y + x^2}{2xy}$

b Using the subtraction rule: $\dfrac{2}{b} - \dfrac{a}{2b} = \dfrac{(2)(2b) - (a)(b)}{(b)(2b)} = \dfrac{4b - ab}{2b^2}$

$$= \dfrac{b(4 - a)}{2b^2} = \dfrac{4 - a}{2b}$$

Note: There are different ways of working out fraction calculations. Part **b** could have been done by making the denominator of each fraction the same. Namely,

$$\dfrac{(2)2}{(2)b} - \dfrac{a}{2b} = \dfrac{4 - a}{2b}$$

EXAMPLE 2

Simplify   **a** $\dfrac{x}{3} \times \dfrac{x+2}{x-2}$ **b** $\dfrac{x}{3} \div \dfrac{2x}{7}$

a Using the multiplication rule: $\dfrac{x}{3} \times \dfrac{x+2}{x-2} = \dfrac{(x)(x+2)}{(3)(x-2)} = \dfrac{x^2+2x}{3x-6}$

Remember that the line that separates the top from the bottom of an algebraic fraction acts as a bracket as well as a divide sign. Note that it is sometimes preferable to leave an algebraic fraction in a factorised form.

b Using the division rule: $\dfrac{x}{3} \div \dfrac{2x}{7} = \dfrac{(\cancel{x})(7)}{(3)(2\cancel{x})} = \dfrac{7}{6}$

EXAMPLE 3

Solve this equation. $\dfrac{x+1}{3} - \dfrac{x-3}{2} = 1$

Use the rule for combining fractions, and also **cross-multiply** the denominator of the left-hand side to the right-hand side.

$$\dfrac{(2)(x+1) - (3)(x-3)}{(2)(3)} = 1$$

$$2(x+1) - 3(x-3) = 6 \ (= 1 \times 2 \times 3)$$

Note the brackets. These will avoid problems with signs and help you to expand to get a linear equation.

$$2x + 2 - 3x + 9 = 6 \quad \Rightarrow \quad -x = -5 \quad \Rightarrow \quad x = 5$$

EXAMPLE 4

Solve this equation. $\dfrac{3}{x-1} - \dfrac{2}{x+1} = 1$

Use the rule for combining fractions, and cross multiply the denominator as in Example 3. Use brackets to help with expanding and to avoid problems with minus signs.

$$3(x+1) - 2(x-1) = (x-1)(x+1)$$

$$3x + 3 - 2x + 2 = x^2 - 1 \quad \text{(Right-hand side is the difference of two squares.)}$$

Rearrange into the general quadratic form (see Chapter 12).

$$x^2 - x - 6 = 0$$

Factorise and solve $(x-3)(x+2) = 0 \quad \Rightarrow \quad x = 3 \text{ or } -2$

Note that when your equation is rearranged into the quadratic form it should factorise. If it doesn't, then you have almost certainly made a mistake. If the question required an answer as a decimal or a surd it would say so.

EXAMPLE 5

Simplify: $\dfrac{2x^2 + x - 3}{4x^2 - 9}$

Factorise the numerator and denominator: $\dfrac{(2x + 3)(x - 1)}{(2x + 3)(2x - 3)}$

Denominator is the difference of two squares.

Cancel any common factors: $\dfrac{\cancel{(2x + 3)}(x - 1)}{\cancel{(2x + 3)}(2x - 3)}$

If at this stage there isn't a common factor on top and bottom, you should check your factorisations.

Remaining term is the answer: $\dfrac{(x - 1)}{(2x - 3)}$

EXERCISE 20A

1 Simplify each of these.

a $\dfrac{x}{2} + \dfrac{x}{3}$

b $\dfrac{3x}{4} + \dfrac{x}{5}$

c $\dfrac{3x}{4} + \dfrac{2x}{5}$

d $\dfrac{x}{2} + \dfrac{y}{3}$

e $\dfrac{xy}{4} + \dfrac{2}{x}$

f $\dfrac{x + 1}{2} + \dfrac{x + 2}{3}$

g $\dfrac{2x - 1}{2} + \dfrac{3x - 1}{4}$

h $\dfrac{x}{5} + \dfrac{2x - 1}{3}$

i $\dfrac{x - 2}{2} + \dfrac{x + 3}{4}$

j $\dfrac{x - 4}{5} + \dfrac{2x - 3}{2}$

2 Simplify each of these.

a $\dfrac{x}{2} - \dfrac{x}{3}$

b $\dfrac{3x}{4} - \dfrac{x}{5}$

c $\dfrac{3x}{4} - \dfrac{2x}{5}$

d $\dfrac{x}{2} - \dfrac{y}{3}$

e $\dfrac{xy}{4} - \dfrac{2}{y}$

f $\dfrac{x + 1}{2} - \dfrac{x + 2}{3}$

g $\dfrac{2x + 1}{2} - \dfrac{3x + 3}{4}$

h $\dfrac{x}{5} - \dfrac{2x + 1}{3}$

i $\dfrac{x - 2}{2} - \dfrac{x - 3}{4}$

j $\dfrac{x - 4}{5} - \dfrac{2x - 3}{2}$

3 Solve the following equations.

a $\dfrac{x + 1}{2} + \dfrac{x + 2}{5} = 3$

b $\dfrac{x + 2}{4} + \dfrac{x + 1}{7} = 3$

c $\dfrac{4x + 1}{3} - \dfrac{x + 2}{4} = 2$

d $\dfrac{2x - 1}{3} + \dfrac{3x + 1}{4} = 7$

e $\dfrac{2x + 1}{2} - \dfrac{x + 1}{7} = 1$

f $\dfrac{3x + 1}{5} - \dfrac{5x - 1}{7} = 0$

4 Simplify each of these.

a $\dfrac{x}{2} \times \dfrac{x}{3}$

b $\dfrac{2x}{7} \times \dfrac{3y}{4}$

c $\dfrac{4x}{3y} \times \dfrac{2y}{x}$

d $\dfrac{4y^2}{9x} \times \dfrac{3x^2}{2y}$

e $\dfrac{x}{2} \times \dfrac{x-2}{5}$

f $\dfrac{x-3}{15} \times \dfrac{5}{2x-6}$

g $\dfrac{2x+1}{2} \times \dfrac{3x+1}{4}$

h $\dfrac{x}{5} \times \dfrac{2x+1}{3}$

i $\dfrac{x-2}{2} \times \dfrac{4}{x-3}$

j $\dfrac{x-5}{10} \times \dfrac{5}{x^2-5x}$

5 Simplify each of these.

a $\dfrac{x}{2} \div \dfrac{x}{3}$

b $\dfrac{2x}{7} \div \dfrac{4y}{14}$

c $\dfrac{4x}{3y} \div \dfrac{x}{2y}$

d $\dfrac{4y^2}{9x} \div \dfrac{2y}{3x^2}$

e $\dfrac{x}{2} \div \dfrac{x-2}{5}$

f $\dfrac{x-3}{15} \div \dfrac{5}{2x-6}$

g $\dfrac{2x+1}{2} \div \dfrac{4x+2}{4}$

h $\dfrac{x}{6} \div \dfrac{2x^2+x}{3}$

i $\dfrac{x-2}{12} \div \dfrac{4}{x-3}$

j $\dfrac{x-5}{10} \div \dfrac{x^2-5x}{5}$

6 Simplify each of these. Factorise and cancel where appropriate.

a $\dfrac{3x}{4} + \dfrac{x}{4}$

b $\dfrac{3x}{4} - \dfrac{x}{4}$

c $\dfrac{3x}{4} \times \dfrac{x}{4}$

d $\dfrac{3x}{4} \div \dfrac{x}{4}$

e $\dfrac{3x+1}{2} + \dfrac{x-2}{5}$

f $\dfrac{3x+1}{2} - \dfrac{x-2}{5}$

g $\dfrac{3x+1}{2} \times \dfrac{x-2}{5}$

h $\dfrac{x^2-9}{10} \times \dfrac{5}{x-3}$

i $\dfrac{2x+3}{5} \div \dfrac{6x+9}{10}$

j $\dfrac{2x^2}{9} - \dfrac{2y^2}{3}$

7 Show that each algebraic fraction simplifies to the given expression.

a $\dfrac{2}{x+1} + \dfrac{5}{x+2} = 3$ simplifies to $3x^2 + 2x - 3 = 0$

b $\dfrac{4}{x-2} + \dfrac{7}{x+1} = 3$ simplifies to $3x^2 - 14x + 4 = 0$

c $\dfrac{3}{4x+1} - \dfrac{4}{x+2} = 2$ simplifies to $8x^2 + 31x + 2 = 0$

d $\dfrac{2}{2x-1} - \dfrac{6}{x+1} = 11$ simplifies to $22x^2 + 21x - 19 = 0$

e $\dfrac{3}{2x-1} - \dfrac{4}{3x-1} = 1$ simplifies to $x^2 - x = 0$

8 Solve the following equations.

a $\dfrac{4}{x+1} + \dfrac{5}{x+2} = 2$

b $\dfrac{18}{4x-1} - \dfrac{1}{x+1} = 1$

c $\dfrac{2x-1}{2} - \dfrac{6}{x+1} = 1$

d $\dfrac{3}{2x-1} - \dfrac{4}{3x-1} = 1$

9 Simplify the following expressions.

a $\dfrac{x^2 + 2x - 3}{2x^2 + 7x + 3}$

b $\dfrac{4x^2 - 1}{2x^2 + 5x - 3}$

c $\dfrac{6x^2 + x - 2}{9x^2 - 4}$

d $\dfrac{4x^2 + x - 3}{4x^2 - 7x + 3}$

e $\dfrac{4x^2 - 25}{8x^2 - 22x + 5}$

20.2 Linear and non-linear simultaneous equations

In this section you will learn how to:
- solve linear and non-linear simultaneous equations

Key words
linear
non-linear
substitute

You have already seen the method of substitution for solving **linear** simultaneous equations (see Year 10 book, page 98). Example 6 is a reminder.

EXAMPLE 6

Solve these simultaneous equations.

$2x + 3y = 7$ (1)

$x - 4y = 9$ (2)

First, rearrange equation (2) to obtain:

$x = 9 + 4y$

Substitute the expression for x into equation (1), which gives:

$2(9 + 4y) + 3y = 7$

Expand and solve this equation to obtain:

$18 + 8y + 3y = 7$

$\Rightarrow \quad 11y = -11$

$\Rightarrow \quad y = -1$

Now substitute y into either equation (1) or (2) to find x. Using equation (1), we have

$\Rightarrow 2x - 3 = 7$

$\Rightarrow \quad x = 5$

We can use a similar method when we need to solve a pair of equations, one of which is linear and the other of which is **non-linear**. But we must *always* **substitute** from the linear into the non-linear.

EXAMPLE 7

Solve these simultaneous equations.

$$x^2 + y^2 = 5$$
$$x + y = 3$$

Call the equations (1) and (2):

$$x^2 + y^2 = 5 \text{ (1)}$$
$$x + y = 3 \text{ (2)}$$

Rearrange equation (2) to obtain:

$$x = 3 - y$$

Substitute this into equation (1), which gives:

$$(3 - y)^2 + y^2 = 5$$

Expand and rearrange into the general form of the quadratic equation:

$$9 - 6y + y^2 + y^2 = 5$$
$$2y^2 - 6y + 4 = 0$$

Cancel by 2:

$$y^2 - 3y + 2 = 0$$

Factorise:

$$(y - 1)(y - 2) = 0$$
$$\Rightarrow \qquad y = 1 \text{ or } 2$$

Substitute for y in equation (2):

When $y = 1$, $x = 2$; and when $y = 2$, $x = 1$.

Note you should always give answers as a pair of values in x and y.

EXERCISE 20B

1 Solve these pairs of linear simultaneous equations using the substitution method.

a $2x + y = 9$
$x - 2y = 7$

b $3x - 2y = 10$
$4x + y = 17$

c $x - 2y = 10$
$2x + 3y = 13$

2 Solve these pairs of simultaneous equations.

a $xy = 2$
$y = x + 1$

b $xy = -4$
$2y = x + 6$

3 Solve these pairs of simultaneous equations.

a $x^2 + y^2 = 25$
   $x + y = 7$

b $x^2 + y^2 = 9$
   $y = x + 3$

c $x^2 + y^2 = 13$
   $5y + x = 13$

4 Solve these pairs of simultaneous equations.

a $y = x^2 + 2x - 3$
   $y = 2x + 1$

b $y = x^2 - 2x - 5$
   $y = x - 1$

c $y = x^2 - 2x$
   $y = 2x - 3$

5 Solve these pairs of simultaneous equations.

a $y = x^2 + x - 2$
   $y = 5x - 6$

b $y = x^2 + 2x - 3$
   $y = 4x - 4$

c What is the geometrical significance of the answers to parts **a** and **b**?

20.3 Number sequences

In this section you will learn how to:
- recognise how number sequences are built up
- find the *n*th term of a sequence
- recognise some special sequences

Key words
coefficient
consecutive
difference
*n*th term
sequence
term

A number **sequence** is an ordered set of numbers with a rule to find every number in the sequence. The rule which takes you from one number to the next could be a simple addition or multiplication, but often it is more tricky than that. So you need to look most carefully at the pattern of a sequence.

Each number in a sequence is called a **term** and is in a certain position in the sequence.

Look at these sequences and their rules.

3, 6, 12, 24, ... doubling the last term each time ... 48, 96, ...

2, 5, 8, 11, ... adding 3 to the last term each time ... 14, 17, ...

1, 10, 100, 1000, ... multiplying the last term by 10 each time ... 10 000, 100 000, ...

1, 8, 15, 22, ... adding 7 to the last term each time ... 29, 36, ...

These are all quite straightforward once you have looked for the link from one term to the next (**consecutive** terms).

Differences

For some sequences we need to look at the **differences** between consecutive terms to determine the pattern.

EXAMPLE 8

Find the next two terms of the sequence 1, 3, 6, 10, 15, …

Looking at the differences between each pair of consecutive terms, we notice:

1   3   6   10   15
 ↑   ↑   ↑   ↑
 2   3   4   5

So, we can continue the sequence as follows:

1   3   6   10   15   21   28
 ↑   ↑   ↑   ↑
 2   3   4   5 ⌊ +6 ⌋⌊ +7 ⌋

The differences usually form a number sequence of their own, so you need to find out the sequence of the differences before you can expand the original sequence.

Generalising to find the rule

When using a number sequence, we sometimes need to know, say, its 50th term, or even a later term in the sequence. To do so, we need to find the rule which produces the sequence in its general form.

Let's first look at the problem backwards. That is, we'll take a rule and see how it produces a sequence.

EXAMPLE 9

A sequence is formed by the rule $3n + 1$, where $n = 1, 2, 3, 4, 5, 6, …$. Write down the first five terms of the sequence.

Substituting $n = 1, 2, 3, 4, 5$ in turn, we get:

$(3 \times 1 + 1), (3 \times 2 + 1), (3 \times 3 + 1), (3 \times 4 + 1), (3 \times 5 + 1), …$

    4   7   10   13   16

So the sequence is 4, 7, 10, 13, 16, …

Notice that the difference between each term and the next is always 3, which is the **coefficient** of n (the number attached to n). The constant term is the difference between the first term and the coefficient (in this case, $4 - 3 = 1$).

EXAMPLE 10

The **nth term** of a sequence is $4n - 3$. Write down the first five terms of the sequence.

Substituting $n = 1, 2, 3, 4, 5$ in turn, we get

$$(4 \times 1 - 3), (4 \times 2 - 3), (4 \times 3 - 3), (4 \times 4 - 3), (4 \times 5 - 3)$$
$$1 \qquad 5 \qquad 9 \qquad 13 \qquad 17$$

So the sequence is 1, 5, 9, 13, 17, …

Notice that the difference between each term and the next is always 4, which is the coefficient of n. The constant term is the difference between the first term and the coefficient $(1 - 4 = -3)$.

EXERCISE 20C

 1 Look carefully at each number sequence below. Find the next two numbers in the sequence and try to explain the pattern.

a 1, 1, 2, 3, 5, 8, 13, …   **b** 1, 4, 9, 16, 25, 36, …

c 3, 4, 7, 11, 18, 29, …

> **HINTS AND TIPS**
>
> These patterns do not go up by the same value each time so you will need to find another connection between the terms.

 2 Triangular numbers are found as follows.

1   3   6   10

Find the next four triangular numbers.

 3 Hexagonal numbers are found as follows.

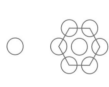 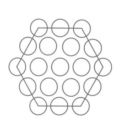 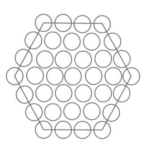

1   7   19   37

Find the next three hexagonal numbers.

 4 The first two terms of the sequence of fractions $\dfrac{n - 1}{n + 1}$ are:

$$n = 1: \frac{1 - 1}{1 + 1} = \frac{0}{2} = 0 \qquad n = 2: \frac{2 - 1}{2 + 1} = \frac{1}{3}$$

Work out the next five terms of the sequence.

A sequence is formed by the rule $\frac{1}{2} \times n \times (n + 1)$ for $n = 1, 2, 3, 4, \ldots$

The first term is given by $n = 1$: $\frac{1}{2} \times 1 \times (1 + 1) = 1$

The second term is given by $n = 2$: $\frac{1}{2} \times 2 \times (2 + 1) = 3$

a Work out the next five terms of this sequence.

b This is a well-known sequence you have met before. What is it?

 5! means "factorial 5", which is $5 \times 4 \times 3 \times 2 \times 1 = 120$

In the same way 7! means $7 \times 6 \times 5 \times 4 \times 3 \times 2 \times 1 = 5040$

a Calculate 2!, 3!, 4! and 6!

b If your calculator has a factorial button, check that it gives the same answers as you get for part **a**. What is the largest factorial you can work out with your calculator before you get an error?

Finding the *n*th term of a linear sequence

A linear sequence has the *same difference* between each term and the next.

For example:

2, 5, 8, 11, 14, … difference of 3

The *n*th term of this sequence is given by $3n - 1$.

Here is another linear sequence:

5, 7, 9, 11, 13, … difference of 2

The *n*th term of this sequence is given by $2n + 3$.

So, you can see that the *n*th term of a linear sequence is *always* of the form $An + b$, where:

- A, the coefficient of n, is the difference between each term and the next term (consecutive terms)
- b is the difference between the first term and A.

EXAMPLE 11

Find the *n*th term of the sequence 5, 7, 9, 11, 13, …

The difference between consecutive terms is 2. So the first part of the *n*th term is 2*n*.

Subtract the difference, 2, from the first term, 5, which gives $5 - 2 = 3$.

So the *n*th term is given by $2n + 3$.

(You can test it by substituting $n = 1, 2, 3, 4, \ldots$.)

EXAMPLE 12

Find the *n*th term of the sequence 3, 7, 11, 15, 19, ...

The difference between consecutive terms is 4. So the first part of the *n*th term is 4*n*.

Subtract the difference 4 from the first term 3, which gives $3 - 4 = -1$.

So the *n*th term is given by $4n - 1$.

EXAMPLE 13

From the sequence 5, 12, 19, 26, 33, ... find the following.

    a the *n*th term   **b** the 50th term   **c** the first term that is greater than 1000

a The difference between consecutive terms is 7. So the first part of the *n*th term is 7*n*.

Subtract the difference 7 from the first term 5, which gives $5 - 7 = -2$.

So the *n*th term is given by $7n - 2$.

b The 50th term is found by substituting $n = 50$ into the rule, $7n - 2$.

So 50th term $= 7 \times 50 - 2 = 350 - 2$
$= 348$

c The first term that is greater than 1000 is given by

$7n - 2 > 1000$

$\Rightarrow \quad 7n > 1000 + 2$

$\Rightarrow \quad n > \dfrac{1002}{7}$

$n > 143.14$

So the first term (which has to be a whole number) over 1000 is the 144th.

Special sequences

There are some number sequences that occur frequently. It is useful to know these as they are very likely to occur in examinations.

Even numbers

The even numbers are 2, 4, 6, 8, 10, 12, ...

The *n*th term of this sequence is 2*n*

Odd numbers

The odd numbers are 1, 3, 5, 7, 9, 11, ...

The *n*th term of this sequence is $2n - 1$

Square numbers

The square numbers are 1, 4, 9, 16, 25, 36, ...

The *n*th term of this sequence is n^2

Triangular numbers

The triangular numbers are 1, 3, 6, 10, 15, 21, …

The nth term of this sequence is $\frac{1}{2}n(n + 1)$

Powers of 2

The powers of 2 are 2, 4, 8, 16, 32, 64, ….

The nth term of this sequence is 2^n

Powers of 10

The powers of 10 are 10, 100, 1000, 10 000, 100 000, 1 000 000, ….

The nth term of this sequence is 10^n

Prime numbers

The first 20 prime numbers are 2, 3, 5, 7, 11, 13, 17, 19, 23, 29, 31, 37, 41, 43, 47, 53, 59, 61, 67, 71

A prime number is a number that only has two factors, 1 and itself.

There is no pattern to the prime numbers so they do not have an nth term.

One important fact that you should remember is that there is only one even prime number, 2.

EXERCISE 20D

1 Find the next two terms and the nth term in each of these linear sequences.

		HINTS AND TIPS

Remember to look at the differences and the first term.

   a 3, 5, 7, 9, 11, …   **b** 5, 9, 13, 17, 21, …

   c 8, 13, 18, 23, 28, …   **d** 2, 8, 14, 20, 26, …

   e 5, 8, 11, 14, 17, …   **f** 2, 9, 16, 23, 30, …

   g 1, 5, 9, 13, 17, …   **h** 3, 7, 11, 15, 19, …   **i** 2, 5, 8, 11, 14, …

   j 2, 12, 22, 32, …   **k** 8, 12, 16, 20, …   **l** 4, 9, 14, 19, 24, …

2 Find the nth term and the 50th term in each of these linear sequences.

   a 4, 7, 10, 13, 16, …   **b** 7, 9, 11, 13, 15, …   **c** 3, 8, 13, 18, 23, …

   d 1, 5, 9, 13, 17, …   **e** 2, 10, 18, 26, …   **f** 5, 6, 7, 8, 9, …

   g 6, 11, 16, 21, 26, …   **h** 3, 11, 19, 27, 35, …   **i** 1, 4, 7, 10, 13, …

   j 21, 24, 27, 30, 33, …   **k** 12, 19, 26, 33, 40, …   **l** 1, 9, 17, 25, 33, …

3 **a** Which term of the sequence 5, 8, 11, 14, 17, … is the first one to be greater than 100?

b Which term of the sequence 1, 8, 15, 22, 29, … is the first one to be greater than 200?

c Which term of the sequence 4, 9, 14, 19, 24, … is the closest to 500?

4 For each sequence **a** to **j**, find

i the nth term   **ii** the 100th term   **iii** the term closest to 100.

a 5, 9, 13, 17, 21, …   **b** 3, 5, 7, 9, 11, 13, …

c 4, 7, 10, 13, 16, …   **d** 8, 10, 12, 14, 16, …

e 9, 13, 17, 21, …   **f** 6, 11, 16, 21, …

g 0, 3, 6, 9, 12, …   **h** 2, 8, 14, 20, 26, …

i 7, 15, 23, 31, …   **j** 25, 27, 29, 31, …

5 A sequence of fractions is $\frac{3}{4}, \frac{5}{7}, \frac{7}{10}, \frac{9}{13}, \frac{11}{16}, \ldots$

a Find the nth term in the sequence.

b By changing each fraction to a decimal, can you see a pattern?

c What, as a decimal, will be the value of the

i 100th term?   **ii** 1000th term?

d Use your answers to part **c** to predict what the 10 000th term and the millionth term are. (Check these out on your calculator.)

6 Repeat question **5** for $\frac{3}{6}, \frac{7}{11}, \frac{11}{16}, \frac{15}{21}, \frac{19}{26}, \ldots$

7 The powers of 2 are $2^1, 2^2, 2^3, 2^4, 2^5, \ldots$

This gives the sequence 2, 4, 8, 16, 32, …

The nth term is given by 2^n.

a Continue the sequence for another five terms.

b Give the nth term of these sequences.

i 1, 3, 7, 15, 31, …

ii 3, 5, 9, 17, 33, …

iii 6, 12, 24, 48, 96, …

8 The powers of 10 are $10^1, 10^2, 10^3, 10^4, 10^5, \ldots$

This gives the sequence 10, 100, 1000, 10 000, 100 000, …

The nth term is given by 10^n.

a Describe the connection between the numbers of zeros in each term and the power of the term.

b If $10^n = 1\,000\,000$, what is the value of n?

c   Give the nth term of these sequences.

   i   9, 99, 999, 9 999, 99 999, …

   ii   20, 200, 2000, 20 000, 200 000, …

9 a   Pick any odd number.

Pick any other odd number.

Add the two numbers together. Is the answer odd or even?

Complete this table.

+	Odd	Even
Odd	Even	
Even		

b   Pick any odd number.

Pick any other odd number.

Multiply the two numbers together. Is the answer odd or even?

Complete this table.

×	Odd	Even
Odd	Odd	
Even		

10 The square numbers are 1, 4, 9, 16, 25, …

The nth term of this sequence is n^2.

a   Continue the sequence for another five terms.

b   Give the nth term of these sequences.

   i   2, 5, 10, 17, 26, …

   ii   2, 8, 18, 32, 50, …

   iii   0, 3, 8, 15, 24, …

11 Write down the next two lines of this number pattern.

$$1 = 1 = 1^2$$

$$1 + 3 = 4 = 2^2$$

$$1 + 3 + 5 = 9 = 3^2$$

12 The triangular numbers are 1, 3, 6, 10, 15, 21, …

a   Continue the sequence for another four terms.

b The nth term of this sequence is given by $\frac{1}{2}n(n + 1)$.

Use the formula to find:

i The 20th triangular number

ii the 100th triangular number

c Add consecutive terms of the triangular number sequence.

For example, $1 + 3 = 4$, $3 + 6 = 9$, etc.

What do you notice?

13 p is an odd number, q is an even number. State if the following are odd or even.

a $p + 1$	**b** $q + 1$	**c** $p + q$
d p^2	**e** $qp + 1$	**f** $(p + q)(p - q)$
g $q^2 + 4$	**h** $p^2 + q^2$	**i** p^3

14 p is a prime number, q is an even number.

State if the following are odd or even, or could be either odd or even.

a $p + 1$	**b** $p + q$	**c** p^2
d $qp + 1$	**e** $(p + q)(p - q)$	**f** $2p + 3q$

20.4 General rules from given patterns

In this section you will learn how to:
- find the nth term from practical problems

Key words
difference
pattern
rule

Many problem-solving situations that you are likely to meet involve number sequences. So you need to be able to formulate general **rules** from given number **patterns**.

EXAMPLE 14

The diagram shows a pattern of squares building up.

a How many squares will be on the base of the nth pattern?

b Which pattern has 99 squares in its base?

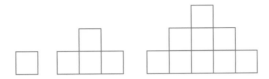

a First, we build up the following table for the patterns.

Pattern number	1	2	3	4	5
Number of squares in base	1	3	5	7	9

Looking at the **difference** between consecutive patterns, we see it is always two squares. So, we use $2n$.

Subtract the difference 2 from the first number, which gives $1 - 2 = -1$.

So the number of squares on the base of the nth pattern is $2n - 1$.

b We have to find n when $2n - 1 = 99$:

$$2n - 1 = 99$$
$$2n = 99 + 1 = 100$$
$$n = 100 \div 2 = 50$$

The pattern with 99 squares in its base is the 50th.

EXERCISE 20E

1 A pattern of squares is built up from matchsticks as shown.

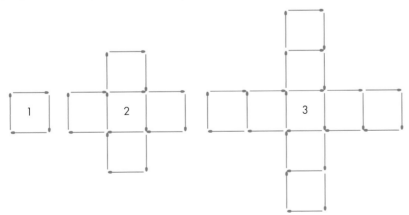

a Draw the 4th diagram.

b How many squares are in the nth diagram?

c How many squares are in the 25th diagram?

d With 200 squares, which is the biggest diagram that could be made?

> **HINTS AND TIPS**
>
> Write out the number sequences to help you see the patterns.

C

2 A pattern of triangles is built up from matchsticks.

   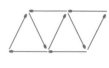

1   2   3   4

a Draw the 5th set of triangles in this pattern.

b How many matchsticks are needed for the *n*th set of triangles?

c How many matchsticks are needed to make the 60th set of triangles?

d If there are only 100 matchsticks, which is the largest set of triangles that could be made?

3 A conference centre had tables each of which could sit six people. When put together, the tables could seat people as shown.

 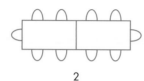 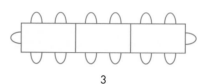

1   2   3

a How many people could be seated at four tables put together this way?

b How many people could be seated at *n* tables put together in this way?

c A conference had 50 people who wished to use the tables in this way. How many tables would they need?

4 Prepacked fencing units come in the shape shown on the right, made of four pieces of wood. When you put them together in stages to make a fence, you also need joining pieces, so the fence will start to build up as shown below.

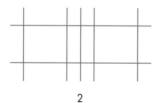 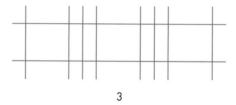

2   3

a How many pieces of wood would you have in a fence made up in:

   i five stages   **ii** *n* stages   **iii** 45 stages?

b I made a fence out of 124 pieces of wood. How many stages did I use?

5 Regular pentagons of side length 1 cm are joined together to make a pattern as shown.

Copy this pattern and write down the perimeter of each shape.

 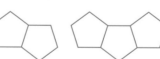 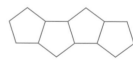

1   2   3   4

a What is the perimeter of patterns like this made from

   i six pentagons?   **ii** *n* pentagons?   **iii** 50 pentagons?

b What is the largest number of pentagons that can be put together like this to have a perimeter less than 1000 cm?

6 Lamp-posts are put at the end of every 100 m stretch of a motorway, as shown.

 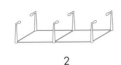 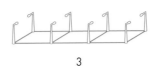

1   2   3

a How many lamp-posts are needed for

i 900 m of this motorway? **ii** 8 km of this motorway?

b The M99 is a motorway being built. The contractor has ordered 1598 lamp-posts. How long is this motorway?

7 A school dining hall had tables in the shape of a trapezium. Each table could seat five people, as shown on the right. When the tables were joined together as shown below, each table could not seat as many people.

 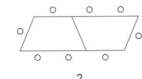 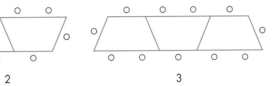

1   2   3

a In this arrangement, how many could be seated if there were:

i four tables? **ii** n tables? **iii** 13 tables?

b For an outside charity event, up to 200 people had to be seated. How many tables arranged like this did they need?

8 When setting out tins to make a display of a certain height, you need to know how many tins to start with at the bottom.

a How many tins are needed on the bottom if you wish the display to be:

i five tins high? **ii** n tins high? **iii** 18 tins high?

b I saw a shop assistant starting to build a display, and noticed he was starting with 20 tins on the bottom. How high was the display when it was finished?

9 a The values of 2 raised to a positive whole-number power are 2, 4, 8, 16, 32, …

What is the nth term of this sequence?

b A supermarket sells four different sized bottles of water: pocket size, 100 ml; standard size, 200 ml; family size, 400 ml; giant size, 800 ml.

i Describe the number pattern that the contents follow.

ii The supermarket introduces a super giant size, which is the next sized bottle in the pattern. How much does this bottle hold?

In this section you will learn how to:

● work out the nth term of a non-linear rule

Some problem-solving situations involve number sequences which are governed by a **quadratic rule**.

You can always identify a pattern as being quadratic from its **second differences**, which are *constant*. (A second difference is the result of subtracting one difference between consecutive terms from the next difference.) Quadratic sequences are not assessed directly on the exam paper but occur in coursework.

The simpler rules

These sequences will nearly always be based on n^2 alone. So you do need to recognise the pattern 1, 4, 9, 16, 25, … .

The differences between consecutive terms of this pattern are the odd numbers 3, 5, 7, 9, … . So if you find that the differences form an odd-number sequence, you know the pattern is based on n^2.

EXAMPLE 15

Find the nth term in the sequence 2, 5, 10, 17, 26, … .

The differences are the odd numbers 3, 5, 7, 9, … so we know the rule is based on n^2.

The second differences are 2, a constant.

Next, we look for a link with the square numbers. We do this by subtracting from each term the corresponding square number:

2	5	10	17	26
−1	−4	−9	−16	−25
1	1	1	1	1

Clearly, the link is +1, so the nth term is $n^2 + 1$.

(You should always quickly check the generalisation by substituting $n = 1, 2, 3, 4$ to see whether it does work.)

EXAMPLE 16

Find the nth term in the sequence 1, 6, 13, 22, 33, … .

The differences are 5, 7, 9, 11, … so we know the pattern is based on n^2.

The second differences are 2, a constant.

Next, we have to find the link. We notice that the first difference is 5 not 3, which means that the series of square numbers we use starts at 4, not at 1.

It follows that to obtain 4, 9, 16, 25, … from the original sequence simply add 3 to each term of that sequence.

So to get from the square numbers to the sequence 1, 6, 13, 22, 33, … we have to use $(n + 1)^2$, since the sequence is based on 4, 9, 16, … .

The final step in finding the rule is to take away the 3, which gives the nth term as $(n + 1)^2 - 3$.

More complicated rules

EXAMPLE 17

Find the *n*th term in the sequence 2, 6, 12, 20, 30, …

Looking at the differences tells us that the sequence is non-linear, and is not based on n^2.

So we split each term into factors to see whether we can find a pattern which shows how the numbers have been formed. Constructing a table like the one below can help us to sort out which factors to use when we have a choice.

Term	2	6	12	20	30
Factors	1×2	2×3	3×4	4×5	5×6

We can break down the factors to obtain:

$1 \times (1 + 1)$ $2 \times (2 + 1)$ $3 \times (3 + 1)$ $4 \times (4 + 1)$ $5 \times (5 + 1)$

We can now see quite easily that the pattern is $n \times (n + 1)$. That is the *n*th term is $n(n + 1)$.

EXAMPLE 18

Find the *n*th term in the sequence of the triangular numbers 1, 3, 6, 10, 15, … .

Looking at the differences tells us that the sequence is non-linear and is not based on n^2.

So we split each term into factors and construct a table. (We have no problem with the choice of factors.)

Term	1	3	6	10	15
Factors	1×1	1×3	2×3	2×5	3×5

At this stage, we may not yet have spotted a pattern. So we investigate the effect of multiplying the smaller of each pair of factors by 2, and obtain an interesting pattern.

Term	1	3	6	10	15
Factors	1×1	1×3	2×3	2×5	3×5
Smaller × 2	2×1	2×3	4×3	4×5	6×5

That is:

1×2 2×3 3×4 4×5 5×6

We can further break down this last set of numbers to obtain:

$1 \times (1 + 1)$ $2 \times (2 + 1)$ $3 \times (3 + 1)$ $4 \times (4 + 1)$ $5 \times (5 + 1)$

the pattern of which is given by $n \times (n + 1)$.

This gives terms twice the size of those in the sequence 1, 3, 6, 10, 15, … so we need to change the expression to $\frac{1}{2} \times n\,(n + 1)$.

So the *n*th term is $\frac{1}{2}n(n + 1)$.

Expressions of the form $an^2 + bn + c$

These expressions are unlikely to appear in a GCSE exam but could easily appear in an AO1 coursework task. This method will give an algebraic means of showing a sequence.

EXAMPLE 19

Find the nth term of the sequence 5, 15, 31, 53, ...

Set up a difference table.

n		1	2	3	4
nth term		5	15	31	53
1st difference			10	16	22
2nd difference				6	6

Now extend the table backwards to get the term for $n = 0$ and call the three lines of the table c, $a + b$ and $2a$.

n	0	1	2	3	4
c	1	5	15	31	53
$a + b$		4	10	16	22
$2a$		6	6	6	

This gives $2a = 6 \implies a = 3$, $\quad a + b = 4 \implies b = 1$, $\quad c = 1$

Giving the nth term as: $\quad 3n^2 + n + 1$

EXAMPLE 20

Find the nth term of the sequence 3, 5, 8, 12, 17, ...

Set up a difference table.

n	0	1	2	3	4	5
c	2	3	5	8	12	17
$a + b$		1	2	3	4	5
$2a$		1	1	1	1	

This gives $2a = 1 \implies a = \frac{1}{2}$, $\quad a + b = 1 \implies b = \frac{1}{2}$, $\quad c = 2$

Giving the nth term as: $\quad \frac{1}{2}n^2 + \frac{1}{2}n + 2$

EXERCISE 20F

1 For each of the sequences **a** to **e**   **i** write down the next two terms   **ii** find the nth term.

    a 0, 3, 8, 15, 24, …   **b** 3, 6, 11, 18, 27, …   **c** 4, 7, 12, 19, 28, …

    d −1, 2, 7, 14, 23, …   **e** 11, 14, 19, 26, …

2 For each of the sequences **a** to **e**   **i** write down the next two terms   **ii** find the nth term.

    a 5, 10, 17, 26, …   **b** 3, 8, 15, 24, …   **c** 9, 14, 21, 30, …

    d 10, 17, 26, 37, …   **e** 8, 15, 24, 35, …

3 Look at each of the following sequences to see whether the rule is linear, quadratic on n^2 alone or fully quadratic. Then

    i write down the nth term   **ii** write down the 50th term.

    a 5, 8, 13, 20, 29, …   **b** 5, 8, 11, 14, 17, …   **c** 3, 8, 15, 24, 35, …

    d 5, 12, 21, 32, 45, …   **e** 3, 6, 11, 18, 27, …   **f** 1, 6, 11, 16, 21, …

4 Find the nth terms of the following sequences in the form $an^2 + bn + c$.

    a 1, 4, 11, 22, 37, ….   **b** 2, 13, 30, 53, 82, ….   **c** 4, 8, 13, 19, 26, …..

20.6 Changing the subject of a formula

In this section you will learn how to:

- change the subject of a formula where the subject occurs more than once

Key words

subject
transpose

You already have met changing the **subject** of a formula in which the subject appears only once (see Year 10 book, page 104). This is like solving an equation but using letters. You have also solved equations in which the unknown appears on both sides of the equation. This requires the unknown (usually x) terms to be collected on one side and the numbers to be collected on the other.

We can do something similar, to **transpose** formulae in which the subject appears more than once. The principle is the same. Collect all the subject terms on the same side and everything else on the other side. Most often, we then need to factorise the subject out of the resulting expression.

EXAMPLE 21

Make x the subject of this formula.

$$ax + b = cx + d$$

First, rearrange the formula to get all the x terms on the left-hand side and all the other terms on the right-hand side. (The rule "change sides – change signs" still applies.)

$$ax - cx = d - b$$

Factorise x out of left-hand side to get:

$$x(a - c) = d - b$$

Divide by the bracket, which gives:

$$x = \frac{d - b}{a - c}$$

EXAMPLE 22

Make p the subject of this formula.

$$5 = \frac{ap + b}{cp + d}$$

First, multiply both sides by the denominator of the algebraic fraction, which gives:

$$5(cp + d) = ap + b$$

Expand the bracket to get:

$$5cp + 5d = ap + b$$

Now continue as in Example 21:

$$5cp - ap = b - 5d$$

$$p(5c - a) = b - 5d$$

$$p = \frac{b - 5d}{5c - a}$$

EXERCISE 20G

In questions **1** to **10**, make the letter in brackets the subject of each formula.

1 $3(x + 2y) = 2(x - y)$ (x)

2 $3(x + 2y) = 2(x - y)$ (y)

3 $5 = \dfrac{a + b}{a - c}$ (a)

4 $p(a + b) = q(a - b)$ (a)

5 $p(a + b) = q(a - b)$ (b)

6 $A = 2\pi rh + \pi rk$ (r)

7 $v^2 = u^2 + av^2$ (v)

8 $s(t - r) = 2r - 3$ (r)

9 $s(t - r) = 2(r - 3)$ (r)

10 $R = \dfrac{x - 3}{x - 2}$ (x)

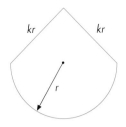

11 **a** The perimeter of the shape shown on the right is given by the formula $P = \pi r + 2kr$. Make r the subject of this formula.

b The area of the same shape is given by $A = \frac{1}{2}[\pi r^2 + r^2\sqrt{(k^2 - 1)}]$

Make r the subject of this formula.

12 When £P is invested for Y years at a simple interest rate of R, the following formula gives the amount, A, at any time:

$$A = P + \frac{PRY}{100}$$

Make P the subject of this formula.

13 When two resistors with values a and b are connected in parallel, the total resistance is given by:

$$R = \frac{ab}{a + b}$$

a Make b the subject of the formula.

b Write the formula when a is the subject.

14 **a** Make x the subject of this formula.

$$y = \frac{x + 2}{x - 2}$$

b Show that the formula $y = 1 + \frac{4}{x - 2}$ can be rearranged to give:

$$x = 2 + \frac{4}{y - 1}$$

c Combine the right-hand sides of each formula in part **b** into single fractions and simplify as much as possible.

d What do you notice?

15 The volume of the solid shown is given by:

$$V = \frac{2}{3}\pi r^3 + \pi r^2 h$$

a Explain why it is not possible to make r the subject of this formula.

b Make π the subject.

c If $h = r$, can the formula be rearranged to make r the subject? If so, rearrange it to make r the subject.

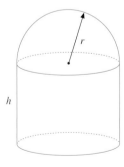

16 Make x the subject of this formula.

$$W = \frac{1}{2}z(x + y) + \frac{1}{2}y(x + z)$$

1
a Here is a sequence of numbers.

   29   25   21   17   13

  i Write down the next two numbers in the sequence.

  ii Write down the rule for continuing the sequence.

b Another sequence of numbers begins:

   2   5   14   41

The rule for continuing this sequence is:

> Multiply by 3 and subtract 1

  i What is the next number in the sequence?

  ii The same rule is used for a sequence that starts with the number 7. What is the second number in this sequence?

  iii The same rule is also used for a sequence that starts with the number –2. What is the second number in this sequence?

2 The first 10 prime numbers are 2, 3, 5, 7, 11, 13, 17, 19, 23, 29.

P is a prime number.

Q is an odd number.

State whether each of the following is always odd, always even or could be either odd or even.

Tick the appropriate box.

a $P(Q + 1)$

  ☐ Always odd   ☐ Always even   ☐ Could be either odd or even

b $Q - P$

  ☐ Always odd   ☐ Always even   ☐ Could be either odd or even

3 The nth term of a sequence is $3n - 1$.

a Write down the first and second terms of the sequence.

b Which term of the sequence is equal to 32?

c Explain why 85 is not a term in this sequence.

4 **a** The nth term of a sequence is $4n - 1$.

  i Write down the first three terms of the sequence.

  ii Is 132 a term in this sequence? Explain your answer.

b Tom builds fencing from pieces of wood as shown.

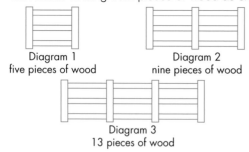

Diagram 1
five pieces of wood

Diagram 2
nine pieces of wood

Diagram 3
13 pieces of wood

How many pieces of wood will be in diagram n?

5 The first four terms of an arithmetic sequence are

   21   17   13   9

Find, in terms of n, an expression for the nth term of this sequence.

Edexcel, Question 2, Paper 10B Higher, January 2005

6 Here is a sequence made from a pattern of dots.

1st pattern   2nd pattern   3rd pattern

a Complete the table.

Pattern	1	2	3	4	5
Number of dots	5	8	11		

b How many dots are in the 7th pattern?

c How many dots are in the nth pattern?

d Which pattern has 62 dots in it?

7 Make x the subject of this formula.

$$t = m - x^2$$

8 A witch's hat shape is made from a rectangular piece of card by cutting out two identical quadrants of a circle, radius r cm.

a Show that the shaded area is given by the formula

$$A = 2r^2 - \tfrac{1}{2}\pi r^2$$

b Find the area of the rectangle if the area of the witch hat is 16 cm².

9 **a** Show that

$$\frac{3}{4x + 1} - \frac{4}{x + 2} = 2$$

simplifies to $8x^2 + 31x + 2 = 0$

b Hence, or otherwise, solve the following equation

$$\frac{3}{4x + 1} - \frac{4}{x + 2} = 2$$

giving your answer to 2 decimal places.

10 Solve the equation

$$\frac{2x + 3}{5} - \frac{3x - 4}{8} = 1$$

11 Make x the subject of this formula.

$$p(q - x) = px + q^2$$

12 Make x the subject of this formula.

$$y = \frac{2x + 3}{x - 5}$$

13 Solve the simultaneous equations

$$xy = 32$$
$$4y - 3x = 26$$

14 A straight line has the equation $\qquad y = 2x + 1$

A curve has the equation $\qquad y^2 = 8x$

Find the point of intersection of the line and the curve.

15 Simplify fully $\qquad \dfrac{3x^2 - 5x - 2}{x^2 + x - 6}$

16 **a** Sketch the graph of $x^2 + y^2 = 20$, indicating the values of x and y where the curve intersects the positive and negative axes in the form $a\sqrt{5}$.

b Find the coordinates of the points where the curve intersects the line $y = \sqrt{11}$ and show these solutions on the sketch.

WORKED EXAM QUESTION

Make g the subject of the following formula.

$$\frac{t(3 + g)}{8 - g} = 2$$

$t(3 + g) = 2(8 - g)$ —— Cross multiply to get rid of the fraction

$3t + gt = 16 - 2g$ —— Expand the brackets

$gt + 2g = 16 - 3t$ —— Collect all the g terms on the left-hand side and other terms on the right-hand side.

$g(t + 2) = 16 - 3t$

$g = \dfrac{16 - 3t}{t + 2}$ —— Simplify, $gt + 2g = g(t + 2)$, and divide by $(t + 2)$.

Walking holiday

A group of friends plan an eight-day walking holiday. The profile of their first four daily walks is shown below.

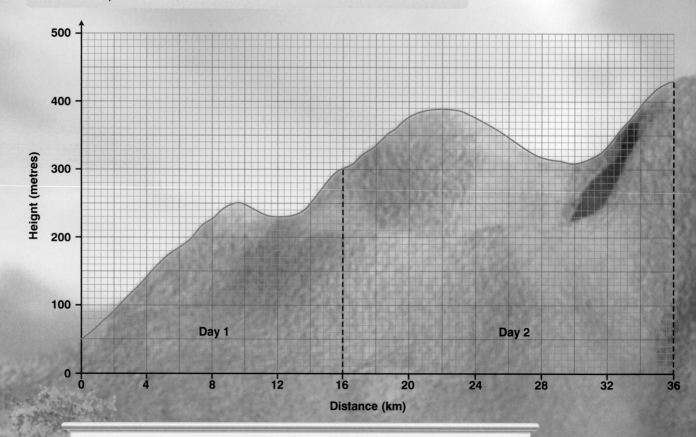

For every day they work out the horizontal distance they walk in kilometres, and the height they climb in metres.

They calculate the time each day's walk will take using the formula

$$T = 15D + \frac{H}{10}$$

where: T = time in minutes D = distance in km
H = height climbed in m

This formula assumes an average walking speed of 4km/h and an extra minute for each 10 metres climbed.

Copy this table and help them complete it. Work out the time each day's walk will take, and the time that the group expects to finish.

Day	Distance in km	Height climbed in metres	Time in minutes	Time in hours and minutes	Start time	Time allowed for breaks	Finish time
1	16	250	265	4h 25m	9:30 am	2 hours	3:55 pm
2					9.00 am	2¾ hours	
3					10:00 am	2½ hours	
4					10:30 am	2¼ hours	

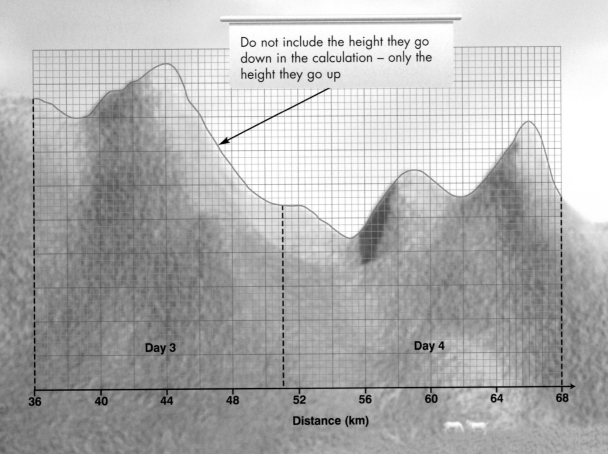

Do not include the height they go down in the calculation – only the height they go up

Day 3

Day 4

Distance (km)

This table shows the information for their walks from Day 5 to Day 8.

Unfortunately coffee has been spilt on the table! Help them to work out the values covered by the coffee.

Day	Distance in km	Height climbed in metres	Time in minutes	Time in hours and minutes	Start time	Time allowed for breaks	Finish time
5	18		282		10:00 am		5:12 pm
6		290	284			2 hours	5:14 pm
7		90		5h 39m	10:00 am	2¾ hours	
8	12			3h 30m	10:30 am		4:15 pm

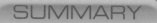

GRADE YOURSELF

D Able to substitute numbers into an *n*th term rule

D Able to understand how odd and even numbers interact in addition, subtraction and multiplication problems

C Able to give the *n*th term of a linear sequence

C Able to give the *n*th term of a sequence of powers of 2 or 10

B Able to find the *n*th term of a quadratic sequence

B Able to solve linear equations involving algebraic fractions where the subject appears as the numerator

A Able to rearrange a formula where the subject appears twice

A Able to combine algebraic fractions using the four rules of addition, subtraction, multiplication and division

A* Able to rearrange more complicated formulae where the subject may appear twice or as a power

A* Able to solve a quadratic equation obtained from algebraic fractions where the variable appears in the denominator

A* Able to simplify algebraic fractions by factorisation and cancellation

A* Able to solve a pair of simultaneous equations where one is linear and the other is non-linear

What you should know now

- Be able to manipulate algebraic fractions and solve equations resulting from the simplified fractions
- Be able to solve a pair of simultaneous equations where one is linear and one is non-linear
- Be able to recognise a linear sequence and find its *n*th term
- Be able to recognise a sequence of powers of 2 or 10
- Be able to recognise a non-linear sequence and find its *n*th term
- Be able to rearrange a formula where the subject appears twice

1 Dimensions of length

2 Dimensions of area

3 Dimensions of volume

4 Consistent dimensions

This chapter will show you ...

- how to decide whether a formula represents a length, an area or a volume
- how to check that a formula has consistent dimensions

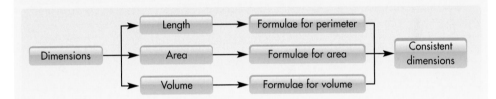

What you should already know

- The formulae for perimeters, areas and volumes of common shapes
- The common units used for length, area and volume

Quick check

Write down a formula for each of the following.

1 The perimeter of a square with side length l.

2 The circumference of a circle with diameter d.

3 The area of a triangle with base b and height h.

4 The area of a circle with radius r.

5 The volume of a cube with side length l.

6 The volume of a cylinder with radius r and height h.

Dimensions of length

In this section you will learn how to:

- find formulae for the perimeter of 2-D shapes

When we have an unknown length or distance in a problem, we represent it by a single letter, followed by the unit in which it is measured. For example,

t centimetres x miles y kilometres

EXAMPLE 1

Find a formula the **perimeter** of each of these shapes.

a 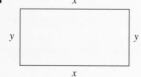   **b**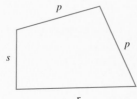

Shape **a** is a rectangle. Its perimeter is given by the formula

$P = x + y + x + y = 2x + 2y$

Shape **b** is an irregular quadrilateral. Its perimeter is given by the formula

$P = p + p + r + s = 2p + r + s$

In the example, each letter is a **length** and has the dimension or measure of length, i.e. centimetre, metre, kilometre, etc. The numbers or coefficients written before the letters are *not* lengths and therefore have *no* dimensions. So, for example, $2x$, $5y$ or $\frac{1}{2}p$ have the same dimension as x, y or p respectively.

When just lengths are involved in a formula, the formula is said to have one dimension or **1-D**, which is sometimes represented by the symbol [L].

EXERCISE 21A

Find a formula for the perimeter of each of these shapes. Each letter represents a length.

1

2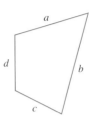

3

4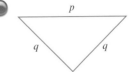

5

6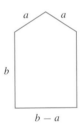

7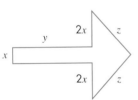

8

9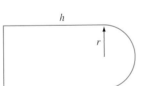

10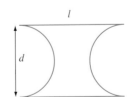

Dimensions of area

In this section you will learn how to:
● find formulae for the area of 2-D shapes

Key words
2-D
area

EXAMPLE 2

Look at these four examples of formulae for calculating area.

$A = lb$ gives the area of a rectangle
$A = x^2$ gives the area of a square
$A = 2ab + 2ac + 2bc$ gives the surface area of a cuboid
$A = \pi r^2$ gives the area of a circle

These formulae have one thing in common. They all consist of terms that are the product of two lengths. You can recognise this by counting the number of letters in each term of the formula. The first formula has two (l and b). The second has two (x and x). The third has three terms, each of two letters (a and b, a and c, b and c). The fourth also has only two letters (r and r) because π is a number (3.14159…) which has no dimension.

We can recognise formulae for **area** because they only have terms that consist of two letters – that is, two lengths multiplied together. Numbers are not defined as lengths, since they have no dimensions. These formulae therefore have two dimensions or **2-D**, which is sometimes represented by the symbol [L^2].

This confirms the units in which area is usually measured. For example,

square metres (m × m or m^2)

square centimetres (cm × cm or cm^2)

EXERCISE 21B

Find a formula for the area of each of these shapes. Each letter represents a length.

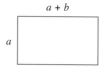

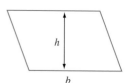

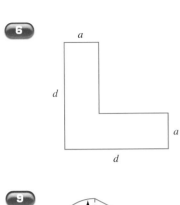

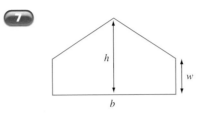

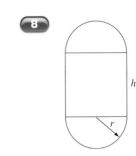

C

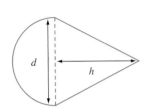

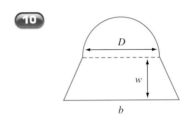

21.3 Dimensions of volume

In this section you will learn how to:

● find formulae for the volume of 3-D shapes

Key words

3-D
volume

EXAMPLE 3

Look at these three examples of formulae for calculating volume.

$V = lbh$ gives the volume of a cuboid
$V = x^3$ gives the volume of a cube
$V = \pi r^2 h + \frac{4}{3}\pi r^3$ gives the volume of a cylinder with hemispherical ends

Again, these formulae have one thing in common. They all consist of terms that are the product of three lengths. You can recognise this by counting the number of letters in each term of the formula. The first formula has three (l, b and h). The second has three (x, x and x). The third has two terms, each of three letters (r, r and h; r, r and r). Remember, π has no dimension.

We can recognise formulae for **volume** because they only have terms that consist of three letters – that is, three lengths multiplied together. They therefore have three dimensions or **3-D**, which is sometimes represented by the symbol $[L^3]$. Once more, numbers are not defined as lengths, since they have no dimensions.

This confirms the units in which volume is usually measured. For example,

cubic metres (m × m × m or m^3)

cubic centimetres (cm × cm × cm or cm^3)

EXERCISE 21C

Find a formula for the volume of each of these shapes. Each letter represents a length.

1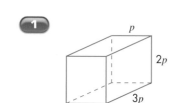

2

3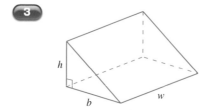

4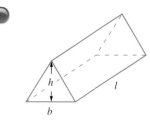

5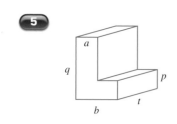

6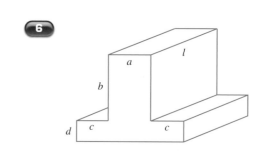

21.4 Consistent dimensions

In this section you will learn how to:

● check that the dimensions of a formula are consistent

Key words

consistency
dimension
formula

One way in which scientists and mathematicians check complicated **formulae** to see whether they are correct is to test for **consistency**. They check that every term in the formula is of the same **dimension**.

Each term in a formula must have the correct number of dimensions. It is not possible to have a formula with a mixture of terms, some of which have, for example, one dimension and some two dimensions. When terms are found to be mixed, the formula is said to be *inconsistent* and is not possible.

We are only concerned with lengths, areas and volumes, so it is easy for us to test for consistency.

EXAMPLE 4

Which of these expressions are consistent? If any are consistent, do they represent a length, an area or a volume?

a $a + bc$ **b** $\pi r^2 + ab$ **c** $r^3 + 2\pi r^2$ **d** $\dfrac{(ab^2 + a^2 b)}{2}$ **e** $\dfrac{\pi(R^2 + r^2)}{x}$

a is inconsistent because the first term has one letter (1-D), and the second has two letters (2-D). Hence, it is a mixture of length and area. So it has no physical meaning, i.e. $[L] + [L^2]$ is not possible.

b is consistent because the first term has two letters (r and r) multiplied by a dimensionless number (π), and the second term also has two letters (a and b). Hence the expression could represent an area, i.e. $[L^2] + [L^2] = [L^2]$ is consistent.

c is inconsistent because the first term is 3-D and the second term is 2-D. It is a mixture of volume and area, so it has no physical meaning, i.e. $[L^3] + [L^2]$ is not possible.

d is consistent. Each term is 3-D and hence the expression could represent a volume, i.e. $[L^3] + [L^3] = [L^3]$ is consistent.

e is consistent. There are two terms which are 2-D in the numerator and the term in the denominator is 1-D. The numerator can be cancelled to give two terms which are both 1-D. Hence the expression could represent a length, i.e. $[L^2]/[L] = [L]$ is consistent.

EXERCISE 21D

1 Each of these expressions represents a length, an area or a volume. Indicate which it is by writing L, A or V. Each letter represents a length.

a x^2 **b** $2y$ **c** πa **d** πab

e xyz **f** $3x^3$ **g** $x^2 y$ **h** $2xy$

i $4y$ **j** $3ab^2$ **k** $4xz$ **l** $5z$

m abc **n** $ab + bc$ **o** $abc + d^3$ **p** $2ab + 3bc$

q $a^2 b + ab^2$ **r** $a^2 + b^2$ **s** πa^2 **t** $\dfrac{abc}{d}$

u $\dfrac{(ab + bc)}{d}$ **v** $\dfrac{ab}{2}$ **w** $(a + b)^2$ **x** $4a^2 + 2ab$

y $3abc + 2abd + 4bcd + 2acd$ **z** $4\pi r^3 + \pi r^2 h$

2 Indicate whether each of these expressions is consistent (C) or inconsistent (I). Each letter represents a length.

a $a + b$ **b** $a^2 + b$ **c** $a^2 + b^2$ **d** $ab + c$

e $ab + c^2$ **f** $a^3 + bc$ **g** $a^3 + abc$ **h** $a^2 + abc$

i $3a^2 + bc$ **j** $4a^3 b + 2ab^2$ **k** $3abc + 2x^2 y$ **l** $3a(ab + bc)$

m $4a^2 + 3ab$ **n** $\pi a^2(a + b)$ **o** $\pi a^2 + 2r^2$ **p** $\pi r^2 h + \pi rh$

C

q $\pi r^2(R + r)$ **r** $\dfrac{(ab + bc)}{d}$ **s** $a(b^2 + c)$ **t** $\pi ab + \pi bc$

u $(a + b)(c + d)$ **v** $\pi(a + b)(a^2 + b^2)$ **w** $\pi(a^2 + b^2)$ **x** $\pi^2(a + b)$

y $\pi r^2 h + \pi r^3$

3 Write down whether each of these expressions is consistent (C) or inconsistent (I). When it is consistent, say whether it represents a length (L), an area (A) or a volume (V). Each letter represents a length.

a $\pi a + \pi b$ **b** $2\pi r^2 + h$ **c** $\pi r^2 h + 2\pi r^3$ **d** $2\pi r + h$

e $2\pi rh + 4\pi r^3$ **f** $\dfrac{\pi r}{6} + \pi a^2$ **g** $r^2 h + \pi rh^2$ **h** $\pi r^2(r + h)$

i $\pi r^2 h + 2r^3 + \dfrac{h^2 r}{6}$ **j** $2\pi r^3 + 3\pi r^2 h$ **k** $4\pi a + 3x$ **l** $3\pi r^2 a + 2\pi r$

m $\dfrac{\pi r^2 h}{3} + \dfrac{\pi r^3}{3} + x^3$

4 What power * would make each expression consistent?

a $\pi abc + a^* b$ **b** $\dfrac{\pi r^* h}{2} + \pi h^* + \dfrac{rh^2}{2}$

c $\pi a(b^* + ac)$ **d** $a^* b + ab^* + c^3$

5 Kerry has worked out a volume formula as

$$V = \dfrac{(2hD^2 + hd)}{4}$$

It is wrong. Why?

6 The diagram shows a cuboid with sides a, b and c, with a circular hole radius r drilled through it. Three of the following formulae represent

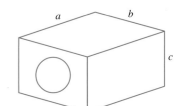

A: the total length of all straight edges

B: the total surface area of the six flat sides

C: the volume.

a Match the correct formula to each of the quantities A, B and C.

F_1: $4\pi r$ F_2: $4(a + b + c)$

F_3: $abc - \pi r^2 a$ F_4: $2a(b + c) + 2(bc - \pi r^2)$

b Say what quantity the fourth formula represents.

1 In this question, the letters a, b and c represent lengths. State whether each expression could represent a length, an area or a volume.

   a $2abc$

   b $3a + 2b + c$

   c $\pi(a^2 - b^2)$

2 In this question, the letters x, y and z represent lengths. State whether each expression could represent a length, an area or a volume.

   a $xy + yz$

   b πxyz

   c $3(x + y + z)$

3 This table shows some expressions.

The letters x, y and z represent lengths.

Copy the table below. Place a tick in the appropriate column for each expression to show whether the expression can be used to represent a length, an area, a volume or none of these.

Expresion	Length	Area	Volume	None of these
$x + y + z$				
xyz				
$xy + yz + xz$				

Edexcel, Question 8, Paper 5 Higher, June 2003

4 Here are some expressions.

$(a + b)c$	$ac + b$	$2abc$	$\pi a^2 + \pi b^2$	$2\pi c$

The letters a, b, and c represent lengths. π and 2 are numbers that have no dimension.

Two of the expressions could represent areas.

Copy the table and tick the boxes (✔) underneath these two expressions.

Edexcel, Question 11, Paper 17 Intermediate, June 2003

5 The diagram shows an ellipse of width $2a$ cm and height $2b$ cm.

Which of the following is a formula for the area of the ellipse?

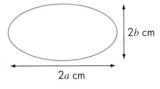

2b cm
2a cm

   a $\pi(2a + 2b)$

   b πab

   c $4a^2b^2$

6 Here are some expressions.

$\frac{1}{2}ac$	πc	$2b$	$2ab^2$	abc	$a(b + c)$	$\frac{ab}{c}$	πa^2

The letters a, b and c represent lengths. π, 2 and $\frac{1}{2}$ are numbers which have no dimension.

Three of the expressions could represent areas. Copy the table and tick (✔) the boxes underneath the *three* expressions which could represent areas.

Edexcel, Question 2, Paper 10B Higher, January 2005

WORKED EXAM QUESTION

r, a and b are all lengths. Which of the following expressions could be a volume? Write Yes or No for each one. If the expression could not be a volume, give a reason.

$$\frac{ar}{2}(4b + \pi r) \qquad 2a^2 + \pi r^2 \qquad 4a^2b + rb^3 \qquad 2abr + \frac{\pi ar^2}{2}$$

Solution

1 Yes, $[L^2] \times [L + L] = [L^2] \times [L] = [L^3]$

2 No, $[L^2] + [L^2]$ is an area

3 No, $[L^3] + [L^4]$ inconsistent

4 Yes, $[L^3] + [L^3] = [L^3]$

> Convert the letters in each term. If the term is a product of three letters, it can represent a volume.

GRADE YOURSELF

D Able to work out a formula for the perimeter, area or volume of simple shapes

C Able to work out a formula for the perimeter, area or volume of complex shapes

C Able to work out whether an expression or formula is dimensionally consistent and whether it represents a length, an area or a volume

What you should know now

● How to work out a formula for the length, area or volume of a shape

● How to recognise whether a formula is 1-D, 2-D or 3-D

● How to recognise when a formula or expression is consistent

Variation

 Direct variation

 Inverse variation

This chapter will show you ...

- how to solve problems where two variables are connected by a relationship that varies in direct or inverse proportion

Direct proportion ⟶ Inverse proportion

What you should already know

- Squares, square roots, cubes and cube roots of integers
- How to substitute values into algebraic expressions
- How to solve simple algebraic equations

Quick check

1 Write down the value of each of the following.

   a 5^2 **b** $\sqrt{81}$ **c** 3^3 **d** $\sqrt[3]{64}$

2 Calculate the value of y if $x = 4$.

   a $y = 3x^2$ **b** $y = \dfrac{1}{\sqrt{x}}$

This section will introduce you to:
- direct variation and show you how to work out the constant of proportionality

Key words
constant of proportionality, k
direct proportion
direct variation

The term **direct variation** has the same meaning as **direct proportion**.

There is direct variation (or direct proportion) between two variables when one variable is a simple multiple of the other. That is, their ratio is a constant.

For example:

1 kilogram = 2.2 pounds   There is a multiplying factor of 2.2 between kilograms and pounds.

Area of a circle = πr^2 There is a multiplying factor of π between the area of a circle and the square of its radius.

An examination question involving direct variation usually requires you first to find this multiplying factor (called the **constant of proportionality**), then to use it to solve a problem.

The symbol for variation or proportion is $\propto$.

So the statement "Pay is directly proportional to time" can be mathematically written as

$Pay \propto Time$

which implies that

$Pay = k \times Time$

where k is the constant of proportionality.

There are three steps to be followed when solving a question involving proportionality.

Step 1: set up the proportionality equation (you may have to define variables).

Step 2: use the given information to find the constant of proportionality.

Step 3: substitute the constant of proportionality in the original equation and use this to find unknown values.

EXAMPLE 1

The cost of an article is directly proportional to the time spent making it. An article taking 6 hours to make costs £30. Find the following.

a the cost of an article that takes 5 hours to make

b the length of time it takes to make an article costing £40

Step 1: Let C be the cost of making an article and t the time it takes. We then have:

$$C \propto t$$

$$\Rightarrow C = kt$$

where k is the constant of proportionality.

Note that we can "replace" the proportionality sign $\propto$ with $= k$ to obtain the proportionality equation.

Step 2: Since $C = £30$ when $t = 6$ hours, then $30 = 6k$

$$\Rightarrow \frac{30}{6} = k$$

$$\Rightarrow k = 5$$

Step 3: So the formula is $C = 5t$

a When $t = 5$ hours $C = 5 \times 5 = 25$

So the cost is £25.

b When $C = £40$ $40 = 5 \times t$

$$\Rightarrow \frac{40}{5} = t \Rightarrow t = 8$$

So the making time is 8 hours.

EXERCISE 22A

In each case, first find k, the constant of proportionality, and then the formula connecting the variables.

1 T is directly proportional to M. If $T = 20$ when $M = 4$, find the following.

    a T when $M = 3$ **b** M when $T = 10$

2 W is directly proportional to F. If $W = 45$ when $F = 3$, find the following.

    a W when $F = 5$ **b** F when $W = 90$

3 Q varies directly with P. If $Q = 100$ when $P = 2$, find the following.

    a Q when $P = 3$ **b** P when $Q = 300$

4 X varies directly with Y. If $X = 17.5$ when $Y = 7$, find the following.

    a X when $Y = 9$ **b** Y when $X = 30$

5 The distance covered by a train is directly proportional to the time taken. The train travels 105 miles in 3 hours.

a What distance will the train cover in 5 hours?

b What time will it take for the train to cover 280 miles?

6 The cost of fuel delivered to your door is directly proportional to the weight received. When 250 kg is delivered, it costs £47.50.

a How much will it cost to have 350 kg delivered?

b How much would be delivered if the cost were £33.25?

7 The number of children who can play safely in a playground is directly proportional to the area of the playground. A playground with an area of 210 m^2 is safe for 60 children.

a How many children can safely play in a playground of area 154 m^2?

b A playgroup has 24 children. What is the smallest playground area in which they could safely play?

Direct proportions involving squares, cubes and square roots

The process is the same as for a linear direct variation, as the next example shows.

EXAMPLE 2

The cost of a circular badge is directly proportional to the square of its radius. The cost of a badge with a radius of 2 cm is 68p.

a Find the cost of a badge of radius 2.4 cm.

b Find the radius of a badge costing £1.53.

Step 1: Let C be the cost and r the radius of a badge. Then

$$C \propto r^2$$

$$\Rightarrow C = kr^2 \text{ where } k \text{ is the constant of proportionality.}$$

Step 2: $C = 68p$ when $r = 2$ cm. So

$$68 = 4k$$

$$\Rightarrow \frac{68}{4} = k \Rightarrow k = 17$$

Hence the formula is $C = 17r^2$

a When $r = 2.4$ cm $C = 17 \times 2.4^2 p = 97.92p$

Rounding off gives the cost as 98p.

b When $C = 153p$ $153 = 17r^2$

$$\Rightarrow \frac{153}{17} = 9 = r^2$$

$$\Rightarrow r = \sqrt{9} = 3$$

Hence, the radius is 3 cm.

EXERCISE 22B

In each case, first find k, the constant of proportionality, and then the formula connecting the variables.

 1 T is directly proportional to x^2. If $T = 36$ when $x = 3$, find the following.

    a T when $x = 5$ **b** x when $T = 400$

 2 W is directly proportional to M^2. If $W = 12$ when $M = 2$, find the following.

    a W when $M = 3$ **b** M when $W = 75$

 3 E varies directly with $\sqrt{C}$. If $E = 40$ when $C = 25$, find the following.

    a E when $C = 49$ **b** C when $E = 10.4$

 4 X is directly proportional to $\sqrt{Y}$. If $X = 128$ when $Y = 16$, find the following.

    a X when $Y = 36$ **b** Y when $X = 48$

 5 P is directly proportional to f^3. If $P = 400$ when $f = 10$, find the following.

    a P when $f = 4$ **b** f when $P = 50$

 6 The cost of serving tea and biscuits varies directly with the square root of the number of people at the buffet. It costs £25 to serve tea and biscuits to 100 people.

    a How much will it cost to serve tea and biscuits to 400 people?

    b For a cost of £37.50, how many could be served tea and biscuits?

 7 In an experiment, the temperature, in °C, varied directly with the square of the pressure, in atmospheres. The temperature was 20 °C when the pressure was 5 atm.

    a What will the temperature be at 2 atm?   **b** What will the pressure be at 80 °C?

 8 The weight, in grams, of ball bearings varies directly with the cube of the radius measured in millimetres. A ball bearing of radius 4 mm has a weight of 115.2 g.

    a What will a ball bearing of radius 6 mm weigh?

    b A ball bearing has a weight of 48.6 g. What is its radius?

 9 The energy, in J, of a particle varies directly with the square of its speed in m/s. A particle moving at 20 m/s has 50 J of energy.

    a How much energy has a particle moving at 4 m/s?

    b At what speed is a particle moving if it has 200 J of energy?

 10 The cost, in £, of a trip varies directly with the square root of the number of miles travelled. The cost of a 100-mile trip is £35.

    a What is the cost of a 500-mile trip (to the nearest £1)?

    b What is the distance of a trip costing £70?

Inverse variation

This section will introduce you to:

- inverse variation and show you how to work out the constant of proportionality

Key words

constant of proportionality, k
inverse proportion

There is **inverse variation** between two variables when one variable is directly proportional to the reciprocal of the other. That is, the product of the two variables is constant. So, as one variable increases, the other decreases.

For example, the faster you travel over a given distance, the less time it takes. So there is an inverse variation between speed and time. We say speed is inversely proportional to time.

$$S \propto \frac{1}{T} \text{ and so } S = \frac{k}{T}$$

which can be written as $ST = k$.

EXAMPLE 3

M is **inversely proportional** to R. If $M = 9$ when $R = 4$, find the following.

a M when $R = 2$ **b** R when $M = 3$

Step 1: $M \propto \frac{1}{R} \Rightarrow M = \frac{k}{R}$ where k is the **constant of proportionality**.

Step 2: When $M = 9$ and $R = 4$, we get $9 = \frac{k}{4}$

$\Rightarrow 9 \times 4 = k \Rightarrow k = 36$

Step 3: So the formula is $M = \frac{36}{R}$

a When $R = 2$, then $M = \frac{36}{2} = 18$

b When $M = 3$, then $3 = \frac{36}{R} \Rightarrow 3R = 36 \Rightarrow R = 12$

EXERCISE 22C

In each case, first find the formula connecting the variables.

1 T is inversely proportional to m. If $T = 6$ when $m = 2$, find the following.

     a T when $m = 4$ **b** m when $T = 4.8$

2 W is inversely proportional to x. If $W = 5$ when $x = 12$, find the following.

     a W when $x = 3$ **b** x when $W = 10$

3 Q varies inversely with $(5 - t)$. If $Q = 8$ when $t = 3$, find the following.

a Q when $t = 10$ **b** t when $Q = 16$

4 M varies inversely with t^2. If $M = 9$ when $t = 2$, find the following.

a M when $t = 3$ **b** t when $M = 1.44$

5 W is inversely proportional to $\sqrt{T}$. If $W = 6$ when $T = 16$, find the following.

a W when $T = 25$ **b** T when $W = 2.4$

6 The grant available to a section of society was inversely proportional to the number of people needing the grant. When 30 people needed a grant, they received £60 each.

a What would the grant have been if 120 people had needed one?

b If the grant had been £50 each, how many people would have received it?

7 While doing underwater tests in one part of an ocean, a team of scientists noticed that the temperature in °C was inversely proportional to the depth in kilometres. When the temperature was 6 °C, the scientists were at a depth of 4 km.

a What would the temperature have been at a depth of 8 km?

b To what depth would they have had to go to find the temperature at 2 °C?

8 A new engine was being tested, but it had serious problems. The distance it went, in km, without breaking down was inversely proportional to the square of its speed in m/s. When the speed was 12 m/s, the engine lasted 3 km.

a Find the distance covered before a breakdown, when the speed is 15 m/s.

b On one test, the engine broke down after 6.75 km. What was the speed?

9 In a balloon it was noticed that the pressure, in atmospheres, was inversely proportional to the square root of the height, in metres. When the balloon was at a height of 25 m, the pressure was 1.44 atm.

a What was the pressure at a height of 9 m?

b What would the height have been if the pressure was 0.72 atm?

10 The amount of waste which a firm produces, measured in tonnes per hour, is inversely proportional to the square root of the size of the filter beds, measured in m². At the moment, the firm produces 1.25 tonnes per hour of waste, with filter beds of size 0.16 m².

a The filter beds used to be only 0.01 m². How much waste did the firm produce then?

b How much waste could be produced if the filter beds were 0.75 m²?

1 y is proportional to $\sqrt{x}$. Complete the table.

x	25		400
y	10	20	

2 The energy, E, of an object moving horizontally is directly proportional to the speed, v, of the object. When the speed is 10 m/s the energy is 40 000 Joules.

a   Find an equation connecting E and v.

b   Find the speed of the object when the energy is 14 400 Joules.

3 y is inversely proportional to the cube root of x. When $y = 8$, $x = \frac{1}{8}$.

a   Find an expression for y in terms of x,

b   Calculate

   i   the value of y when $x = \frac{1}{125}$,

   ii   the value of x when $y = 2$.

4 The mass of a cube is directly proportional to the cube of its side. A cube with a side of 4 cm has a mass of 320 grams. Calculate the side length of a cube made of the same material with a mass of 36 450 grams

5 y is directly proportional to the cube of x. When $y = 16$, $x = 3$. Find the value of y when $x = 6$.

6 d is directly proportional to the square of t. $d = 80$ when $t = 4$

a   Express d in terms of t.

b   Work out the value of d when $t = 7$.

c   Work out the positive value of t when $d = 45$.

Edexcel, Question 16, Paper 5 Higher, June 2005

7 The force, F, between two magnets is inversely proportional to the square of the distance, x, between them.

When $x = 3$, $F = 4$.

a   Find an expression for F in terms of x.

b   Calculate F when $x = 2$.

c   Calculate x when $F = 64$.

Edexcel, Question 17, Paper 5 Higher, June 2003

8 Two variables, x and y, are known to be proportional to each other. When $x = 10$, $y = 25$.

Find the constant of proportionality, k, if:

a $y \propto x$

b $y \propto x^2$

c $y \propto \frac{1}{x}$

d $\sqrt{y} \propto \frac{1}{x}$

9 y is directly proportional to the cube root of x. When $x = 27$, $y = 6$.

a   Find the value of y when $x = 125$.

b   Find the value of x when $y = 3$.

10 The surface area, A, of a solid is directly proportional to the square of the depth, d. When $d = 6$, $A = 12\pi$.

a   Find the value of A when $d = 12$. Give your answer in terms of π.

b   Find the value of d when $A = 27\pi$.

11 r is inversely proportional to t. $r = 12$ when $t = 0.2$

Calculate the value of r when $t = 4$.

Edexcel, Question 4, Paper 13B Higher, January 2003

12 The frequency, f, of sound is inversely proportional to the wavelength, w. A sound with a frequency of 36 hertz has a wavelength of 20.25 metres.

Calculate the frequency when the frequency and the wavelength have the same numerical value.

13 t is proportional to m^3.

a   When $m = 6$, $t = 324$. Find the value of t when $m = 10$.

Also, m is inversely proportional to the square root of w.

b   When $t = 12$, $w = 25$. Find the value of w when $m = 4$.

14 P and Q are positive quantities. P is inversely proportional to Q^2. When $P = 160$, $Q = 20$. Find the value of P when $P = Q$.

WORKED EXAM QUESTION

y is inversely proportional to the square of x. When y is 40, $x = 5$.

a Find an equation connecting x and y.

b Find the value of y when $x = 10$.

Solution

a $y \propto \dfrac{1}{x^2}$

$y = \dfrac{k}{x^2}$

$40 = \dfrac{k}{25}$

$\Rightarrow \quad k = 40 \times 25 = 1000$

$y = \dfrac{1000}{x^2}$

or $yx^2 = 1000$

> First set up the proportionality relationship and replace the proportionality sign with $= k$.

> Substitute the given values of y and x into the proportionality equation to find the value of k.

> Substitute the value of k to get the final equation connecting y and x.

b When $x = 10$, $y = \dfrac{1000}{10^2} = \dfrac{1000}{100} = 10$

> Substitute the value of x into the equation to find y.

The mass of a solid, M, is directly proportional to the cube of its height, h. When $h = 10$, $M = 4000$.

The surface area, A, of the solid is directly proportional to the square of the height, h. When $h = 10$, $A = 50$.

Find A, when $M = 32\,000$.

Solution

$M = kh^3$

$4000 = k \times 1000 \Rightarrow k = 4$

So, $M = 4h^3$

> First, find the relationship between M and h using the given information.

$A = ph^2$

$50 = p \times 100 \Rightarrow p = \dfrac{1}{2}$

So, $A = \dfrac{1}{2}h^2$

> Next, find the relationship between A and h using the given information.

$32\,000 = 4h^3$

$h^3 = 8000 \Rightarrow h = 20$

> Find the value of h when $M = 32\,000$.

$A = \dfrac{1}{2}(20)^2 = \dfrac{400}{2} = 200$

> Now find the value of A for that value of h.

Wind Power

An electricity company wants to build some offshore wind turbines (as shown below). The company is concerned about how big the turbines will look to a person standing on the shore. It asks an engineer to calculate the angle of elevation from the shore to the highest point of a turbine, when it is rotating, if the turbine was placed at different distances out to sea. Help the engineer to complete the first table below.

Distance of turbine out to sea	Angle of elevation from shore
3km	2.29°
4km	
5km	
6km	
7km	
8km	

50m

70m

The power available in the wind is measured in watts per metre squared of rotor area (W/m^2). Wind speed is measured in metres per second (m/s). The power available in the wind is proportional to the cube of its speed. A wind speed of 7 m/s can provide 210 W/m^2 of energy. Complete the table below to show the available power at different wind speeds.

Wind speed (m/s)	Available power (W/m^2)
6	
7	210
8	
9	
10	
11	
12	

The engineer investigates the different amounts of power produced by different length rotor blades at different wind speeds. He calculates the rotor area for each blade length – this is the area of the circle made by the rotors – and then works out the power produced by these blades at the different wind speeds shown. Help him to complete the table.

Remember

1 W = 1 watt
1000 W = 1 kW = 1 kilowatt
1000 kW = 1 MW = 1 megawatt

Wind speed (m/s)	Available power (W/m²)	Rotor area for 50 m blade (m²)	Power (MW)	Rotor area for 60 m blade (m²)	Power (MW)	Rotor area for 70 m blade (m²)	Power (MW)
7	210	7854	1.65				
8		7854					
9		7854					
10		7854					

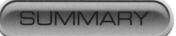

SUMMARY

Number and limits of accuracy

1 Limits of accuracy

2 Problems involving limits of accuracy

This chapter will show you ...

- how to find the limits of numbers rounded to certain accuracies
- how to use limits of accuracy in calculations

Limits of accuracy → Calculating with limits of accuracy

What you should already know

- How to round numbers to various degrees of accuracy

Quick check

1 Round off 6374 to

  a the nearest 10,

  b the nearest 100,

  c the nearest 1000.

2 Round off 2.389 to

  a one decimal place,

  b two decimal places.

3 Round off 47.28 to

  a one significant figure,

  b three significant figures.

Limits of accuracy

This section will show you how to:

- find the limits of accuracy of numbers that have been rounded to different degrees of accuracy

Key words

continuous data
discrete data
limits of accuracy
lower bound
rounding error
upper bound

Any recorded measurement will have been rounded off to some degree of accuracy. This defines the possible true value before rounding off took place, and hence the **limits of accuracy**. The range of values between the limits of accuracy is called the **rounding error**.

EXAMPLE 1

A stick of wood is measured as 32 cm to the nearest centimetre.

Between what limits does the actual length of the stick lie?

The lower limit is 31.5 cm as a halfway value is always rounded up.

The upper limit is 32.499999999… cm. In other words it can get as close to 32.5 cm as possible but not be 32.5 cm. However 32.5 cm is the upper limit. So we say

   31.5 cm ⩽ length of stick < 32.5 cm.

Note the use of the strict inequality for the upper limit.

EXAMPLE 2

53.7 is accurate to one decimal place. What are the limits of accuracy?

The smallest possible value is 53.65.

The largest possible value is 53.749999999… but once again we say 53.75 is the upper limit.

Hence the limits of accuracy are 53.65 ⩽ 53.7 < 53.75

EXAMPLE 3

A skip has a mass of 220 kg measured to three significant figures. What are the limits of accuracy of the mass of the skip?

The smallest possible value is 219.5 kg.

The largest possible value is 220.49999999… kg but once again we say 220.5 kg is the upper limit.

Hence the limits of accuracy are 219.5 kg ⩽ mass of skip < 220.5 kg

---

Note that the limits of accuracy are always given to one more degree of accuracy than the rounded value. For example 32 is the nearest integer and the limits are to half a unit; 53.7 is to 1 decimal place and the limits are to 2 decimal places; 220 is to 3 significant figures and the limits are to 4 significant figures.

EXAMPLE 4

A coach carrying 50 people measured to the nearest 10, is travelling at 50 mph measured to the nearest 10 mph. What are the actual limits of the number of people and the speed?

This is an example of the difference between **discrete** and **continuous data**. The number of people is discrete data as it can only take integer values, but speed is continuous data as it can take any value in a range.

The limits are 45 ⩽ number of people ⩽ 54, 45 mph ⩽ speed < 55 mph.

Be careful as questions sometimes ask about the limits of discrete data.

EXERCISE 23A

1 Write down the limits of accuracy of the following.

a 7 cm measured to the nearest centimetre

b 120 grams measured to the nearest 10 grams

c 3400 kilometres measured to the nearest 100 kilometres

d 50 mph measured to the nearest mph

e £6 given to the nearest £

f 16.8 cm to the nearest tenth of a centimetre

g 16 kg to the nearest kilogram

h a football crowd of 14 500 given to the nearest 100

i 55 miles given to the nearest mile

j 55 miles given to the nearest 5 miles

2 Write down the limits of accuracy for each of the following values which are rounded to the given degree of accuracy.

a 6 cm (1 significant figure)	**b** 17 kg (2 significant figures)	**c** 32 min (2 significant figures)
d 238 km (3 significant figures)	**e** 7.3 m (1 decimal place)	**f** 25.8 kg (1 decimal place)
g 3.4 h (1 decimal place)	**h** 87 g (2 significant figures)	**i** 4.23 mm (2 decimal places)
j 2.19 kg (2 decimal places)	**k** 12.67 min (2 decimal places)	**l** 25 m (2 significant figures)
m 40 cm (1 significant figure)	**n** 600 g (2 significant figures)	**o** 30 min (1 significant figure)
p 1000 m (2 significant figures)	**q** 4.0 m (1 decimal place)	**r** 7.04 kg (2 decimal places)
s 12.0 s (1 decimal place)	**t** 7.00 m (2 decimal places)	

Upper and lower bounds

A journey of 26 miles measured to the nearest mile could actually be as long as 26.4999999... miles or as short as 25.5 miles. It could not be 26.5 miles, as this would round up to 27 miles. However, 26.4999999... is *virtually the same* as 26.5.

We overcome this difficulty by saying that 26.5 is the **upper bound** of the measured value and 25.5 is its **lower bound**. We can therefore write

$$25.5 \text{ miles} \leqslant \text{actual distance} < 26.5 \text{ miles}$$

which states that the actual distance is *greater than or equal to* 25.5 miles but *less than* 26.5 miles.

Although it is not wrong to give the upper bound as 26.49999... it is mathematically neater to give 26.5. It is wrong, however, to give the upper bound as 26.4 or 26.49. So, when stating an upper bound, always follow the accepted practice, as demonstrated here, which eliminates the difficulties that arise with recurring decimals.

A mathematical peculiarity

Let $x = 0.999\ 999\dots$ (1)

Multiply by 10 $10x = 9.999\ 999\dots$ (2)

Subtract (1) from (2) $9x = 9$

Divide by 9 $x = 1$

So, we have $0.\dot{9} = 1$

Hence, it is valid to give the upper bound without using recurring decimals.

EXERCISE 23B

1 Write down the lower and upper bounds of each of these values, rounded to the accuracy stated.

   a 8 m (1 significant figure)   **b** 26 kg (2 significant figures)   **c** 25 min (2 significant figures)

   d 85 g (2 significant figures)   **e** 2.40 m (2 decimal places)   **f** 0.2 kg (1 decimal place)

   g 0.06 s (2 decimal places)   **h** 300 g (1 significant figure)   **i** 0.7 m (1 decimal place)

   j 366 d (3 significant figures)   **k** 170 weeks (2 significant figures)   **l** 210 g (2 significant figures)

2 Billy has 40 identical marbles. Each marble weighs 65 g (to the nearest gram).

   a What is the greatest possible weight of one marble?

   b What is the least possible weight of one marble?

   c What is the greatest possible weight of all the marbles?

   d What is the least possible weight of all the marbles?

In this section you will learn how to:

- Combine limits of two or more variables together to solve problems

Key words

limits of
  accuracy
maximum
minimum

When we calculate an area or a volume, the errors in the linear measures will be compounded and, hence, will produce a still larger error in the calculated value. There are four operations to perform on limits – addition, subtraction, multiplication and division.

To get the **maximum** value when adding two numbers given to a certain **limit of accuracy**, the maximum values of the two numbers should be added. However, to get the maximum value when two numbers are subtracted then the lower limit of the second number should be subtracted from the upper limit of the first number.

Let a and b be two numbers that lie within limits $a_{min} \leqslant a < a_{max}$ and $b_{min} \leqslant b < b_{max}$

The following table shows the combinations to give the maximum and **minimum** values for the four rules of arithmetic.

Operation	Maximum	Minimum
Addition $(a + b)$	$a_{max} + b_{max}$	$a_{min} + b_{min}$
Subtraction $(a - b)$	$a_{max} - b_{min}$	$a_{min} - b_{max}$
Multiplication $(a \times b)$	$a_{max} \times b_{max}$	$a_{min} \times b_{min}$
Division $(a \div b)$	$a_{max} \div b_{min}$	$a_{min} \div b_{max}$

Be very careful about the order when doing subtraction or division.

When solving problems involving limits, start by writing down the limits of the variables involved, as this will get you some credit in the exam, then think about which combination of limits is needed to get the required answer.

Sometimes, especially when dividing, the upper and lower limits will be given to many decimal places. Be careful where rounding these off as the rounded answer may be outside the acceptable range of the limits. If you do round answers off, give your answer to at least 3 significant figures.

EXAMPLE 5

A rectangle has sides given as 6 cm by 15 cm, to the nearest centimetre.

Calculate the limits of accuracy of the area of the rectangle.

Write down the limits: 5.5 cm ⩽ width < 6.5 cm, 14.5 cm ⩽ length < 15.5 cm

For maximum area, multiply maximum width by maximum length, and for minimum area, multiply minimum width by minimum length.

The upper bound of the width is 6.5 cm and of the length is 15.5 cm. Hence the upper bound of the area of the rectangle is

$$6.5 \text{ cm} \times 15.5 \text{ cm} = 100.75 \text{ cm}^2$$

The lower bound of the width is 5.5 cm and of the length is 14.5 cm. Hence the lower bound of the area of the rectangle is

$$5.5 \text{ cm} \times 14.5 \text{ cm} = 79.75 \text{ cm}^2$$

Therefore, the limits of accuracy for the area of the rectangle are

$$79.75 \text{ cm}^2 \leqslant \text{area} < 100.75 \text{ cm}^2$$

EXAMPLE 6

The distance from Barnsley to Sheffield is 15 miles to the nearest mile. The time Jeff took to drive between Barnsley and Sheffield was 40 minutes to the nearest 10 minutes.

Calculate the upper limit of Jeff's average speed.

Write down the limits: 14.5 miles ⩽ distance < 15.5 miles, 35 mins ⩽ time < 45 mins

$$speed = distance \div time$$

To get the maximum speed we need the maximum distance ÷ minimum time.

$$15.5 \text{ miles} \div 35 \text{ mins} = 0.443 \text{ (3 significant figures) miles per minute}$$

$$0.443 \text{ mph} \times 60 = 26.6 \text{ mph}$$

The upper limit of Jeff's average speed = 26.6 mph.

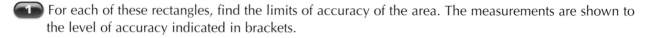

EXERCISE 23C

1 For each of these rectangles, find the limits of accuracy of the area. The measurements are shown to the level of accuracy indicated in brackets.

    a 5 cm × 9 cm (nearest cm)   **b** 4.5 cm × 8.4 cm (1 decimal place)

    c 7.8 cm × 18 cm (2 significant figures)

2 A rectangular garden has sides of 6 m and 4 m, measured to the nearest metre.

    a Write down the limits of accuracy for each length.

    b What is the maximum area of the garden?

    c What is the minimum perimeter of the garden?

A

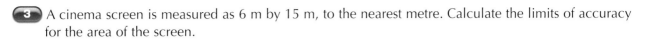 A cinema screen is measured as 6 m by 15 m, to the nearest metre. Calculate the limits of accuracy for the area of the screen.

 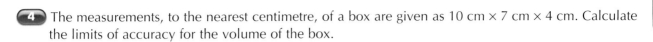 The measurements, to the nearest centimetre, of a box are given as 10 cm × 7 cm × 4 cm. Calculate the limits of accuracy for the volume of the box.

 The area of a field is given as 350 m², to the nearest 10 m². One length is given as 16 m, to the nearest metre. Find the limits of accuracy for the other length of the field.

 In triangle ABC, AB = 9 cm, BC = 7 cm, and ∠ABC = 37°. All the measurements are given to the nearest unit. Calculate the limits of accuracy for the area of the triangle.

 The price of pure gold is £18.25 per gram. The density of gold is 19.3 g/cm³. (Assume these figures are exact.) A solid gold bar in the shape of a cuboid has sides 4.6 cm, 2.2 cm and 6.6 cm. These measurements are made to the nearest 0.1 cm.

a i What are the limits of accuracy for the volume of this gold bar?

ii What are the upper and lower limits of the cost of this bar?

The gold bar was weighed and given a value of 1296 g, to the nearest gram.

b What are the upper and lower limits for the cost of the bar now?.

c Explain why the price ranges are so different.

 A stopwatch records the time for the winner of a 100-metre race as 14.7 seconds, measured to the nearest one-tenth of a second.

a What are the greatest and least possible times for the winner?

b The length of the 100-metre track is correct to the nearest 1 m. What are the greatest and least possible lengths of the track?

c What is the fastest possible average speed of the winner, with a time of 14.7 seconds in the 100-metre race?

 A cube has a side measured as 8 cm, to the nearest millimetre. What is the greatest percentage error of the following?

a the calculated area of one face

b the calculated volume of the cube

 A cube has a volume of 40 cm³, to the nearest cm³. Find the range of possible values of the side length of the cube.

 A cube has a volume of 200 cm³, to the nearest 10 cm³. Find the limits of accuracy of the side length of the cube.

 A model car travels 40 m, measured to one significant figure, at a speed of 2 m/s, measured to one significant figure. Between what limits does the time taken lie?

1 A school has 1850 pupils to the nearest 10.

a What is the least number of pupils at the school

b What is the greatest number of pupils at the school?

2 The longest river in Britain is the River Severn. It is 220 miles long to the nearest 10 miles. What is the least length it could be?

3 Jerry measures a piece of wood as 60 cm correct to the nearest centimetre.

a Write down the minimum possible length of the piece of wood.

b Write down the maximum possible length of the piece of wood.

Edexcel, Question 1, Paper 13A Higher, March 2005

4 The base of a triangle is 10 cm measured to the nearest centimetre. The area of the triangle is 100 cm² measured to the nearest square centimetre. Calculate the least and greatest values of the height of the triangle.

5 A circle has an area of 70 cm², measured to the nearest square centimetre. What is the lower bound of the radius?

6 $x = 1.8$ measured to 1 decimal place,
$y = 4.0$ measured to 2 significant figures,
$z = 2.56$ measured to 3 significant figures.

Calculate the upper limit of $\dfrac{x^2 + y}{z}$.

7 Correct to 2 significant figures, the area of a rectangle is 470 cm².

Correct to 2 significant figures, the length of the rectangle is 23 cm.

Calculate the upper bound for the width of the rectangle.

Edexcel, Question 5, Paper 13B Higher, March 2004

8 A girl runs 60 metres in a time of 8.0 seconds. The distance is measured to the nearest metre and the time is measured to 2 significant figures.
What is the least possible speed?

9 Elliot did an experiment to find the value of g m/s², the acceleration due to gravity. He measured the time, T seconds, that a block took to slide L m down a smooth slope of angle $x°$.

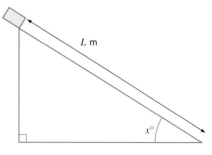

He then used the formula $\quad g = \dfrac{2L}{T^2 \sin x°}$

to calculate an estimate for g.

$T = 1.3$ correct to 1 decimal place.
$L = 4.50$ correct to 2 decimal places.
$x = 30$ correct to the nearest integer.

a Calculate the lower bound and the upper bound for the value of g. Give your answers correct to 3 decimal places.

b Use your answers to part **a** to write down the value of g to a suitable degree of accuracy.
Explain your reasoning.

Edexcel, Question 16, Paper 6 Higher, June 2003

10 a Calculate the length of the diagonal x in this cube of side 3 m.

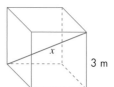

b A man is carrying a pole of length 5 m down a long corridor. The pole is measured to the nearest centimetre. At the end of the corridor is a right-angled corner. The corridor is 3 m wide and 3 m high, both measurements correct to the nearest 10 cm. Will the pole be certain to get round the corner?

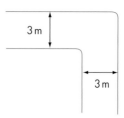

WORKED EXAM QUESTION

The magnification of a lens is given by the formula

$$m = \frac{v}{u}$$

In an experiment, u is measured as 8.5 cm and v is measured as 14.0 cm, both correct to the nearest 0.1 cm. Find the least possible value of m, You must show full details of your calculation.

Solution

$8.45 \leqslant u < 8.55$

$13.95 \leqslant v < 14.05$

> Write down the limits of both variables.

Least m = least u ÷ greatest v = 8.45 ÷ 14.05 = 0.6014234875

> As the calculation is a division the least value will be given by least u ÷ greatest v.

= 0.601 or 0.6

> Round off to a suitable degree of accuracy.

A long rod with a square cross-section is made with a side of 5 cm. A circular hole is drilled with a radius of 3.6 cm. All measurements are to the nearest $\frac{1}{10}$ cm. Will the rod fit into the circle?

> This is a using and applying maths question. You need to have a strategy to solve it. Step 1: find the largest possible diagonal of the square using Pythagoras. Step 2: work out the smallest possible diameter of the circle. Step 3: Compare the values to see if the diagonal is smaller than the diameter. Always start with writing down the limits of the variables in the question.

Solution

Limits of side of square

$4.95 < \text{side} < 5.05$

Limits of radius

$3.55 < \text{radius} < 3.65$

Largest diagonal = $\sqrt{(5.05^2 + 5.05^2)}$

= 7.14177849

= 7.142 (4 significant figures)

> Step 1: Work out the largest possible diagonal, do not round off to less than 4 significant figures.

Smallest diameter = 2 × 3.55 = 7.1

> Step 2: Work out the smallest diameter.

As 7.142 > 7.1,
the rod may not fit in the circle.

> Step 3: Compare the results.

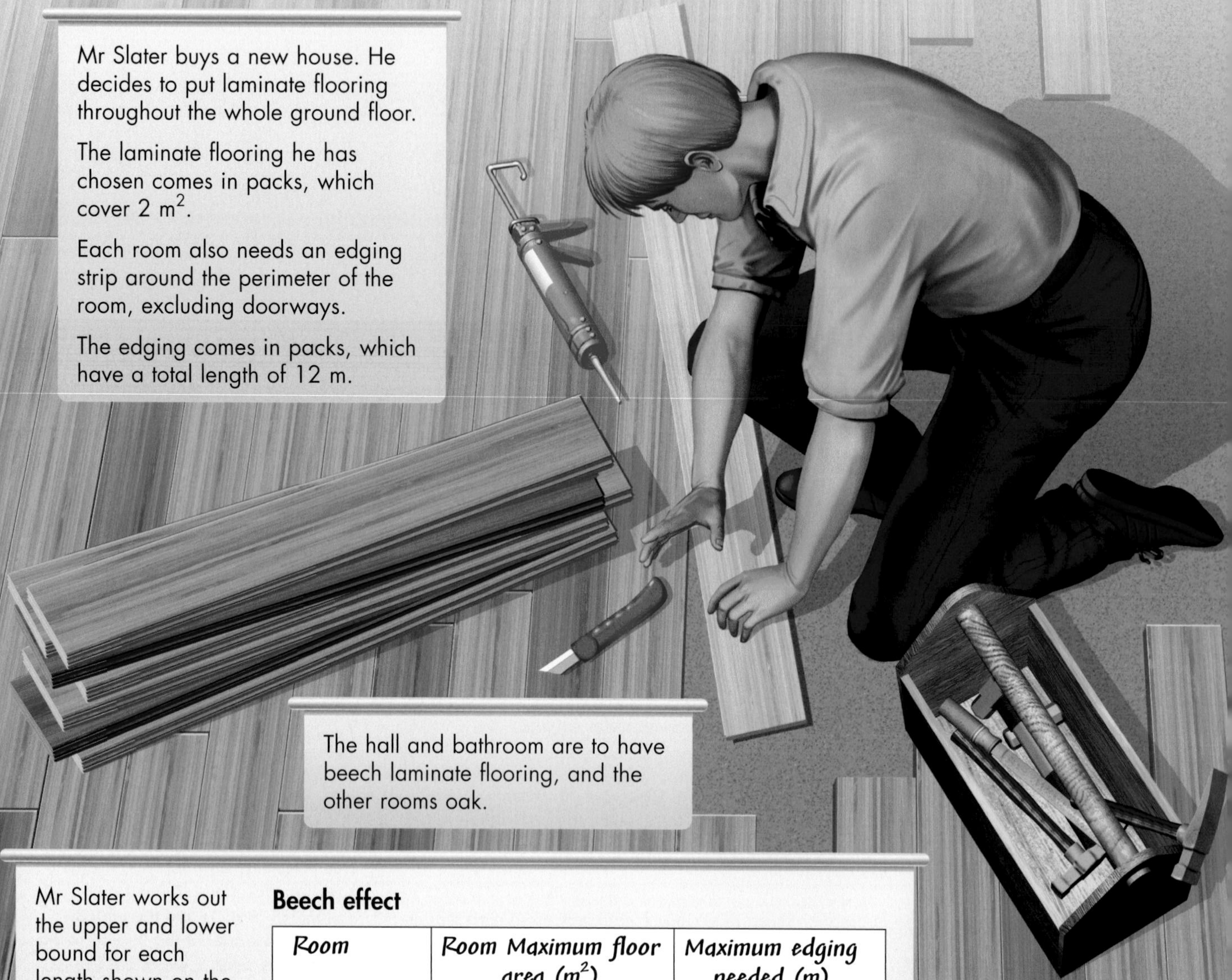

Mr Slater buys a new house. He decides to put laminate flooring throughout the whole ground floor.

The laminate flooring he has chosen comes in packs, which cover 2 m².

Each room also needs an edging strip around the perimeter of the room, excluding doorways.

The edging comes in packs, which have a total length of 12 m.

The hall and bathroom are to have beech laminate flooring, and the other rooms oak.

Mr Slater works out the upper and lower bound for each length shown on the sketch. He then calculates the maximum floor area of each room and the maximum length of edging needed for every room. Help him complete the table to find the total maximum floor area and edging he needs.

Beech effect

Room	Room Maximum floor area (m²)	Maximum edging needed (m)
Hall		
Bathroom		
Total		

Oak effect

Room	Room Maximum floor area (m²)	Maximum edging needed (m)
Lounge		
Sitting room		
Kitchen/diner		
Conservatory		
Total		

This is a sketch showing the ground floor dimensions.

All measurements are to the nearest 0.1 m.

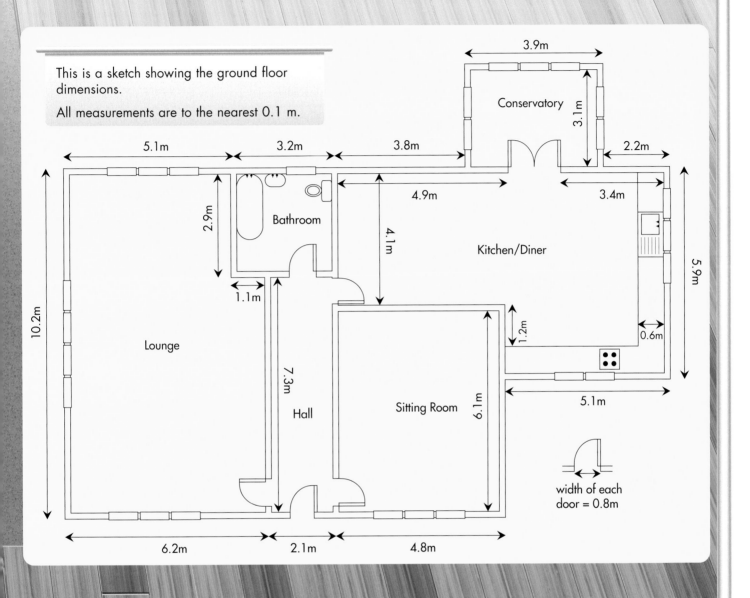

Calculate for Mr Slater the total cost of the flooring and edging.

Oak effect

	Number of packs	Price per pack	Total cost
Beech flooring		£56.40	
Beech edging		£21.15	
Oak flooring		£61.10	
Oak edging		£25.85	
		Total:	

This total price is inclusive of VAT.

VAT is 17½%.

What is the total price, exclusive of VAT?

GRADE YOURSELF

B Able to find measures of accuracy for numbers given to whole number accuracies

A Able to find measures of accuracy for numbers given to decimal place or significant figure accuracies

A* Able to calculate the limits of compound measures

What you should know now

- How to find the limits of numbers given to various accuracies

- How to find the limits of compound measures by combining the appropriate limits of the variables involved

Chapter

24

Inequalities and regions

① Solving inequalities

② Graphical inequalities

③ Problem solving

This chapter will show you ...

- how to solve a linear inequality
- how to find a region on a graph that obeys a linear inequality in two variables
- how inequalities can be used to represent and solve problems

Visual overview

| Linear inequalities | → | Inequalities in two variables | → | Problem solving |

What you should already know

- How to solve linear equations
- How to draw linear graphs

Quick check

1 Solve these equations.

a $\dfrac{2x + 5}{3} = 7$ 　　　　**b** $2x - 7 = 13$

2 On a grid with x and y axes from 0 to 10, draw the graphs of these equations.

a $y = 3x + 1$ 　　　　**b** $2x + 3y = 12$

This section will show you how to:
- solve a simple linear inequality

Key words
inequality
number line

Inequalities behave similarly to equations which you have already met. In the case of linear inequalities, we use the same rules to solve them as we use for linear equations. There are four inequality signs, $<$ which means "less than", $>$ which means "greater than", $\leqslant$ which means "less than or equal to" and $\geqslant$ which means "greater than or equal to".

EXAMPLE 1

Solve $2x + 3 < 14$.

This is rewritten as:

$$2x < 14 - 3$$
$$2x < 11$$

Divide both sides by 2:

$$\frac{2x}{2} < \frac{11}{2}$$

$$\Rightarrow x < 5.5$$

This means that x can take any value below 5.5 but *not* the value 5.5.

Note: The inequality sign given in the problem is the sign to give in the answer.

EXAMPLE 2

Solve $\frac{x}{2} + 4 \geqslant 13$.

Solve just like an equation but leave the inequality sign in place of the equals sign.

Subtract 4 from both sides:

$$\frac{x}{2} \geqslant 9$$

Multiply both sides by 2:

$$x \geqslant 18$$

This means that x can take any value above and including 18.

EXAMPLE 3

Solve $\dfrac{3x + 7}{2} < 14$.

This is rewritten as: $\quad\quad\quad 3x + 7 < 14 \times 2$

That is: $\quad\quad\quad\quad\quad\quad\quad 3x + 7 < 28$

$\quad\quad\quad\quad\quad\quad\quad\quad\Rightarrow\quad 3x < 28 - 7$

$\quad\quad\quad\quad\quad\quad\quad\quad\Rightarrow\quad 3x < 21$

$\quad\quad\quad\quad\quad\quad\quad\quad\Rightarrow\quad x < 21 \div 3$

$\quad\quad\quad\quad\quad\quad\quad\quad\Rightarrow\quad x < 7$

EXAMPLE 4

Solve $1 < 3x + 4 \leqslant 13$.

Divide the inequality into two parts, and treat each part separately.

$\quad\quad\quad\quad 1 < 3x + 4 \quad\quad\quad\quad\quad\quad\quad 3x + 4 \leqslant 13$

$\quad\Rightarrow\quad 1 - 4 < 3x \quad\quad\quad\quad\quad\Rightarrow\quad 3x \leqslant 13 - 4$

$\quad\Rightarrow\quad -3 < 3x \quad\quad\quad\quad\quad\quad\Rightarrow\quad 3x \leqslant 9$

$\quad\Rightarrow\quad -\dfrac{3}{3} < x \quad\quad\quad\quad\quad\quad\Rightarrow\quad x \leqslant \dfrac{9}{3}$

$\quad\quad\quad\quad\quad\quad\quad\quad\quad\quad\quad\quad\Rightarrow\quad -1 < x \Rightarrow$

3

Hence, $-1 < x \leqslant 3$.

EXERCISE 24A

1 Solve the following linear inequalities.

a $x + 4 < 7$ **b** $t - 3 > 5$ **c** $p + 2 \geqslant 12$

d $2x - 3 < 7$ **e** $4y + 5 \leqslant 17$ **f** $3t - 4 > 11$

g $\dfrac{x}{2} + 4 < 7$ **h** $\dfrac{y}{5} + 3 \leqslant 6$ **i** $\dfrac{t}{3} - 2 \geqslant 4$

j $3(x - 2) < 15$ **k** $5(2x + 1) \leqslant 35$ **l** $2(4t - 3) \geqslant 34$

2 Write down the largest integer value of x that satisfies each of the following.

a $x - 3 \leqslant 5$, where x is positive

b $x + 2 < 9$, where x is positive and even

c $3x - 11 < 40$, where x is a square number

d $5x - 8 \leqslant 15$, where x is positive and odd

e $2x + 1 < 19$, where x is positive and prime

3 Write down the smallest integer value of x that satisfies each of the following.

a $x - 2 \geqslant 9$, where x is positive

b $x - 2 > 13$, where x is positive and even

c $2x - 11 \geqslant 19$, where x is a square number

4 Solve the following linear inequalities.

a $4x + 1 \geqslant 3x - 5$ **b** $5t - 3 \leqslant 2t + 5$ **c** $3y - 12 \leqslant y - 4$

d $2x + 3 \geqslant x + 1$ **e** $5w - 7 \leqslant 3w + 4$ **f** $2(4x - 1) \leqslant 3(x + 4)$

5 Solve the following linear inequalities.

a $\dfrac{x + 4}{2} \leqslant 3$ **b** $\dfrac{x - 3}{5} > 7$ **c** $\dfrac{2x + 5}{3} < 6$

d $\dfrac{4x - 3}{5} \geqslant 5$ **e** $\dfrac{3t - 2}{7} > 4$ **f** $\dfrac{5y + 3}{5} \leqslant 2$

6 Solve the following linear inequalities.

a $7 < 2x + 1 < 13$ **b** $5 < 3x - 1 < 14$ **c** $-1 < 5x + 4 \leqslant 19$

d $1 \leqslant 4x - 3 < 13$ **e** $11 \leqslant 3x + 5 < 17$ **f** $-3 \leqslant 2x - 3 \leqslant 7$

The number line

The solution to a linear inequality can be shown on the **number line** by using the following conventions.

Below are five examples.

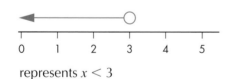

represents $x < 3$

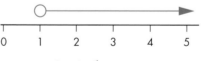

represents $x > 1$

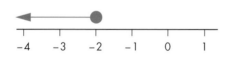

represents $x \leqslant -2$

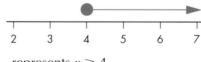

represents $x \geqslant 4$

represents $-1 \leqslant x < 2$

EXAMPLE 5

a Write down the inequality shown by this diagram.

b i Solve the following inequality $2x + 3 < 11$.

ii Mark the solution on a number line.

c Write down the integers that satisfy both the inequalities in **a** and **b**.

a The inequality shown is $x \geqslant 1$.

b i $2x + 3 < 11 \quad \Rightarrow \quad 2x < 8 \quad \Rightarrow \quad x < 4$

ii

c The integers that satisfy both inequalities are 1, 2 and 3.

EXERCISE 24B

1 Write down the inequality that is represented by each diagram below.

a

b

c

d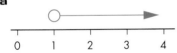

e

f

2 Draw diagrams to illustrate the following.

a $x \leqslant 3$ **b** $x > -2$ **c** $x \geqslant 0$ **d** $x < 5$

e $x \geqslant -1$ **f** $2 < x \leqslant 5$ **g** $-1 \leqslant x \leqslant 3$ **h** $-3 < x < 4$

3 Solve the following inequalities and illustrate their solutions on number lines.

a $x + 4 \geqslant 8$ **b** $x + 5 < 3$ **c** $4x - 2 \geqslant 12$ **d** $2x + 5 < 3$

e $2(4x + 3) < 18$ **f** $\dfrac{x}{2} + 3 \leqslant 2$ **g** $\dfrac{x}{5} - 2 > 8$ **h** $\dfrac{x}{3} + 5 \geqslant 3$

4 Solve the following inequalities and illustrate their solutions on number lines.

a $\dfrac{2x + 5}{3} > 3$ **b** $\dfrac{3x + 4}{2} \geqslant 11$ **c** $\dfrac{2x + 8}{3} \leqslant 2$ **d** $\dfrac{2x - 1}{3} \geqslant -3$

Inequalities involving x^2

When we have an inequality such as $x^2 < 9$, we have to think very carefully because there are two possible solutions to $x^2 = 9$. They are $x = 3$ and $x = -3$.

The solution $x = 3$ to the equation $x^2 = 9$ would suggest the condition $x < 3$ is a solution to $x^2 < 9$. Clearly, $x < 3$ does satisfy the inequality $x^2 < 9$. The condition to be obtained from the solution $x = -3$ is not $x < -3$. (Think about $(-5)^2$.) So it must be $x > -3$. That is, the inequality sign is *changed*. For convenience, $x > -3$ can be turned to give $-3 < x$.

Show this situation on a number line and the solution becomes clear.

Namely, $-3 < x < 3$.

EXAMPLE 6

Solve the inequality $x^2 > 16$ and show your solution on a number line.

The solution to $x^2 > 16$ will be $x > 4$ and $x < -4$, which is represented as

---

Notice the difference between inequalities of the type $x^2 < a^2$ and those of the type $x^2 > a^2$.

EXERCISE 24C

Solve the following inequalities, showing their solutions on number lines.

1. $x^2 \leqslant 4$
2. $x^2 > 25$
3. $x^2 < 49$

4. $x^2 \geqslant 1$
5. $x^2 \geqslant 9$
6. $x^2 - 1 > 8$

7. $x^2 + 2 \leqslant 6$
8. $x^2 - 3 < 13$
9. $x^2 + 5 > 6$

10. $x^2 - 4 \geqslant 5$
11. $2x^2 - 1 > 7$
12. $3x^2 - 5 < 22$

13. $5x^2 + 3 \leqslant 8$
14. $2x^2 - 4 < 28$
15. $3x^2 - 9 \geqslant 66$

16. $x^2 \geqslant 100$
17. $x^2 < 2.25$
18. $x^2 \geqslant 0.25$

19. $x^2 - 5 \leqslant 76$
20. $x^2 > 0$

This section will show you how to:
● show a graphical inequality and how to find regions that satisfy more than one graphical inequality

Key words
boundary
included
origin
region

A linear inequality can be plotted on a graph. The result is a **region** that lies on one side or the other of a straight line. You will recognise an inequality by the fact that it looks like an equation but instead of the equals sign it has an inequality sign: $<$, $>$, $\leqslant$, or $\geqslant$.

The following are examples of linear inequalities which can be represented on a graph.

$$y < 3 \qquad x > 7 \qquad -3 \leqslant y < 5 \qquad y \geqslant 2x + 3 \qquad 2x + 3y < 6 \qquad y \leqslant x$$

The method for graphing an inequality is to draw the **boundary** line that defines the inequality. This is found by replacing the inequality sign with an equals sign. When a strict inequality is stated ($<$ or $>$), the boundary line should be drawn as a *dashed* line to show that it is not included in the range of values. When $\leqslant$ or $\geqslant$ are used to state the inequality, the boundary line should be drawn as a *solid* line to show that the boundary is **included**.

After the boundary line has been drawn, the *required region is shaded*.

To confirm on which side of the line the region lies, choose any point that is not on the boundary line and test it in the inequality. If it satisfies the inequality, that is the side required. If it doesn't, the other side is required.

Work through the six inequalities on this page and the next, to see how the procedure is applied.

EXAMPLE 7

Show each of the following inequalities on a graph.

a $y \leqslant 3$ **b** $x > 7$ **c** $-3 \leqslant y < 5$ **d** $y \leqslant 2x + 3$ **e** $2x + 3y < 6$ **f** $y \leqslant x$

a Draw the line $y = 3$. Since the inequality is stated as $\leqslant$, the line is *solid*. Test a point that is not on the line. The **origin** is always a good choice if possible, as 0 is easy to test.

Putting 0 into the inequality gives $0 \leqslant 3$. The inequality is satisfied and so the region containing the origin is the side we want.

Shade it in.

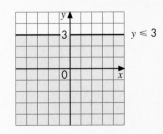

b Since the inequality is stated as $>$, the line is *dashed*. Draw the line $x = 7$.

Test the origin $(0, 0)$, which gives $0 > 7$. This is not true, so we want the other side of the line from the origin.

Shade it in.

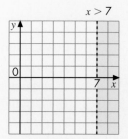

c Draw the lines $y = -3$ (solid for $\leqslant$) and $y = 5$ (dashed for $<$).

Test a point that is not on either line, say $(0, 0)$. Zero is between -3 and 5, so the required region lies between the lines.

Shade it in.

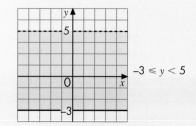

d Draw the line $y = 2x + 3$. Since the inequality is stated as $\leqslant$, the line is solid.

Test a point that is not on the line, $(0, 0)$. Putting these x and y-values in the inequality gives $0 \leqslant 2(0) + 3$, which is true. So the region that includes the origin is what we want.

Shade it in.

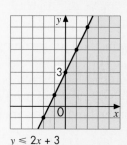

e Draw the line $2x + 3y = 6$. Since the inequality is stated as $<$, the line is dashed.

Test a point that is not on the line, say $(0, 0)$. Is it true that $2(0) + 3(0) < 6$? The answer is yes, so the origin is in the region that we want.

Shade it in.

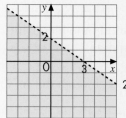

f Draw the line $y = x$. Since the inequality is stated as $\leqslant$, the line is solid.

This time the origin is on the line, so pick any other point, say $(1, 3)$. Putting $x = 1$ and $y = 3$ in the inequality gives $3 \leqslant 1$. This is not true, so the point $(1, 3)$ is not in the region we want.

Shade in the other side to $(1, 3)$.

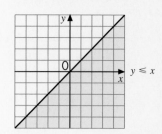

More than one inequality

When we have to show a region that satisfies more than one inequality, it is clearer to *shade* the regions *not required*, so that the *required region* is left *blank*.

EXAMPLE 8

a On the same grid, show the regions that represent the following inequalities by shading the unwanted regions.

 i $x > 2$ ii $y \geqslant x$ iii $x + y < 8$

b Are the points (3, 4), (2, 6) and (3, 3) in the region that satisfies all three inequalities?

i 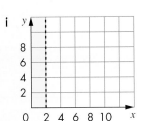   ii 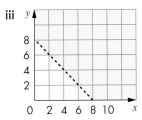   iii

a i This region is shown unshaded in diagram **i**.

   The boundary line is $x = 2$ (dashed).

   ii This region is shown unshaded in diagram **ii**.

   The boundary line is $y = x$ (solid).

   iii This region is shown unshaded in diagram **iii**.

   The boundary line is $x + y = 8$ (dashed). The regions have first been drawn separately so that each may be clearly seen. The diagram on the right shows all three regions on the same grid. The white triangular area defines the region that satisfies all three inequalities.

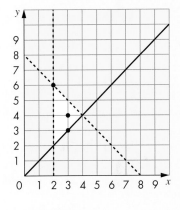

b i The point (3, 4) is clearly within the region that satisfies all three inequalities.

   ii The point (2, 6) is on the boundary lines $x = 2$ and $x + y = 8$. As these are dashed lines, they are not included in the region defined by all three inequalities. So, the point (2, 6) is not in this region.

   iii The point (3, 3) is on the boundary line $y = x$. As this is a solid line, it is included in the region defined by all three inequalities. So, the point (3, 3) is included in this region.

EXERCISE 24D

1 a Draw the line $x = 2$ (as a solid line).

   b Shade the region defined by $x \leqslant 2$.

2 a Draw the line $y = -3$ (as a dashed line).

   b Shade the region defined by $y > -3$.

3 **a** Draw the line $x = -2$ (as a solid line).

b Draw the line $x = 1$ (as a solid line) on the same grid.

c Shade the region defined by $-2 \leqslant x \leqslant 1$.

4 **a** Draw the line $y = -1$ (as a dashed line).

b Draw the line $y = 4$ (as a solid line) on the same grid.

c Shade the region defined by $-1 < y \leqslant 4$.

5 **a** On the same grid, draw the regions defined by these inequalities.

i $-3 \leqslant x \leqslant 6$ **ii** $-4 < y \leqslant 5$

b Are the following points in the region defined by both inequalities?

i (2, 2)   **ii** (1, 5)   **iii** (−2, −4)

6 **a** Draw the line $y = 2x - 1$ (as a dashed line).

b Shade the region defined by $y < 2x - 1$.

7 **a** Draw the line $3x - 4y = 12$ (as a solid line).

b Shade the region defined by $3x - 4y \leqslant 12$.

8 **a** Draw the line $y = \frac{1}{2}x + 3$ (as a solid line).

b Shade the region defined by $y \geqslant \frac{1}{2}x + 3$.

9 Shade the region defined by $y < -3$.

10 **a** Draw the line $y = 3x - 4$ (as a solid line).

b Draw the line $x + y = 10$ (as a solid line) on the same diagram.

c Shade the diagram so that the region defined by $y \geqslant 3x - 4$ is left *unshaded*.

d Shade the diagram so that the region defined by $x + y \leqslant 10$ is left *unshaded*.

e Are the following points in the region defined by both inequalities?

i (2, 1)   **ii** (2, 2)   **iii** (2, 3)

11 **a** Draw the line $y = x$ (as a solid line).

b Draw the line $2x + 5y = 10$ (as a solid line) on the same diagram.

c Draw the line $2x + y = 6$ (as a dashed line) on the same diagram.

d Shade the diagram so that the region defined by $y \geqslant x$ is left *unshaded*.

e Shade the diagram so that the region defined by $2x + 5y \geqslant 10$ is left *unshaded*.

f Shade the diagram so that the region defined by $2x + y < 6$ is left *unshaded*.

g Are the following points in the region defined by these inequalities?

i (1, 1)   **ii** (2, 2)   **iii** (1, 3)

> **HINTS AND TIPS**
>
> In exams it is always made clear which region is to be labelled or shaded. Make sure you do as the question asks, and label or shade as required otherwise you could lose a mark.

12 **a** On the same grid, draw the regions defined by the following inequalities. (Shade the diagram so that the overlapping region is left blank.)

    i $y > x - 3$ **ii** $3y + 4x \leqslant 24$ **iii** $x \geqslant 2$

  b Are the following points in the region defined by all three inequalities?

    i $(1, 1)$ **ii** $(2, 2)$ **iii** $(3, 3)$ **iv** $(4, 4)$

24.3 Problem solving

This section will show you:

- some of the problems that can be solved using inequalities

Inequalities can arise in the solution of certain kinds of problem. The next example illustrates such a situation.

EXAMPLE 9

James has to buy drinks for himself and four friends. He has £2.50 to spend. A can of Cola costs 60 pence and a can of Orange costs 40 pence. He buys x cans of Cola and y cans of Orange.

a Explain why   **i** $x + y \geqslant 5$ **ii** $6x + 4y \leqslant 25$

b Write down all the possible numbers of each type of drink he can buy.

a **i** James needs to buy at least five cans as there are five people. So the total number of cans of Cola and Orange must be at least five. This is expressed as $x + y \geqslant 5$.

    ii x cans of Cola cost $60x$ pence, and y cans of Orange cost $40y$ pence. So

    total cost $= 60x + 40y$

    But he has only 250 pence to spend, so total cost cannot exceed 250 pence. Hence,

    $60x + 40y \leqslant 250$

    This cancels through by 10 to give

    $6x + 4y \leqslant 25$

b By trying different values of x and y, the following four combinations are found to satisfy the condition.

    one can of Cola and four cans of Orange

    two cans of Cola and three cans of Orange

    five or six cans of Orange

EXERCISE 24E

1 A company sells two types of bicycle, the Chapper and the Graffiti. A Chapper costs £148 and a Graffiti cost £125.

  a How much do *x* Chappers cost?

  b How much do *y* Graffitis cost?

  c How much do *x* Chappers and *y* Graffitis cost altogether?

2 A computer firm makes two types of machine. The Z210 and the Z310. The price of the Z210 is £*A* and that of the Z310 is £*B*. How much are the following?

  a *x* Z210s and *y* Z310s

  b *x* Z210s and twice as many Z310s

  c 9 Z210s and (9 + *y*) Z310s

3 If $x + y > 40$, which of the following *may* be true?

  a $x > 40$ **b** $x + y \leqslant 20$ **c** $x - y = 10$ **d** $x \leqslant 5$

4 A bookshelf holds *P* paperback and *H* hardback books. The bookshelf can hold a total of 400 books. Which of the following *may* be true?

  a $P + H < 300$ **b** $P \geqslant H$ **c** $P + H > 500$

5 A school uses two coach firms, Excel and Storm, to take pupils home from school. An Excel coach holds 40 pupils and a Storm coach holds 50 pupils. 1500 pupils need to be taken home by coach. If *E* Excel coaches and *S* Storm coaches are used, explain why:

  $4E + 5S \geqslant 150$

6 A boy goes to the fair with £6.00 in his pocket. He only likes rides on the big wheel and eating hot-dogs. A big wheel ride costs £1.50 and a hot-dog costs £2.00. He has *W* big wheel rides and *D* hot-dogs. Explain why:

  a $W \leqslant 4$ **b** $D \leqslant 3$ **c** $3W + 4D \leqslant 12$

  d If he cannot eat more than two hot-dogs without being ill, write down an inequality that *must* be true.

  e Which of these combinations of big wheel rides and hot-dogs are possible if they obey all of the above conditions?

    i two big wheel rides and one hot-dog

    ii three big wheel rides and two hot-dogs

    iii two big wheel rides and two hot-dogs

    iv one big wheel ride and one hot-dog

7 Pens cost 45p each and pencils cost 25p each. Jane has £2.00 with which to buy pens and pencils. She buys x pens and y pencils.

 a Write down an inequality that must be true.

 b She must have at least two more pencils than pens. Write down an inequality that must be true.

8 Mushtaq has to buy some apples and some pears. He has £3.00 to spend. Apples cost 30p each and pears cost 40p each. He must buy at least two apples and at least three pears, and at least seven fruits altogether. He buys x apples and y pears.

 a Explain each of these inequalities.

   i $3x + 4y \leqslant 30$ **ii** $x \geqslant 2$ **iii** $y \geqslant 3$ **iv** $x + y \geqslant 7$

 b Which of these combinations satisfy all of the above inequalities?

   i three apples and three pears

   ii four apples and five pears

   iii no apples and seven pears

   iv three apples and five pears

9 A shop decides to stock only sofas and beds. A sofa takes up 4 m² of floor area and is worth £300. A bed takes up 3 m² of floor area and is worth £500. The shop has 48 m² of floor space for stock. The insurance policy will allow a total of only £6000 of stock to be in the shop at any one time. The shop stocks x sofas and y beds.

 a Explain each of these inequalities.

   i $4x + 3y \leqslant 48$ **ii** $3x + 5y \leqslant 60$

 b Which of these combinations satisfy both of the above inequalities?

   i ten sofas and no beds

   ii eight sofas and six beds

   iii ten sofas and five beds

   iv six sofas and eight beds

10 The 300 pupils in Year 7 are to go on a trip to Adern Towers theme park. The local bus company has six 40-seat coaches and five 50-seat coaches. The school hires x 40-seat coaches and y 50-seat coaches.

 a Explain each of these inequalities.

   i $4x + 5y \geqslant 30$ **ii** $x \leqslant 6$ **iii** $y \leqslant 5$

 b Check that each of these combinations obeys each of the inequalities above.

   i six 40-seaters and two 50-seaters

   ii two 40-seaters and five 50-seaters

   iii four 40-seaters and three 50-seaters

   iv three 40-seaters and four 50-seaters

 c The cost of hiring each coach is £100 for a 40-seater and £120 for a 50-seater. Which of the combinations in part **b** would be the cheapest option?

 d There is one combination that is even cheaper than the answer to part **c**. What is it?

1 *n* is a whole number such that

$$7 \leqslant 3n < 15$$

List all the possible values of *n*.

Edexcel, Question 2, Paper 13A Higher, January 2004

2 **a** Solve the inequality $4x + 3 < 13$

b Write down the largest integer that is a solution of $4x + 3 < 13$

3 **a** Solve the inequality $5x + 12 > 2$

b Expand and simplify $(x - 6)(x + 4)$

Edexcel, Question 2, Paper 13A Higher, January 2003

4 **a** Solve the inequality $5x - 9 \geqslant 6$

b **i** Solve the inequality $2x + 7 > 15 - 3x$

ii If *x* is an integer, what is the smallest possible value of *x*?

5 Find all the integer values of *n* that satisfy the inequality

$$-3 \leqslant 2n + 1 < 9$$

6 **a** Solve the inequality $4x - 9 < x + 3$

b Solve the inequality $x^2 < 25$

7 On a grid show the region that is defined by the three inequalities

$$x \geqslant 1 \qquad y \leqslant 3 \qquad x + y \leqslant 5$$

Mark the region with an **R**.

8 On a grid show the region that is defined by the three inequalities

$$x \geqslant 0 \qquad y \leqslant 2x + 1 \qquad x + y \leqslant 4$$

Mark the region with an **R**.

9 **a** $-2 < x \leqslant 1$

x is an integer.

Write down all the possible values of *x*.

b $-2 < x \leqslant 1 \qquad y > -2 \qquad y < x + 1$

x and *y* are integer.

On a copy of the grid, mark with a cross (**X**), each of the six points which satisfies *all* these 3 inequalities.

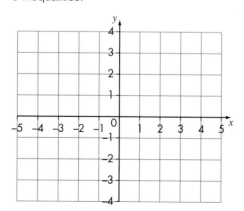

Edexcel, Question 4, Paper 5 Higher, June 2003

10 Copy the grid below and indicate clearly on it the region defined by the three inequalities

$$y \leqslant 5$$

$$x \geqslant -2$$

$$y \geqslant 2x - 1$$

Mark the region with an **R**.

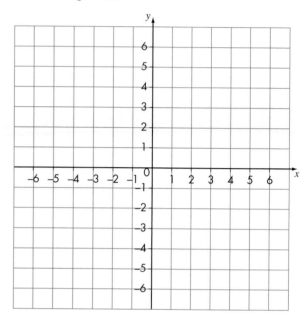

11 *n* is an integer that satisfies the inequality

$$\frac{121}{n^2} \geqslant 8$$

List all the possible values of *n*.

WORKED EXAM QUESTION

a On the number lines show the inequalities

i $-2 \leqslant n < 4$

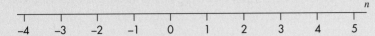

ii $n < 2$

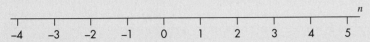

b n is an integer. Find the values of n that satisfy both inequalities in part **a**

c Solve the inequalities

i $3x + 8 > 2$

ii $3(x - 4) \leqslant \frac{1}{2}(x + 1)$

Solution

a i

ii

> Remember that a strict inequality has an open circle to show the boundary and an inclusive inequality has a solid circle to show the boundary.

b $\{-2, -1, 0, 1\}$

> The integers that satisfy both inequalities are in the overlap of both lines.

c i $3x + 8 > 2$
$3x > -6$
$x > -2$

> As when solving an equation do the same thing to both sides. First subtract 8, then divide by 3.

ii $3(x - 4) \leqslant \frac{1}{2}(x + 1)$
$6(x - 4) \leqslant x + 1$
$6x - 24 < x + 1$
$5x < 25$
$x < 5$

> First multiply by 2 to get rid of the fraction, then expand the brackets. Then collect all the x terms on the left-hand side and the number terms on the right-hand side. Then simplify and divide by 5.

GRADE YOURSELF

C Able to solve inequalities such as $3x + 2 < 5$ and represent the solution on a number line

B Able to represent a region that satisfies a linear inequality graphically, and to solve more complex linear inequalities

B Able to represent a region that simultaneously satisfies more than one linear inequality graphically

A Able to translate a problem into inequalities

What you should know now

- How to solve simple inequalities
- How to create algebraic inequalities from verbal statements
- How to represent linear inequalities on a graph
- How to depict a region satisfying more than one linear inequality

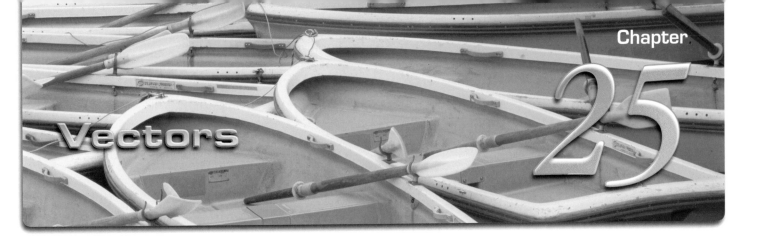

Vectors

1 Properties of vectors

2 Vectors in geometry

This chapter will show you ...

- the properties of vectors
- how to add and subtract vectors
- how to use vectors to solve geometrical problems

Visual overview

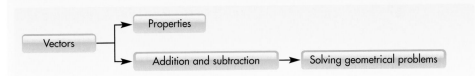

What you should already know

- Vectors are used to describe translations

Quick check

Use column vectors to describe these translations.

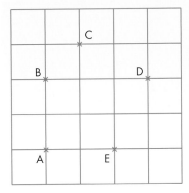

a A to C

b B to D

c C to D

d D to E

Properties of vectors

In this section you will learn how to:
- add and subtract vectors

Key words
direction
magnitude
vector

A **vector** is a quantity which has both **magnitude** and **direction**. It can be represented by a straight line which is drawn in the direction of the vector and whose length represents the magnitude of the vector. Usually, the line includes an arrowhead.

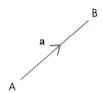

The translation or movement from A to B is represented by the vector **a**.

a is always printed in bold type, but is written as <u>a</u>.

a can also be written as $\overrightarrow{AB}$.

A quantity which is completely described by its magnitude, and has no direction associated with it, is called a scalar. The mass of a bus (10 tonnes) is an example of a scalar. Another example is a linear measure, such as 25.4 mm.

Multiplying a vector by a number (scalar) alters its magnitude (length) but not its direction. For example, the vector 2**a** is twice as long as the vector **a**, but in the same direction.

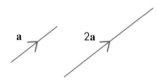

A negative vector, for example –**b**, has the same magnitude as the vector **b**, but is in the opposite direction.

Addition and subtraction of vectors

Take two non-parallel vectors **a** and **b**, then **a** + **b** is defined to be the translation of **a** followed by the translation of **b**. This can easily be seen on a vector diagram.

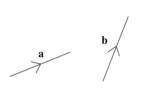

Similarly, **a** − **b** is defined to be the translation of **a** followed by the translation of −**b**.

Look at the parallelogram grid below. **a** and **b** are two independent vectors that form the basis of this grid. It is possible to define the position, with reference to O, of any point on this grid by a vector expressed in terms of **a** and **b**. Such a vector is called a position vector.

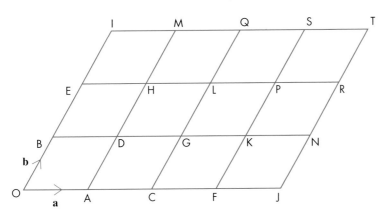

For example, the position vector of K is $\overrightarrow{OK}$ or **k** = 3**a** + **b**, the position vector of E is $\overrightarrow{OE}$ or **e** = 2**b**. The vector $\overrightarrow{HT}$ = 3**a** + **b**, the vector $\overrightarrow{PN}$ = **a** − **b**, the vector $\overrightarrow{MK}$ = 2**a** − 2**b**, and the vector $\overrightarrow{TP}$ = −**a** − **b**.

Note $\overrightarrow{OK}$ and $\overrightarrow{HT}$ are called equal vectors because they have exactly the same length and are in the same direction. $\overrightarrow{MK}$ and $\overrightarrow{PN}$ are parallel vectors but $\overrightarrow{MK}$ is twice the magnitude of $\overrightarrow{PN}$.

EXAMPLE 1

    a Using the grid above, write down the following vectors in terms of **a** and **b**.

        i $\overrightarrow{BH}$ **ii** $\overrightarrow{HP}$ **iii** $\overrightarrow{GT}$

        iv $\overrightarrow{TI}$ **v** $\overrightarrow{FH}$ **vi** $\overrightarrow{BQ}$

    b What is the relationship between the following vectors?

        i $\overrightarrow{BH}$ and $\overrightarrow{GT}$ **ii** $\overrightarrow{BQ}$ and $\overrightarrow{GT}$ **iii** $\overrightarrow{HP}$ and $\overrightarrow{TI}$

    c Show that B, H and Q lie on the same straight line.

    a **i** **a** + **b**   **ii** 2**a**   **iii** 2**a** + 2**b**   **iv** −4**a**   **v** −2**a** + 2**b**   **vi** 2**a** + 2**b**

    b **i** $\overrightarrow{BH}$ and $\overrightarrow{GT}$ are parallel and $\overrightarrow{GT}$ is twice the length of $\overrightarrow{BH}$.

        ii $\overrightarrow{BQ}$ and $\overrightarrow{GT}$ are equal.

        iii $\overrightarrow{HP}$ and $\overrightarrow{TI}$ are in opposite directions and $\overrightarrow{TI}$ is twice the length of $\overrightarrow{HP}$.

    c $\overrightarrow{BH}$ and $\overrightarrow{BQ}$ are parallel and start at the same point B. Therefore, B, H and Q must lie on the same straight line.

EXAMPLE 2

Use a vector diagram to show that   **a** + **b** = **b** + **a**

Take two independent vectors **a** and **b**

a + **b** and **b** + **a** have the same magnitude and direction and are therefore equal.

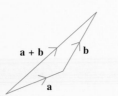

EXERCISE 25A

1 On this grid, $\overrightarrow{OA}$ is **a** and $\overrightarrow{OB}$ is **b**.

   a Name three other vectors equivalent to **a**.

   b Name three other vectors equivalent to **b**.

   c Name three vectors equivalent to –**a**.

   d Name three vectors equivalent to –**b**.

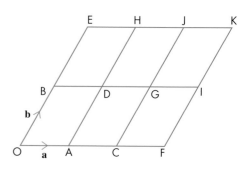

2 Using the same grid as in question **1**, give the following vectors in terms of **a** and **b**.

   a $\overrightarrow{OC}$ **b** $\overrightarrow{OE}$ **c** $\overrightarrow{OD}$ **d** $\overrightarrow{OG}$ **e** $\overrightarrow{OJ}$

   f $\overrightarrow{OH}$ **g** $\overrightarrow{AG}$ **h** $\overrightarrow{AK}$ **i** $\overrightarrow{BK}$ **j** $\overrightarrow{DI}$

   k $\overrightarrow{GJ}$ **l** $\overrightarrow{DK}$

3 **a** What do the answers to parts **2c** and **2g** tell you about the vectors $\overrightarrow{OD}$ and $\overrightarrow{AG}$?

   b On the grid in question **1**, there are three vectors equivalent to $\overrightarrow{OG}$. Name all three.

4 **a** What do the answers to parts **2c** and **2e** tell you about vectors $\overrightarrow{OD}$ and $\overrightarrow{OJ}$?

   b On the grid in question **1**, there is one other vector that is twice the size of $\overrightarrow{OD}$. Which is it?

   c On the grid in question **1**, there are three vectors that are three times the size of $\overrightarrow{OA}$. Name all three.

5 On a copy of this grid, mark on the points C to P
to show the following.

a $\overrightarrow{OC} = 2\mathbf{a} + 3\mathbf{b}$ b $\overrightarrow{OD} = 2\mathbf{a} + \mathbf{b}$

c $\overrightarrow{OE} = \mathbf{a} + 2\mathbf{b}$ d $\overrightarrow{OF} = 3\mathbf{b}$

e $\overrightarrow{OG} = 4\mathbf{a}$ f $\overrightarrow{OH} = 4\mathbf{a} + 2\mathbf{b}$

g $\overrightarrow{OI} = 3\mathbf{a} + 3\mathbf{b}$ h $\overrightarrow{OJ} = \mathbf{a} + \mathbf{b}$

i $\overrightarrow{OK} = 2\mathbf{a} + 2\mathbf{b}$ j $\overrightarrow{OM} = 2\mathbf{a} + \frac{3}{2}\mathbf{b}$ k $\overrightarrow{ON} = \frac{1}{2}\mathbf{a} + 2\mathbf{b}$ l $\overrightarrow{OP} = \frac{5}{2}\mathbf{a} + \frac{3}{2}\mathbf{b}$

6 a Look at the diagram in question **5**. What can you say about the points O, J, K and I?

b How could you tell this by looking at the vectors for parts **5g**, **5h** and **5i**?

c There is another point on the same straight line as O and D. Which is it?

d Copy and complete these statements and then mark the appropriate points on the diagram you
drew for question **5**.

  i The point Q is on the straight line ODH. The vector $\overrightarrow{OQ}$ is given by

  $\overrightarrow{OQ} = \mathbf{a} + \dots \mathbf{b}$

  ii The point R is on the straight line ODH. The vector $\overrightarrow{OR}$ is given by

  $\overrightarrow{OR} = 3\mathbf{a} + \dots \mathbf{b}$

e Copy and complete the following statement.

  Any point on the line ODH has a vector $n\mathbf{a} + \dots \mathbf{b}$, where n is any number.

7 On this grid, $\overrightarrow{OA}$ is **a** and $\overrightarrow{OB}$ is **b**.

Give the following vectors in terms of **a** and **b**.

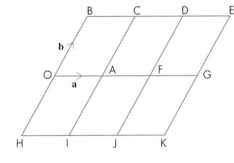

a $\overrightarrow{OH}$ b $\overrightarrow{OK}$

c $\overrightarrow{OJ}$ d $\overrightarrow{OI}$

e $\overrightarrow{OC}$ f $\overrightarrow{CO}$

g $\overrightarrow{AK}$ h $\overrightarrow{DI}$

i $\overrightarrow{JE}$ j $\overrightarrow{AB}$ k $\overrightarrow{CK}$ l $\overrightarrow{DK}$

8 a What do the answers to parts **7e** and **7f** tell you about the vectors $\overrightarrow{OC}$ and $\overrightarrow{CO}$?

b On the grid in question **7**, there are five other vectors opposite to $\overrightarrow{OC}$. Name at least three.

9 a What do the answers to parts **7j** and **7k** tell you about vectors $\overrightarrow{AB}$ and $\overrightarrow{CK}$?

b On the grid in question **7**, there are two vectors that are twice the size of $\overrightarrow{AB}$ and in the opposite
direction. Name both of them.

c On the grid in question **7**, there are three vectors that are three times the size of $\overrightarrow{OA}$ and in the
opposite direction. Name all three.

10 On a copy of this grid, mark on the points C to P to show the following.

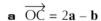

a $\overrightarrow{OC} = 2\mathbf{a} - \mathbf{b}$ **b** $\overrightarrow{OD} = 2\mathbf{a} + \mathbf{b}$

c $\overrightarrow{OE} = \mathbf{a} - 2\mathbf{b}$ **d** $\overrightarrow{OF} = \mathbf{b} - 2\mathbf{a}$

e $\overrightarrow{OG} = -\mathbf{a}$ **f** $\overrightarrow{OH} = -\mathbf{a} - 2\mathbf{b}$

g $\overrightarrow{OI} = 2\mathbf{a} - 2\mathbf{b}$ **h** $\overrightarrow{OJ} = -\mathbf{a} + \mathbf{b}$

i $\overrightarrow{OK} = -\mathbf{a} - \mathbf{b}$ **j** $\overrightarrow{OM} = -\mathbf{a} - \frac{3}{2}\mathbf{b}$ **k** $\overrightarrow{ON} = -\frac{1}{2}\mathbf{a} - 2\mathbf{b}$ **l** $\overrightarrow{OP} = \frac{3}{2}\mathbf{a} - \frac{3}{2}\mathbf{b}$

11 This grid shows the vectors $\overrightarrow{OA} = \mathbf{a}$ and $\overrightarrow{OB} = \mathbf{b}$.

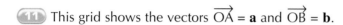

a Name three vectors equivalent to $\mathbf{a} + \mathbf{b}$.

b Name three vectors equivalent to $\mathbf{a} - \mathbf{b}$.

c Name three vectors equivalent to $\mathbf{b} - \mathbf{a}$.

d Name three vectors equivalent to $-\mathbf{a} - \mathbf{b}$.

e Name three vectors equivalent to $2\mathbf{a} - \mathbf{b}$.

f Name three vectors equivalent to $2\mathbf{b} - \mathbf{a}$.

g For each of these, name one equivalent vector.

     i $3\mathbf{a} - \mathbf{b}$ **ii** $2(\mathbf{a} + \mathbf{b})$ **iii** $3\mathbf{a} - 2\mathbf{b}$

     iv $3(\mathbf{a} - \mathbf{b})$ **v** $3(\mathbf{b} - \mathbf{a})$ **vi** $3(\mathbf{a} + \mathbf{b})$

     vii $-3(\mathbf{a} + \mathbf{b})$ **viii** $2\mathbf{a} + \mathbf{b} - 3\mathbf{a} - 2\mathbf{b}$ **ix** $2(2\mathbf{a} - \mathbf{b}) - 3(\mathbf{a} - \mathbf{b})$

12 The points P, Q and R lie on a straight line. The vector $\overrightarrow{PQ}$ is $2\mathbf{a} + \mathbf{b}$, where $\mathbf{a}$ and $\mathbf{b}$ are vectors. Which of the following vectors could be the vector $\overrightarrow{PR}$ and which could not be the vector $\overrightarrow{PR}$ (two of each).

     a $2\mathbf{a} + 2\mathbf{b}$ **b** $4\mathbf{a} + 2\mathbf{b}$ **c** $2\mathbf{a} - \mathbf{b}$ **d** $-6\mathbf{a} - 3\mathbf{b}$

13 The points P, Q and R lie on a straight line. The vector $\overrightarrow{PQ}$ is $3\mathbf{a} - \mathbf{b}$, where $\mathbf{a}$ and $\mathbf{b}$ are vectors.

a Write down any other vector that could represent $\overrightarrow{PR}$.

b How can you tell from the vector $\overrightarrow{PS}$ that S lies on the same straight line as P, Q and R?

14 Use the diagram in question **11** to prove the following results.

a KB is parallel to IE.

b L, A and F are on a straight line.

15 Use a vector diagram to show that $\mathbf{a} + (\mathbf{b} + \mathbf{c}) = (\mathbf{a} + \mathbf{b}) + \mathbf{c}$.

Vectors in geometry

In this section you will learn how to:
● use vectors to solve geometrical problems

Vectors can be used to prove many results in geometry, as the following examples show.

EXAMPLE 3

In the diagram, $\overrightarrow{OA} = \mathbf{a}$, $\overrightarrow{OB} = \mathbf{b}$, and $\overrightarrow{BC} = 1.5\mathbf{a}$. M is the midpoint of BC, N is the midpoint of AC and P is the midpoint of OB.

a Find these vectors in terms of **a** and **b**.

   i $\overrightarrow{AC}$ **ii** $\overrightarrow{OM}$ **iii** $\overrightarrow{BN}$

b Prove that $\overrightarrow{PN}$ is parallel to $\overrightarrow{OA}$.

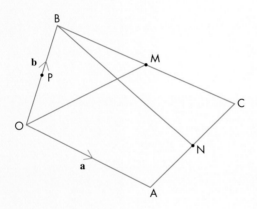

a i You have to get from A to C in terms of vectors that you know.

$$\overrightarrow{AC} = \overrightarrow{AO} + \overrightarrow{OB} + \overrightarrow{BC}$$

Now $\overrightarrow{AO} = -\overrightarrow{OA}$, so you can write

$$\overrightarrow{AC} = -\mathbf{a} + \mathbf{b} + \tfrac{3}{2}\mathbf{a}$$
$$= \tfrac{1}{2}\mathbf{a} + \mathbf{b}$$

Note that the letters "connect up" as we go from A to C, and that the negative of a vector represented by any pair of letters is formed by reversing the letters.

ii In the same way

$$\overrightarrow{OM} = \overrightarrow{OB} + \overrightarrow{BM} = \overrightarrow{OB} + \tfrac{1}{2}\overrightarrow{BC}$$
$$= \mathbf{b} + \tfrac{1}{2}(\tfrac{3}{2}\mathbf{a})$$
$$\overrightarrow{OM} = \tfrac{3}{4}\mathbf{a} + \mathbf{b}$$

iii $\overrightarrow{BN} = \overrightarrow{BC} + \overrightarrow{CN} = \overrightarrow{BC} - \frac{1}{2}\overrightarrow{AC}$

$\qquad = \frac{3}{2}\mathbf{a} - \frac{1}{2}(\frac{1}{2}\mathbf{a} + \mathbf{b})$

$\qquad = \frac{3}{2}\mathbf{a} - \frac{1}{4}\mathbf{a} - \frac{1}{2}\mathbf{b}$

$\qquad = \frac{5}{4}\mathbf{a} - \frac{1}{2}\mathbf{b}$

Note that if you did this as $\overrightarrow{BN} = \overrightarrow{BO} + \overrightarrow{OA} + \overrightarrow{AN}$, you would get the same result.

b $\overrightarrow{PN} = \overrightarrow{PO} + \overrightarrow{OA} + \overrightarrow{AN}$

$\qquad = \frac{1}{2}(-\mathbf{b}) + \mathbf{a} + \frac{1}{2}(\frac{1}{2}\mathbf{a} + \mathbf{b})$

$\qquad = -\frac{1}{2}\mathbf{b} + \mathbf{a} + \frac{1}{4}\mathbf{a} + \frac{1}{2}\mathbf{b}$

$\qquad = \frac{5}{4}\mathbf{a}$

$\overrightarrow{PN}$ is a multiple of $\mathbf{a}$ only, so must be parallel to $\overrightarrow{OA}$.

EXAMPLE 4

OACB is a parallelogram. $\overrightarrow{OA}$ is represented by the vector $\mathbf{a}$. $\overrightarrow{OB}$ is represented by the vector $\mathbf{b}$. P is a point $\frac{2}{3}$ the distance from O to C, and M is the midpoint of AC. Show that B, P and M lie on the same straight line.

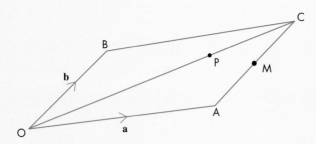

$\overrightarrow{OC} = \overrightarrow{OA} + \overrightarrow{AC} = \mathbf{a} + \mathbf{b}$

$\overrightarrow{OP} = \frac{2}{3}\overrightarrow{OC} = \frac{2}{3}\mathbf{a} + \frac{2}{3}\mathbf{b}$

$\overrightarrow{OM} = \overrightarrow{OA} + \overrightarrow{AM} = \overrightarrow{OA} + \frac{1}{2}\overrightarrow{AC} = \mathbf{a} + \frac{1}{2}\mathbf{b}$

$\overrightarrow{BP} = \overrightarrow{BO} + \overrightarrow{OP} = -\mathbf{b} + \frac{2}{3}\mathbf{a} + \frac{2}{3}\mathbf{b} = \frac{2}{3}\mathbf{a} - \frac{1}{3}\mathbf{b} = \frac{1}{3}(2\mathbf{a} - \mathbf{b})$

$\overrightarrow{BM} = \overrightarrow{BO} + \overrightarrow{OM} = -\mathbf{b} + \mathbf{a} + \frac{1}{2}\mathbf{b} = \mathbf{a} - \frac{1}{2}\mathbf{b} = \frac{1}{2}(2\mathbf{a} - \mathbf{b})$

Therefore, $\overrightarrow{BM}$ is a multiple of $\overrightarrow{BP}$ ($\overrightarrow{BM} = \frac{3}{2}\overrightarrow{BP}$).

Therefore, $\overrightarrow{BP}$ and $\overrightarrow{BM}$ are parallel and as they have a common point, B, they must lie on the same straight line.

EXERCISE 25B

1 The diagram shows the vectors $\overrightarrow{OA}$ = **a** and $\overrightarrow{OB}$ = **b**. M is the midpoint of AB.

  a i Work out the vector $\overrightarrow{AB}$.

  ii Work out the vector $\overrightarrow{AM}$.

  iii Explain why $\overrightarrow{OM}$ = $\overrightarrow{OA}$ + $\overrightarrow{AM}$.

  iv Using your answers to parts **ii** and **iii**, work out $\overrightarrow{OM}$ in terms of **a** and **b**.

  b i Work out the vector $\overrightarrow{BA}$.

  ii Work out the vector $\overrightarrow{BM}$.

  iii Explain why $\overrightarrow{OM}$ = $\overrightarrow{OB}$ + $\overrightarrow{BM}$.

  iv Using your answers to parts **ii** and **iii**, work out $\overrightarrow{OM}$ in terms of **a** and **b**.

  c Copy the diagram and show on it the vector $\overrightarrow{OC}$ which is equal to **a** + **b**.

  d Describe in geometrical terms the position of M in relation to O, A, B and C.

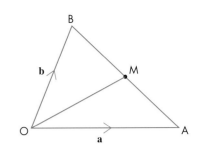

2 The diagram shows the vectors $\overrightarrow{OA}$ = **a** and $\overrightarrow{OC}$ = –**b**. N is the midpoint of AC.

  a i Work out the vector $\overrightarrow{AC}$.

  ii Work out the vector $\overrightarrow{AN}$.

  iii Explain why

  $\overrightarrow{ON}$ = $\overrightarrow{OA}$ + $\overrightarrow{AN}$.

  iv Using your answers to parts **ii** and **iii**, work out $\overrightarrow{ON}$ in terms of **a** and **b**.

  b i Work out the vector $\overrightarrow{CA}$.

  ii Work out the vector $\overrightarrow{CN}$.

  iii Explain why $\overrightarrow{ON}$ = $\overrightarrow{OC}$ + $\overrightarrow{CN}$.

  iv Using your answers to parts **ii** and **iii**, work out $\overrightarrow{ON}$ in terms of **a** and **b**.

  c Copy the diagram above and show on it the vector $\overrightarrow{OD}$ which is equal to **a** – **b**.

  d Describe in geometrical terms the position of N in relation to O, A, C and D.

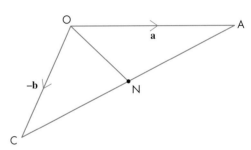

3 Copy this diagram and on it draw vectors that represent

  a **a** + **b**   **b** **a** – **b**

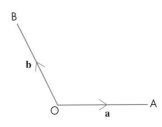

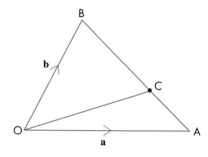

4 The diagram shows the vectors $\overrightarrow{OA} = \mathbf{a}$ and $\overrightarrow{OB} = \mathbf{b}$.

The point C divides the line AB in the ratio 1:2

(i.e. AC is $\frac{1}{3}$ the distance from A to B).

a i Work out the vector $\overrightarrow{AB}$.

ii Work out the vector $\overrightarrow{AC}$.

iii Work out the vector $\overrightarrow{OC}$ in terms of **a** and **b**.

b If C now divides the line AB in the ratio 1:3 (i.e. AC is $\frac{1}{4}$ the distance from A to B), write down the vector that represents $\overrightarrow{OC}$.

5 The diagram shows the vectors $\overrightarrow{OA} = \mathbf{a}$ and $\overrightarrow{OB} = \mathbf{b}$.

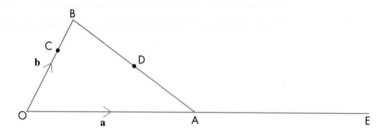

The point C divides OB in the ratio 2:1 (i.e. OC is $\frac{2}{3}$ the distance from O to B). The point E is such that $\overrightarrow{OE} = 2\overrightarrow{OA}$. D is the midpoint of AB.

a Write down (or work out) these vectors in terms of **a** and **b**.

i $\overrightarrow{OC}$ **ii** $\overrightarrow{OD}$ **iii** $\overrightarrow{CO}$

b The vector $\overrightarrow{CD}$ can be written as $\overrightarrow{CD} = \overrightarrow{CO} + \overrightarrow{OD}$. Use this fact to work out $\overrightarrow{CD}$ in terms of **a** and **b**.

c Write down a similar rule to that in part **b** for the vector $\overrightarrow{DE}$. Use this rule to work out $\overrightarrow{DE}$ in terms of **a** and **b**.

d Explain why C, D and E lie on the same straight line.

6 ABCDEF is a regular hexagon. $\overrightarrow{AB}$ is represented by the vector **a**, and $\overrightarrow{BC}$ by the vector **b**.

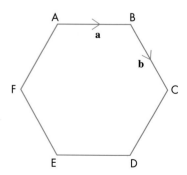

a By means of a diagram, or otherwise, explain why $\overrightarrow{CD} = \mathbf{b} - \mathbf{a}$.

b Express these vectors in terms of **a** and **b**.

i $\overrightarrow{DE}$ **ii** $\overrightarrow{EF}$ **iii** $\overrightarrow{FA}$

c Work out the answer to

$$\overrightarrow{AB} + \overrightarrow{BC} + \overrightarrow{CD} + \overrightarrow{DE} + \overrightarrow{EF} + \overrightarrow{FA}$$

Explain your answer.

d Express these vectors in terms of **a** and **b**.

i $\overrightarrow{AD}$ **ii** $\overrightarrow{BE}$ **iii** $\overrightarrow{CF}$ **iv** $\overrightarrow{AE}$ **v** $\overrightarrow{DF}$

7 ABCDEFGH is a regular octagon. $\overrightarrow{AB}$ is represented by the vector **a**, and $\overrightarrow{BC}$ by the vector **b**.

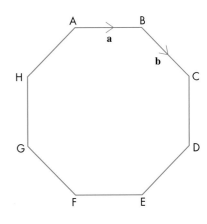

a By means of a diagram, or otherwise, explain why $\overrightarrow{CD} = \sqrt{2}\mathbf{b} - \mathbf{a}$.

b By means of a diagram, or otherwise, explain why $\overrightarrow{DE} = \mathbf{b} - \sqrt{2}\mathbf{a}$.

c Express the following vectors in terms of **a** and **b**.

   i $\overrightarrow{EF}$ ii $\overrightarrow{FG}$ iii $\overrightarrow{GH}$ iv $\overrightarrow{HA}$

   v $\overrightarrow{HC}$ vi $\overrightarrow{AD}$ vii $\overrightarrow{BE}$ viii $\overrightarrow{BF}$

8 In the quadrilateral OABC, M, N, P and Q are the midpoints of the sides as shown. $\overrightarrow{OA}$ is represented by the vector **a**, and $\overrightarrow{OC}$ by the vector **c**. The diagonal $\overrightarrow{OB}$ is represented by the vector **b**.

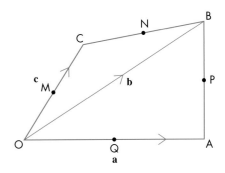

a Express these vectors in terms of **a**, **b** and **c**.

   i $\overrightarrow{AB}$ ii $\overrightarrow{AP}$ iii $\overrightarrow{OP}$

   Give your answers as simply as possible.

b i Express the vector $\overrightarrow{ON}$ in terms of **b** and **c**.

   ii Hence express the vector $\overrightarrow{PN}$ in terms of **a** and **c**.

c i Express the vector $\overrightarrow{QM}$ in terms of **a** and **c**.

   ii What relationship is there between $\overrightarrow{PN}$ and $\overrightarrow{QM}$?

   iii What sort of quadrilateral is PNMQ?

d Prove that $\overrightarrow{AC} = 2\overrightarrow{QM}$.

9 L, M, N, P, Q, R are the midpoints of the line segments, as shown. $\overrightarrow{OA} = \mathbf{a}$, $\overrightarrow{OB} = \mathbf{b}$, $\overrightarrow{OC} = \mathbf{c}$.

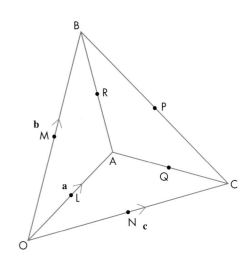

a Express these vectors in terms of **a** and **c**.

   i $\overrightarrow{OL}$ ii $\overrightarrow{AC}$

   iii $\overrightarrow{OQ}$ iv $\overrightarrow{LQ}$

b Express these vectors in terms of **a** and **b**.

   i $\overrightarrow{LM}$ ii $\overrightarrow{QP}$

c Prove that the quadrilateral LMPQ is a parallelogram.

d Find two other sets of four points that form parallelograms.

1 In triangle ABC, M is the mid-point of BC.
$\overrightarrow{AB}$ = **a** and $\overrightarrow{AC}$ = **b**

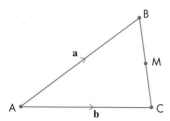

Find $\overrightarrow{AM}$ in terms of **a** and **b**.

Give your answer in its simplest form.

2 The diagram shows two vectors **a** and **b**.

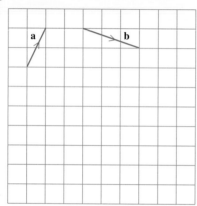

On a copy of the grid, draw the vector 2**a** − **b**

3 OAB is a triangle with X the mid-point of OA and Y the mid-point of AB.
$\overrightarrow{OA}$ = **a** and $\overrightarrow{OB}$ = **b**

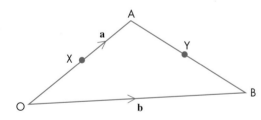

a Find, in terms of **a** and **b**
   i $\overrightarrow{BA}$
   ii $\overrightarrow{OY}$

b What type of quadrilateral is OXYB?
Give a reason for your answer.

4 OPQ is a triangle. T is the point on PQ for which
PT : TQ = 2 : 1
$\overrightarrow{OP}$ = **a** and $\overrightarrow{OQ}$ = **b**

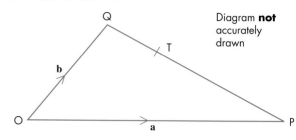

Diagram **not** accurately drawn

a Write down, in terms of **a** and **b**, an expression for $\overrightarrow{PQ}$.

b Express $\overrightarrow{OT}$ in terms of **a** and **b**. Give your answer in its simplest form.

Edexcel, Question 19, Paper 5 Higher, November 2003

5

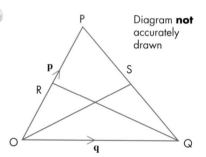

Diagram **not** accurately drawn

OPQ is a triangle.
R is the midpoint of OP.
S is the midpoint of PQ.
$\overrightarrow{OP}$ = **p** and $\overrightarrow{OQ}$ = **q**

a Find $\overrightarrow{OS}$ in terms of **p** and **q**.

b Show that RS is parallel to OQ.

Edexcel, Question 21, Paper 5 Higher, November 2004

6 The diagram shows a regular hexagon ABCDEF with centre O.
$\overrightarrow{OA}$ = 6**a**
$\overrightarrow{OB}$ = 6**b**

Diagram **not** accurately drawn

a Express in terms of **a** and/or **b**
   i $\overrightarrow{AB}$,
   ii $\overrightarrow{EF}$

X is the midpoint of BC.

b Express $\overrightarrow{EX}$ in terms of **a** and/or **b**

Y is the point on AB extended, such that AB : BY = 3 : 2

c Prove that E, X and Y lie on the same straight line.

Edexcel, Question 23, Paper 5 Higher, June 2003

In the triangle OAB, P is the midpoint of AB, X is the midpoint of OB, $\overrightarrow{OA}$ = **a** and $\overrightarrow{OB}$ = **b**. Q is the point that divides OP in the ratio 2 : 1.

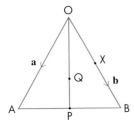

a Express these vectors in terms of **a** and **b**.

   i $\overrightarrow{AB}$ **ii** $\overrightarrow{AP}$

   iii $\overrightarrow{OP}$ **iv** $\overrightarrow{OQ}$

   v $\overrightarrow{AQ}$ **vi** $\overrightarrow{AX}$

b Deduce that $\overrightarrow{AX} = k\overrightarrow{AQ}$, where k is a scalar, and find the value of k.

WORKED EXAM QUESTION

OABC is a trapezium with AB parallel to OC.

P, Q and R are the mid-points of AB, BC and OC respectively.

OC is three times the length of AB.

$\overrightarrow{OA}$ = **a** and $\overrightarrow{AP}$ = **b**

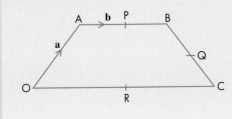

a Express, in terms of **a** and **b**, the following vectors.

   i $\overrightarrow{BC}$ **ii** $\overrightarrow{OQ}$ **iii** $\overrightarrow{PQ}$

b S is the mid-point of $\overrightarrow{PR}$.

   Prove that $\overrightarrow{SQ}$ is parallel to $\overrightarrow{OC}$.

Solution

a i $\overrightarrow{BC} = \overrightarrow{BA} + \overrightarrow{AO} + \overrightarrow{OC} = -2\mathbf{b} - \mathbf{a} + 6\mathbf{b} = 4\mathbf{b} - \mathbf{a}$

  ii $\overrightarrow{OQ} = \overrightarrow{OC} + \overrightarrow{CQ} = \overrightarrow{OC} - \frac{1}{2}\overrightarrow{BC} = 6\mathbf{b} - \frac{1}{2}(4\mathbf{b} - \mathbf{a}) = 6\mathbf{b} - 2\mathbf{b} + \frac{1}{2}\mathbf{a} = \frac{1}{2}\mathbf{a} + 4\mathbf{b}$

  iii $\overrightarrow{PQ} = \overrightarrow{PB} + \overrightarrow{BQ} = \overrightarrow{PB} + \frac{1}{2}\overrightarrow{BC} = \mathbf{b} + \frac{1}{2}(4\mathbf{b} - \mathbf{a}) = \mathbf{b} + 2\mathbf{b} - \frac{1}{2}\mathbf{a} = 3\mathbf{b} - \frac{1}{2}\mathbf{a}$

b $\overrightarrow{PR} = \overrightarrow{PA} + \overrightarrow{AO} + \overrightarrow{OR} = -\mathbf{b} - \mathbf{a} + 3\mathbf{b} = 2\mathbf{b} - \mathbf{a}$

  So $\overrightarrow{PS} = \frac{1}{2}\overrightarrow{PR} = \mathbf{b} - \frac{1}{2}\mathbf{a}$

  $\overrightarrow{SQ} = \overrightarrow{SP} + \overrightarrow{PQ} = \frac{1}{2}\mathbf{a} - \mathbf{b} + 3\mathbf{b} - \frac{1}{2}\mathbf{a} = 2\mathbf{b}$

  $\overrightarrow{OC} = 6\mathbf{b}$, so $\overrightarrow{SQ}$ is parallel to $\overrightarrow{OC}$

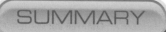

GRADE YOURSELF

A Able to solve problems using addition and subtraction of vectors

A* Able to solve more complex geometrical problems

What you should know now

- How to add and subtract vectors
- How to apply vector methods to solve geometrical problems

Chapter 26

Transformation of graphs

1 Transformations of the graph $y = f(x)$

This chapter will show you ...

- how to transform a graph
- how to recognise the relationships between graphs and their equations

Visual overview

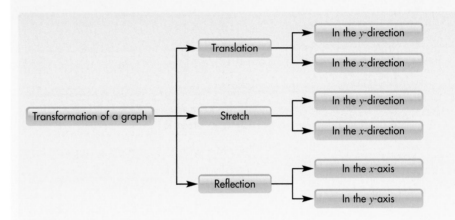

What you should already know

- How to transform a shape by a translation and a reflection
- A translation is described by a column vector
- A reflection is described by a mirror line

continued

● The graphs of $y = x^2$, $y = x^3$, $y = \dfrac{1}{x}$, $y = \sin x$, $y = \cos x$ and $y = \tan x$

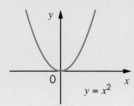

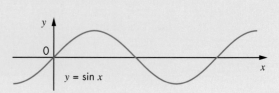

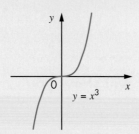

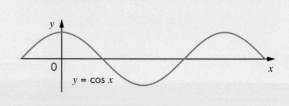

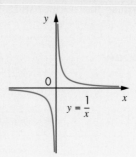

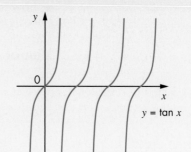

Quick check

Starting with the shaded triangle every time, do the following transformations.

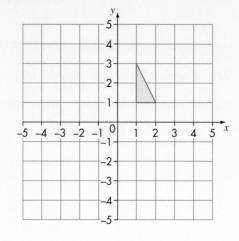

a translation

   i $\begin{pmatrix} 3 \\ 0 \end{pmatrix}$ **ii** $\begin{pmatrix} 0 \\ -2 \end{pmatrix}$

b reflection in the   **i** y-axis   **ii** x-axis

c rotation of 180° about the origin

This section will show you how to:

- transform a graph

Key words

function
reflection
scale factor
stretch
transform
translation
vector

We use the notation f(x) to represent a **function** of x. A function of x is any algebraic expression in which x is the only variable. Examples of functions are: f(x) = x + 3, f(x) = 5x, f(x) = 2x – 7, f(x) = x^2, f(x) = x^3 + 2x – 1, f(x) = sin x and f(x) = $\frac{1}{x}$.

Below and on page 214 are six general statements or rules about **transforming** graphs.

This work is much easier to understand if you have access to a graphics calculator or a graph-drawing computer program.

The graph on the right represents any function y = f(x).

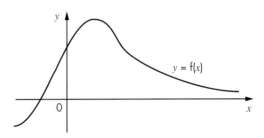

Rule 1 The graph of y = f(x) + a is a **translation** of the graph of y = f(x) by a **vector** $\begin{pmatrix} 0 \\ a \end{pmatrix}$.

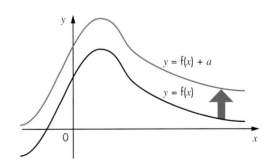

Rule 2 The graph of y = f(x – a) is a translation of the graph of y = f(x) by a vector $\begin{pmatrix} a \\ 0 \end{pmatrix}$.

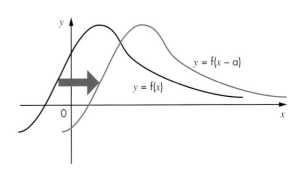

A **stretch** is an enlargement that takes place in one direction only. It is described by a **scale factor** and the direction of the stretch

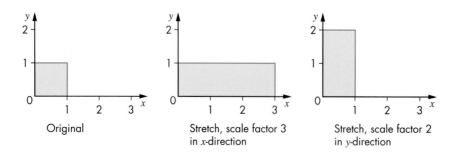

Original | Stretch, scale factor 3 in *x*-direction | Stretch, scale factor 2 in *y*-direction

Rule 3 The graph of $y = kf(x)$ is a stretch of the graph $y = f(x)$ by a scale factor of k in the y-direction.

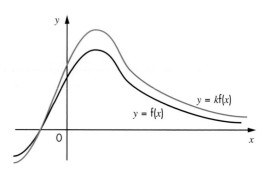

Rule 4 The graph of $y = f(tx)$ is a stretch of the graph $y = f(x)$ by a scale factor of $\dfrac{1}{t}$ in the x-direction.

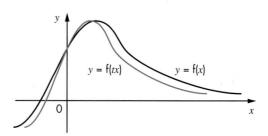

Rule 5 The graph of $y = -f(x)$ is the **reflection** of the graph $y = f(x)$ in the x-axis.

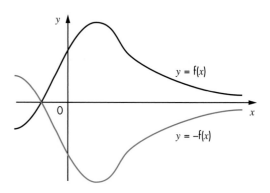

Rule 6 The graph of $y = f(-x)$ is the reflection of the graph $y = f(x)$ in the y-axis.

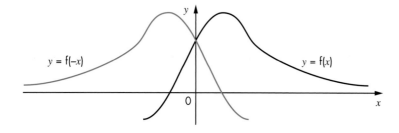

EXAMPLE 1

Sketch the following graphs.

a $y = x^2$

b $y = 5x^2$

c $y = x^2 - 5$

d $y = -x^2$

e $y = (x - 5)^2$

f $y = 2x^2 + 3$

Describe the transformation(s) that change(s) graph **a** to each of the other graphs.

Graph **a** is the basic graph to which we apply the rules to make the necessary transformations: graph **b** uses Rule 3, graph **c** uses Rule 1, graph **d** uses Rule 5, graph **e** uses Rule 2, and graph **f** uses Rules 3 and 1.

The graphs are

a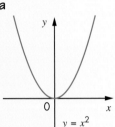

b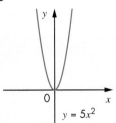

c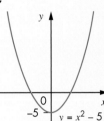

d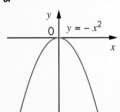

e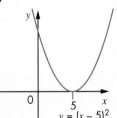

f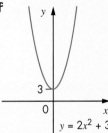

The transformations are:

graph **b** is a stretch of scale factor 5 in the y-direction,

graph **c** is a translation of $\begin{pmatrix} 0 \\ -5 \end{pmatrix}$,

graph **d** is a reflection in the x-axis,

graph **e** is a translation of $\begin{pmatrix} 5 \\ 0 \end{pmatrix}$,

graph **f** is a stretch of scale factor 2 in the y-direction, followed by a translation of $\begin{pmatrix} 0 \\ 3 \end{pmatrix}$.

Note that two of the transformations cause problems because they seem to do the opposite of what is expected. These are:

$y = f(x + a)$ (Rule 2)

The translation is $\begin{pmatrix} -a \\ 0 \end{pmatrix}$, so the sign of the constant inside the bracket changes in the vector (see part **e** in Example 1).

$y = f(ax)$ (Rule 4)

This is not a stretch. It actually closes the graph up. Just like an enlargement (see Chapter 8) can make something smaller, a stretch can make it squeeze closer to the axes.

1 On the same axes sketch the following graphs.

    a $y = x^2$ **b** $y = 3x^2$ **c** $y = \frac{1}{2}x^2$ **d** $y = 10x^2$

    e Describe the transformation(s) that take(s) the graph in part **a** to each of the graphs in parts **b** to **d**.

2 On the same axes sketch the following graphs.

    a $y = x^2$ **b** $y = x^2 + 3$ **c** $y = x^2 - 1$ **d** $y = 2x^2 + 1$

    e Describe the transformation(s) that take(s) the graph in part **a** to each of the graphs in parts **b** to **d**.

3 On the same axes sketch the following graphs.

    a $y = x^2$ **b** $y = (x + 3)^2$ **c** $y = (x - 1)^2$ **d** $y = 2(x - 2)^2$

    e Describe the transformation(s) that take(s) the graph in part **a** to each of the graphs in parts **b** to **d**.

4 On the same axes sketch the following graphs.

    a $y = x^2$ **b** $y = (x + 3)^2 - 1$ **c** $y = 4(x - 1)^2 + 3$

    d Describe the transformation(s) that take(s) the graph in part **a** to each of the graphs in parts **b** and **c**.

5 On the same axes sketch the following graphs.

    a $y = x^2$ **b** $y = -x^2 + 3$ **c** $y = -3x^2$ **d** $y = -2x^2 + 1$

    e Describe the transformation(s) that take(s) the graph in part **a** to each of the graphs in parts **b** to **d**.

6 On the same axes sketch the following graphs.

    a $y = \sin x$ **b** $y = 2\sin x$ **c** $y = \frac{1}{2}\sin x$ **d** $y = 10\sin x$

    e Describe the transformation(s) that take(s) the graph in part **a** to each of the graphs in parts **b** to **d**.

7 On the same axes sketch the following graphs.

    a $y = \sin x$ **b** $y = \sin 3x$ **c** $y = \sin \dfrac{x}{2}$ **d** $y = 5\sin 2x$

    e Describe the transformation(s) that take(s) the graph in part **a** to each of the graphs in parts **b** to **d**.

8 On the same axes sketch the following graphs.

    a $y = \sin x$ **b** $y = \sin (x + 90°)$ **c** $y = \sin (x - 45°)$ **d** $y = 2\sin (x - 90°)$

    e Describe the transformation(s) that take(s) the graph in part **a** to the graphs in parts **b** to **d**.

9 On the same axes sketch the following graphs.

   a $y = \sin x$ **b** $y = \sin x + 2$ **c** $y = \sin x - 3$ **d** $y = 2\sin x + 1$

   e Describe the transformation(s) that take(s) the graph in part **a** to each of the graphs parts **b** to **d**.

10 On the same axes sketch the following graphs.

   a $y = \sin x$ **b** $y = -\sin x$ **c** $y = \sin (-x)$ **d** $y = -\sin (-x)$

   e Describe the transformation(s) that take(s) the graph in part **a** to each of the graphs in parts **b** to **d**.

11 On the same axes sketch the following graphs.

   a $y = \cos x$ **b** $y = 2\cos x$ **c** $y = \cos (x - 60°)$ **d** $y = \cos x + 2$

   e Describe the transformation(s) that take(s) the graph in part **a** to each of the graphs in parts **b** to **d**.

12 **a** Describe the transformations of the graph of $y = x^2$ needed to obtain these graphs.

     i $y = 4x^2$ **ii** $y = 9x^2$ **iii** $y = 16x^2$

   b Describe the transformations of the graph of $y = x^2$ needed to obtain these graphs.

     i $y = (2x)^2$ **ii** $y = (3x)^2$ **iii** $y = (4x)^2$

   c Describe two different transformations that take the graph of $y = x^2$ to the graph of $y = (ax)^2$, where a is a positive number.

13 On the right is a sketch of the function $y = f(x)$. Use this to sketch the following.

   a $y = f(x) + 2$ **b** $y = 2f(x)$

   c $y = f(x - 3)$ **d** $y = -f(x)$

   e $y = 2f(x) + 3$ **f** $y = -f(x) - 2$

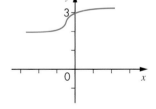

14 What is the equation of the graph obtained when the following transformations are performed on the graph of $y = x^2$?

   a stretch by a factor of 5 in the y-direction

   b translation of $\begin{pmatrix} 0 \\ 7 \end{pmatrix}$

   c translation of $\begin{pmatrix} -3 \\ 0 \end{pmatrix}$

   d translation of $\begin{pmatrix} -2 \\ -3 \end{pmatrix}$

   e stretch by a factor of 3 in the y-direction followed by a translation of $\begin{pmatrix} 0 \\ 4 \end{pmatrix}$

   f reflection in the x-axis, followed by a stretch, scale factor 3, in the y-direction

15 What is the equation of the graph obtained when the following transformations are performed on the graph of $y = \cos x$?

   a stretch by a factor of 6 in the y-direction

   b translation of $\begin{pmatrix} 0 \\ 3 \end{pmatrix}$

   c translation of $\begin{pmatrix} -30 \\ 0 \end{pmatrix}$

   d translation of $\begin{pmatrix} 45 \\ -2 \end{pmatrix}$

   e stretch by a factor of 3 in the y-direction followed by a translation of $\begin{pmatrix} 0 \\ -2 \end{pmatrix}$

16 a Sketch the graph $y = x^3$.

   b Use your sketch in part **a** to draw the graphs obtained after $y = x^3$ is transformed as follows.

     i reflection in the x-axis   **ii** translation of $\begin{pmatrix} 0 \\ -2 \end{pmatrix}$

     iii stretch by a scale factor of 3 in the y-direction   **iv** translation of $\begin{pmatrix} -2 \\ 0 \end{pmatrix}$

   c Give the equation of each of the graphs obtained in part **b**.

17 a Sketch the graph of $y = \dfrac{1}{x}$.

   b Use your sketch in part **a** to draw the graphs obtained after $y = \dfrac{1}{x}$ is transformed as follows.

     i translation of $\begin{pmatrix} 0 \\ 4 \end{pmatrix}$

     ii translation of $\begin{pmatrix} 4 \\ 0 \end{pmatrix}$

     iii stretch, scale factor 3 in the y-direction

     iv stretch, scale factor $\frac{1}{2}$ in the x-direction

   c Give the equation of each of the graphs obtained in part **b**.

18 The graphs below are all transformations of $y = x^2$. Two points through which each graph passes are indicated. Use this information to work out the equation of each graph.

a 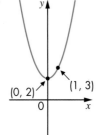   **b** 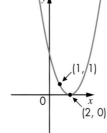   **c** 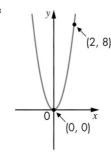   **d**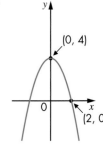

19 The graphs below are all transformations of $y = \sin x$. Two points through which each graph passes are indicated. Use this information to work out the equation of each graph.

a

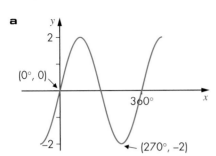

b

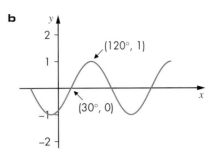

c

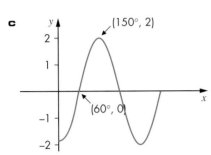

d

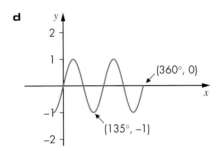

20 Below are the graphs of $y = \sin x$ and $y = \cos x$.

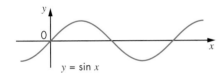

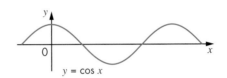

a Describe a series of transformations that would take the first graph to the second.

b Which of these is equivalent to $y = \cos x$?

   i $y = \sin (x + 90°)$ **ii** $y = -\sin (x - 90°)$ **iii** $y = 2\cos \dfrac{x}{2}$

21 **A**   **B**   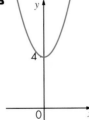   **C**   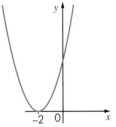

D 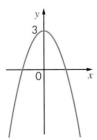   **E**   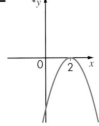

Match each of the graphs **A**, **B**, **C**, **D** and **E** to one of these equations.

  i $y = x^2$ **ii** $y = -x^2 + 3$ **iii** $y = -(x - 2)^2$ **iv** $y = (x + 2)^2$ **v** $y = x^2 + 4$

1 A sketch of the graph $y = x^2$ is given below.

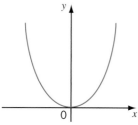

Write down the equations of the two transformed graphs below.

a

b

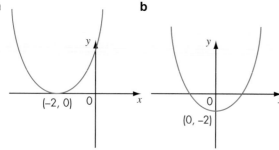

(−2, 0)

(0, −2)

2 The graph of $y = \sin x°$ for $0 \le x \le 360$ is drawn below.

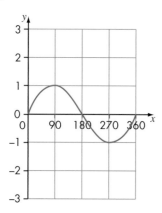

On copies of the same axes draw sketches of the following graphs.

a $y = 2 \sin x°$

b $y = \sin 2x°$

c $y = \sin x° - 2$

3 The graph of $y = f(x)$ is shown below.

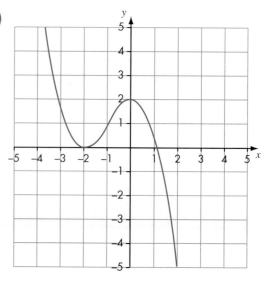

On copies of the grid, sketch the following graphs:

a $y = f(x + 1)$

b $y = 2f(x)$

Edexcel, Question 20, Paper 6 Higher, June 2005

4 This is a sketch of the curve with equation $y = f(x)$. It passes through the origin O.

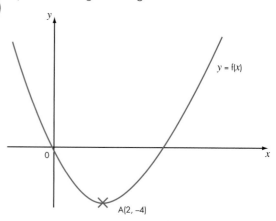

y = f(x)

A(2, −4)

The only vertex of the curve is at A(2, −4)

a Write down the coordinates of the vertex of the curve with equation

  i $y = f(x - 3)$,

  ii $y = f(x) - 5$,

  iii $y = -f(x)$,

  iv $y = f(2x)$.

The curve with equation $y = x^2$ has been translated to give the curve $y = f(x)$.

b Find $f(x)$ in terms of x.

Edexcel, Question 15, Paper 18 Higher, June 2003

WORKED EXAM QUESTION

The sketch shows the graph $y = x^3$.

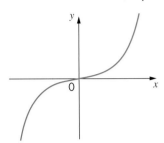

On the axes below sketch the graphs indicated.
(The graph $y = x^3$ is shown dotted to help you.)

a $y = x^3 - 3$

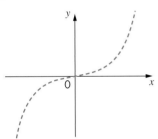

b $y = (x + 2)^3$

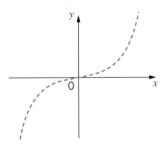

c $y = -x^3$

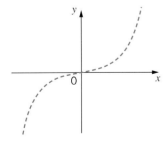

Solution

a This is a translation of $y = x^3$ by the vector $\begin{pmatrix} 0 \\ -3 \end{pmatrix}$

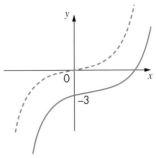

b This is a translation of $y = x^3$ by the vector $\begin{pmatrix} -2 \\ 0 \end{pmatrix}$.

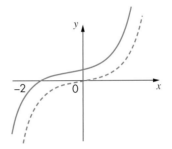

c This is a reflection of $y = x^3$ in the x-axis.

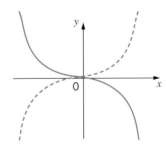

You do not know what the actual value of p is so make sure that the translation is clear. Alternatively, make a value for p up, say 2.

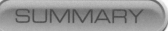

GRADE YOURSELF

A* Able to transform the graph of a given function

A* Able to identify the equation of a function from its graph, which has been formed by a transformation on a known function

What you should know now

- How to sketch the graphs of functions such as $y = f(ax)$ and $y = f(x + a)$ from the known graph of $y = f(x)$

- How to describe from their graphs the transformation of one function into another

- How to identify equations from the graphs of transformations of known graphs

Proof

① Proving standard results

② Algebraic proof

This chapter will show you ...

- the meaning of "a counter-example"
- the difference between a numerical demonstration and a proof
- how to prove results using rigorous and logical mathematical arguments

Visual overview

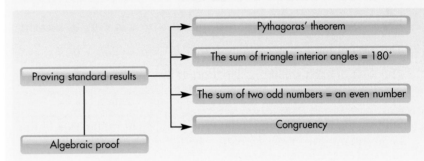

Proving standard results → Pythagoras' theorem

→ The sum of triangle interior angles = 180°

→ The sum of two odd numbers = an even number

→ Congruency

Algebraic proof

What you should already know

The mathematical results in this book, such as:

- The interior angles in a triangle add up to 180°
- The sum of any two odd numbers is always an even number
- The theorems concerning circles
- Pythagoras' theorem

Quick check

1 Give the value of the angle marked z in terms of x and y.

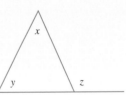

2 Write down a relationship between p, q and r.

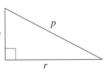

3 Complete this table.

+	even	odd
even	even	
odd		

Proving standard results

This section will remind you of:
- the difference between a proof and a demonstration

Key words

demonstration
proof
prove
show that

Can you **prove** any of the mathematical results listed on the previous page?

The method of mathematical **proof** is to proceed in logical steps, establishing a series of mathematical statements by using facts which are already known to be true. With few exceptions, a proof will also require the use of algebraic manipulation.

In the next pages, we prove four standard results: Pythagoras' theorem, the sum of the interior angles of a triangle is 180°, the sum of any two odd numbers is always an even number, and congruency. Follow them through, making sure that you understand each step in the process.

Proof of Pythagoras' theorem

Draw a square of side c inside a square of side $(a + b)$, as shown.

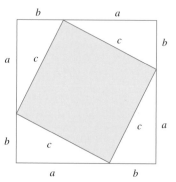

The area of the exterior square is $(a + b)^2 = a^2 + 2ab + b^2$.

The area of each small triangle around the shaded square is $\frac{1}{2}ab$.

The total area of all four triangles is $4 \times \frac{1}{2}ab = 2ab$.

Subtracting the total area of the four triangles from the area of the large square gives the area of the shaded square:

$$a^2 + 2ab + b^2 - 2ab = a^2 + b^2$$

But the area of the shaded square is c^2, so

$$c^2 = a^2 + b^2$$

which is Pythagoras' theorem.

The sum of the interior angles of a triangle is 180°

One of your earlier activities in geometry may have been to draw a triangle, to cut off its corners and to stick them down to **show that** they make a straight line.

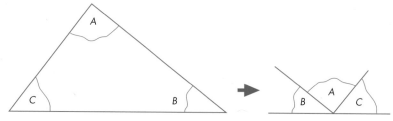

Does this prove that the interior angles make 180° or were you just lucky and picked a triangle that worked? Was the fact that everyone else in the class managed to pick a triangle that worked also a lucky coincidence?

Of course not! But this was a **demonstration**, not a proof. You would have to show that this method worked for *all* possible triangles (there is an infinite number!) to say that you have proved this result.

Your proof must establish that the result is true for *all* triangles.

Look at the following proof.

Start with triangle ABC with angles α, β and γ (figure **i**).

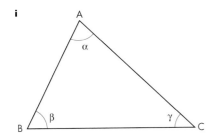 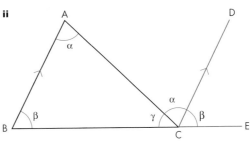

On figure **i** draw a line CD parallel to side AB and extend BC to E, to give figure **ii**.

Since AB is parallel to CD

∠ACD = ∠BAC = α (alternate angles)   ∠DCE = ∠ABC = β (corresponding angles)

BCE is a straight line, so γ + α + β = 180°. Therefore the interior angles of a triangle = 180°.

This proof assumes that alternate angles are equal and that corresponding angles are equal. Strictly speaking, we should prove these results, but we have to accept certain results as true. These are based on Euclid's axioms from which all geometric proofs are derived.

The sum of any two odd numbers is always an even number

If you try this with numbers, you can see that the result is true. For example, 3 + 5 = 8, 11 + 17 = 28. But this is not a proof. Once again, we may have been lucky and found some results that work. Until we have tried an infinite number of different pairs, we cannot be sure.

Look at the following algebraic proof.

Let n be any whole number.

Whatever whole number is represented by n, $2n$ has to be even. So, $2n + 1$ represents any odd number.

Let one odd number be $2n + 1$, and let the other odd number be $2m + 1$.

The sum of these is

$(2n + 1) + (2m + 1) = 2n + 2m + 1 + 1 = 2n + 2m + 2 = 2(n + m + 1)$, which must be even.

Congruency

There are four conditions to prove congruency. These are commonly known as SSS (three sides the same), SAS (two sides and the included angle the same), ASA (or AAS) (two angles and one side the same) and RHS (right-angled triangle, hypotenuse, and one short side the same). **Note:** AAA (three angles the same) is not a condition for congruency.

When you prove a result, you must explain or justify every statement or line. Proofs have to be rigorous and logical.

EXAMPLE 1

ABCD is a parallelogram. X is the point where the diagonals meet.

Prove that triangles AXB and CXD are congruent.

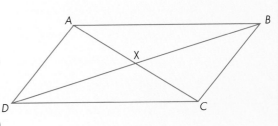

∠BAX = ∠DCX (alternate angles)

∠ABX = ∠CDX (alternate angles)

AB = CD (opposite sides in a parallelogram)

Hence ΔAXB is congruent to ΔCXD (ASA).

Note that you could have used ∠AXB = ∠CXD (vertically opposite angles) as the second line but whichever approach is used you *must* give a reason for each statement.

EXERCISE 27A

In some questions, a numerical example is used to give you a clue which will help you to write down an algebraic proof.

1 **a** Choose any odd number and any even number. Add these together. Is the result odd or even? Does this always work for any odd number and even number you choose?

b Let any odd number be represented by $2n + 1$. Let any even number be represented by $2m$, where m and n are integers. Prove that the sum of an odd number and an even number always gives an odd number.

2 Prove the following results.

a the sum of two even numbers is even

b the product of two even numbers is even

c the product of an odd number and an even number is even

d the product of two odd numbers is odd

e the sum of four consecutive numbers is always even

f half the sum of four consecutive numbers is always odd

3 **a** Show that the triangle ABC (figure **i**) is isosceles.

b Prove that the triangle DEF (figure **ii**) with one angle of $x°$ and an exterior angle of $90°$ $+ \dfrac{x°}{2}$ is isosceles.

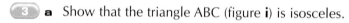

4 Prove that a triangle with an interior angle of $\dfrac{x°}{2}$ and an exterior angle of $x°$ is isosceles.

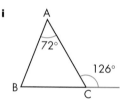

5 **a** Using the theorem that the angle subtended by an arc at the centre of a circle is twice the angle subtended by the same arc at the circumference, find the values of angles DAB and ACB in the circle shown in figure **i**.

b Prove that the sum of the opposite angles of a cyclic quadrilateral is 180°. (You may find figure **ii** useful.)

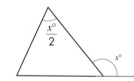
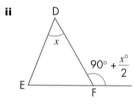

6 A Fibonacci sequence is formed by adding the previous two terms to get the next term. For example, if we start with 3 and 4, the series is

3, 4, 7, 11, 18, 29, 47, 76, 123, 199, ...

a Continue the Fibonacci sequence up to 10 terms. 1, 1, 2, ...

b Continue the Fibonacci sequence up to 10 terms. $a, b, a + b, a + 2b, 2a + 3b, ...$

c Prove that the difference between the 8th term and the 5th term of any Fibonacci sequence is twice the sixth term.

7 The nth term in the sequence of triangular numbers 1, 3, 6, 10, 15, 21, 28, ... is given by

$\frac{1}{2}n (n + 1)$.

a Show that the sum of the 11th and 12th terms is a perfect square.

b Explain why the $(n + 1)$th term of the triangular number sequence is given by $\frac{1}{2}(n + 1)(n + 2)$.

c Prove that the sum of any two consecutive triangular numbers is always a square number.

8 **a** The triangle ABC is isosceles. **i** BCD and AED are straight lines. Find the value of the angle CED, marked x, in figure **i**.

b Prove that angle ACB = angle CED in figure **ii**.

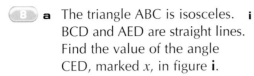
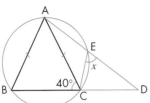
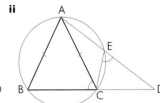

9 The diagram shows part of a 10×10 "hundred square".

a One 2×2 square is marked.

12	13	14	15
22	23	24	25
32	33	34	35
42	43	44	45

  i Work out the difference between the product of the bottom-left and top-right values and the product of the top-left and bottom-right values:

  $$22 \times 13 - 12 \times 23$$

  ii Repeat this for any other 2×2 square of your choosing.

b Prove that this will always give an answer of 10 for any 2×2 square chosen.

c The diagram shows a calendar square (where the numbers are arranged in rows of seven).

Prove that you always get a value of 7 if you repeat the procedure in part **a i**.

1	2	3	4	5	6	7
8	9	10	11	12	13	14
15	16	17	18	19	20	21
22	23	24	25	26	27	28
29	30	31				

d Prove that in a number square that is arranged in rows of n numbers then the difference is always n if you repeat the procedure in part **a i**.

10 Prove that if you add any two-digit number from the 9 times table to the reverse of itself (that is, swap the tens digit and units digit), the result will always be 99.

27.2 Algebraic proof

In this section you will learn how to:
- give a rigorous and logical algebraic proof

Key words
area
length
width

There are three levels of "proof": **Verify** that…, **Show** that…, and **Prove** that… .

- At the lowest level (verification), all you have to do is to substitute numbers into the result to show that it works.
- At the middle level, you have to show that both sides of the result are the same algebraically.
- At the highest level (proof), you have to manipulate the left-hand side of the result to become its right-hand side.

The following example demonstrates these three different procedures.

EXAMPLE 2

You are given that $n^2 + (n + 1)^2 - (n + 2)^2 = (n - 3)(n + 1)$

a Verify that this result is true.

b Show that this result is true.

c Prove that this result is true.

a Choose a number for n, say $n = 5$. Put this value into both sides of the expression, which gives:
$$5^2 + (5 + 1)^2 - (5 + 2)^2 = (5 - 3)(5 + 1)$$
$$25 + 36 - 49 = 2 \times 6$$
$$12 = 12$$
Hence, the result is true.

b Expand the LHS and the RHS of the expression to get:
$$n^2 + n^2 + 2n + 1 - (n^2 + 4n + 4) = n^2 - 2n - 3$$
Collect like terms on each side, which gives:
$$n^2 + n^2 - n^2 + 2n - 4n + 1 - 4 = n^2 - 2n - 3$$
$$n^2 - 2n - 3 = n^2 - 2n - 3$$
That is, both sides are algebraically the same.

c Expand the LHS of the expression to get: $n^2 + n^2 + 2n + 1 - (n^2 + 4n + 4)$

Collect like terms, which gives: $n^2 + n^2 - n^2 + 2n - 4n + 1 - 4 = n^2 - 2n - 3$

Factorise the collected result: $n^2 - 2n - 3 = (n - 3)(n + 1)$ which is the RHS of the original expression.

EXERCISE 27B

1 Speed Cabs charges 45 pence per kilometre for each journey. Evans Taxis has a fixed charge of 90p plus 30p per kilometre.

   a **i** Verify that Speed Cabs is cheaper for a journey of 5 km.

      ii Verify that Evans Taxis is cheaper for a journey of 7 km.

   b Show clearly why both companies charge the same for a journey of 6 km.

   c Show that if Speed Cabs charges a pence per kilometre, and Evans Taxis has a fixed charge of £b plus a charge of c pence per kilometre, both companies charge the same for a journey of $\dfrac{100b}{(a - c)}$ kilometres.

2 You are given that:

$(a + b)^2 + (a - b)^2 = 2(a^2 + b^2)$

   a Verify that this result is true for $a = 3$ and $b = 4$.

   b Show that the LHS is the same as the RHS.

   c Prove that the LHS can be simplified to the RHS.

3 Prove that $(a + b)^2 - (a - b)^2 = 4ab$.

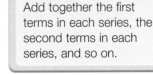

4 The rule for converting from degrees Fahrenheit to degrees Celsius is to subtract 32° and then to multiply by $\frac{5}{9}$.

Prove that the temperature that has the same value in both scales is –40°.

5 The sum of the series $1 + 2 + 3 + 4 + \ldots + (n - 2) + (n - 1) + n$ is given by $\frac{1}{2}n(n + 1)$.

  a Verify that this result is true for $n = 6$.

  b Write down a simplified value, in terms of n, for the sum of these two series.

$$1 + 2 + 3 + \ldots + (n - 2) + (n - 1) + n$$
and $\quad n + (n - 1) + (n - 2) + \ldots + 3 + 2 + 1$

  c Prove that the sum of the first n integers is $\frac{1}{2}n(n + 1)$.

> **HINTS AND TIPS**
>
> Add together the first terms in each series, the second terms in each series, and so on.

6 The following is a "think of a number" trick.

- Think of a number.   ⟶   • Multiply it by 2.
- Add 10.   ⟶   • Divide the result by 2.
- Subtract the original number.

The result is always 5.

  a Verify that the trick works when you pick 7 as the original number.

  b Prove why the trick *always* works.

7 You are told that "when two numbers have a difference of 2, the difference of their squares is twice the sum of the two numbers".

  a Verify that this is true for 5 and 7.

  b Prove that the result is true.

  c Prove that when two numbers have a difference of n, the difference of their squares is n times the sum of the two numbers.

> **HINTS AND TIPS**
>
> Use a and $a + 2$ as the numbers.

8 Four consecutive numbers are 4, 5, 6 and 7.

  a Verify that their product plus 1 is a perfect square.

  b Complete the multiplication square and use it to show that
$$(n^2 - n - 1)^2 = n^4 - 2n^3 - n^2 + 2n + 1$$

	n^2	$-n$	-1
n^2	n^4		$-n^2$
$-n$		n^2	
-1			

  c Let four consecutive numbers be $(n - 2)$, $(n - 1)$, n, $(n + 1)$. Prove that the product of four consecutive numbers plus 1 is a perfect square.

9 Here is another mathematical trick to try on a friend.

- Think of two single-digit numbers.
- Multiply one number (your choice) by 2.
- Add 5 to this answer.
- Multiply this answer by 5.
- Add the second number.
- Subtract 4.
- Ask your friend to state his or her final answer.
- Mentally subtract 21 from his or her answer.

The two digits you get are the two digits your friend first thought of.

Prove why this works.

EXERCISE 27C

You may not be able algebraically to prove all of these results. Some of them can be disproved by a counter-example. You should first try to verify each result, then attempt to prove it – or at least try to demonstrate that the result is probably true by trying lots of examples.

1 T represents any triangular number. Prove the following.

a $8T + 1$ is always a square number

b $9T + 1$ is always another triangular number

2 Lewis Carroll, who wrote *Alice in Wonderland*, was also a mathematician. In 1890, he suggested the following results.

a For any pair of numbers, x and y, if $x^2 + y^2$ is even, then $\frac{1}{2}(x^2 + y^2)$ is the sum of two squares.

b For any pair of numbers, x and y, $2(x^2 + y^2)$ is always the sum of two squares.

c Any number whose square is the sum of two squares is itself the sum of two squares.

Can you prove these statements to be true or false?

3 For all values of n, $n^2 - n + 41$ gives a prime number. True or false?

4 For any integer n, $2n$, $n^2 - 1$ and $n^2 + 1$ form three numbers that obey Pythagoras' theorem. Can you prove this?

5 Waring's theorem states that: "Any whole number can be written as the sum of not more than four square numbers."

For example, $27 = 3^2 + 3^2 + 3^2$ and $23 = 3^2 + 3^2 + 2^2 + 1^2$.

Is this always true?

6 Take a three-digit multiple of 37, for example, $7 \times 37 = 259$. Write these digits in a cycle.

Take all possible three-digit numbers from the cycle, for example, 259, 592 and 925.

Divide each of these numbers by 37 to find that

$259 = 7 \times 37 \qquad 592 = 16 \times 37 \qquad 925 = 25 \times 37$.

Is this true for all three-digit multiples of 37?

Is it true for a five-digit multiple of 41?

7 Prove that the sum of the squares of two consecutive integers is an odd number.

8 PQRS is a parallelogram. Prove that triangles PQS and RQS are congruent.

9 OB is a radius of a circle, centre O. C is the point where the perpendicular bisector of OB meets the circumference. Prove that triangle OBC is equilateral.

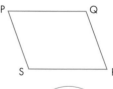

10 In the following grid, $\overrightarrow{OA} = \mathbf{a}$ and $\overrightarrow{OB} = \mathbf{b}$.
Prove that AB is parallel to EF.

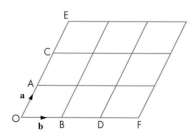

1   T, A and B are points on the circumference of the circle, centre O.

AT is a diameter of the circle.
Angle BTC = 40°
Angle TAB = 30°

Explain why TC cannot be a tangent to the circle.

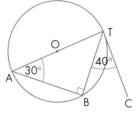

Edexcel, Question 4, Paper 10A Higher, January 2004

2   1 + 2 + 3 = 6
2 + 3 + 4 = 9

Show that every sum of three consecutive integers is a multiple of 3.

3   Lisa said:

> The difference between the cubes of consecutive integers is always a prime number.

a Show an example to illustrate that this statement could be true.

b Show an example to illustrate that this statement is not true.

4 S and T are points on a circle, centre O. PSQ and PTR are tangents to the circle. SOR and TOQ are straight lines.

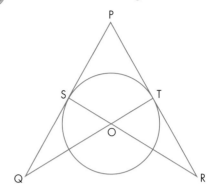

a Prove that triangle PQT and triangle PRS are congruent.

Asif says that triangle STQ and triangle STR have equal areas.

b Explain why Asif is correct.

Edexcel, Question 6, Paper 13B Higher, January 2005

WORKED EXAM QUESTION

a *n* is a positive integer.
  i Explain why $n(n + 1)$ must be an even number.
  ii Explain why $2n + 1$ must be an odd number.
b Expand and simplify $(2n + 1)^2$
c Prove that the square of any odd number is always 1 more than a multiple of 8.

Solution

a i If *n* is odd, *n* + 1 is even
  If *n* is even, *n* + 1 is odd
  Even times odd is always even

> This is a lead in to the rest of the task. An explanation in words is good enough. Keep the words to a minimum.

  ii 2*n* must be even so 2*n* + 1 must be odd

> An explanation in words is good enough.

b $(2n + 1)^2 = (2n + 1)(2n + 1) = 4n^2 + 2n + 2n + 1 = 4n^2 + 4n + 1$

> Always write down a squared bracket twice then expand it by whichever method you prefer.

c $(2n + 1)^2 = 4n^2 + 4n + 1$

> Use the fact that $2n + 1$ is odd, and it has been "squared" in part **b**.

$4n^2 + 4n + 1 = 4n(n + 1) + 1$

> The "one more than" is taken care of with the +1.

$4 \times n(n + 1) + 1 = 4 \times$ even + 1, which must be a multiple of 8 plus 1.

> Show that the $4n^2 + 4n$ is a multiple of 8 using the result in part **a i**.

GRADE YOURSELF

B Able to verify results by substituting numbers into them

B Able to understand the proofs of simple theorems such as an exterior angle of a triangle is the sum of the two opposite interior angles

A Able to show that an algebraic statement is true, using both sides of the statement to justify your answer

A* Able to prove algebraic and geometric results with rigorous and logical mathematical arguments

What you should know now

- The meaning of the terms "verify that", "show that" and "prove"

- How to prove some standard results in mathematics, such as Pythagoras' theorem

- How to use your knowledge of proof to answer the questions throughout the book that are flagged with the proof icon

Really Useful Maths!

Chapter 18
Really Useful Maths!: Are we living longer?

Age distribution in the UK (numbers in millions)			
Age (a) in years	1976	2001	% change
$0 \leqslant a < 15$	12.9	11.1	−14%
$15 \leqslant a < 25$	8.1	7.2	−11%
$25 \leqslant a < 35$	7.9	8.4	6%
$35 \leqslant a < 45$	6.4	8.8	38%
$45 \leqslant a < 55$	9.8	7.8	−20%
$55 \leqslant a < 65$	3.1	6.2	100%
$65 \leqslant a < 75$	5.1	4.9	−4%
$75 \leqslant a < 85$	2.3	3.3	43%
$85 \leqslant a < 105$	0.5	1.1	120%

Midpoint of ages	1976 frequency (millions)	Midpoint × frequency	2001 frequency (millions)	Midpoint × frequency
7.5	12.9	96.75	11.1	83.25
20	8.1	162	7.2	144
30	7.9	237	8.4	252
40	6.4	256	8.8	352
50	9.8	490	7.8	390
60	3.1	186	6.2	372
70	5.1	357	4.9	343
80	2.3	184	3.3	264
95	0.5	47.5	1.1	104.5
Totals	56.1	2016.25	58.8	2304.75
Mean age		35.94		39.20

Cumulative frequencies for age distributions (in millions)									
	<15	<25	<35	<45	<55	<65	<75	<85	<105
1976	12.9	21	28.9	35.3	45.1	48.2	53.3	55.6	56.1
2001	11.1	18.3	26.7	35.5	43.3	49.5	54.4	57.7	58.8

	1976	2001
Mean	36	39
Median	34	38
Upper quartile	52	56
Lower quartile	16	20
IQR	36	36

The missing numbers from the article are:
2.7, $85 \leqslant a < 105$,
120, 20, $45 \leqslant a < 55$,
36, 39, 3, 34, 38, 4, 4

Chapter 20
Really Useful Maths!: Walking holiday

Day	Distance in km	Height climbed in metres	Time in minutes	Time in hours and minutes	Start time	Time allowed for breaks	Finish time
1	16	270	267	4 h 27 m	9:30 am	2 hours	3:57pm
2	20	210	321	5 h 21 m	9:00 am	$2\frac{3}{4}$ hours	5:06pm
3	15	80	233	3 h 53 m	10:00 am	$2\frac{1}{2}$ hours	4:23pm
4	17	210	276	4h 36 m	10:30 am	$2\frac{1}{4}$ hours	5:21pm
5	18	120	282	4 h 42 m	10:00 am	$2\frac{1}{2}$ hours	5:12pm
6	17	290	284	4 h 44 m	10:30 am	2 hours	5:14pm
7	22	90	339	5 h 39 m	10:00 am	$2\frac{3}{4}$ hours	6:24pm
8	12	300	210	3 h 30 m	10:30 am	$2\frac{1}{4}$ hours	4:15pm

Chapter 22
Really Useful Maths!: Windpower

Distance of turbine out to sea	Angle of elevation from shore
3 km	2.29°
4 km	1.72°
5 km	1.37°
6 km	1.15°
7 km	0.98°
8 km	0.86°

Wind speed (m/s)	Available power (W/m²)
6	132.34
7	210
8	313.47
9	446.33
10	612.24
11	814.90
12	1057.96

Wind speed (m/s)	Available power (W/m²)	Rotor area for 50 m blade (m²)	Power (MW)	Rotor area for 60 m blade (m²)	Power (MW)	Rotor area for 70 m blade (m²)	Power (MW)
7	210	7854	1.65	11310	2.38	15394	3.23
8	313.47	7854	2.46	11310	3.55	15394	4.83
9	446.33	7854	3.51	11310	5.05	15394	6.87
10	612.24	7854	4.81	11310	6.92	15394	9.42

Chapter 23
Really Useful Maths!: A new floor

Oak effect Room	Maximum floor area (m²)	Maximum edging needed (m)
Lounge	61.24	32.35
Sitting room	29.8275	21.25
Kitchen/diner	45.175	27.5
Conservatory	12.4425	11.95
Total:	148.685	93.05

Beech effect Room	Maximum floor area (m²)	Maximum edging needed (m)
Hall	15.8025	15.25
Bathroom	9.5875	11.65
Total:	25.39	26.9

The area of the lounge and kitchen/diner may be calculated in several ways. Other possible answers are:

Lounge: 61.07 m² and 61.13 m²   Kitchen/Diner: 44.9675 m²
(if this alternative answer is given, total maximum floor area for oak effect becomes 148.4775 m², the numbers of packs of flooring required is unaffected)

Similarly, the edging required for the Kitchen/Diner could be calculated as 27.35 m (if this alternative answer is given, total maximum edging needed for oak effect becomes 92.9 m, numbers of packs required is unaffected)

	Number of packs	Price per pack	Total cost
Beech flooring	13	£56.40	£733.20
Beech edging	3	£21.15	£63.45
Oak flooring	75	£61.10	£4582.50
Oak edging	8	£25.85	£206.80
		Total:	£5585.95

Total price exclusive of VAT is: £4754.00

Quick check

1 a 13   **b**

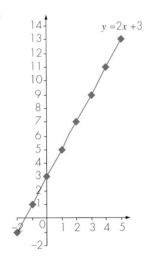

Exercise 16A

1

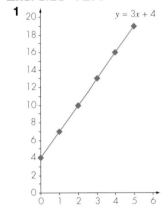

2

3

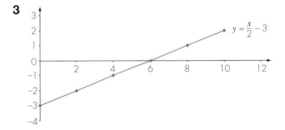

4

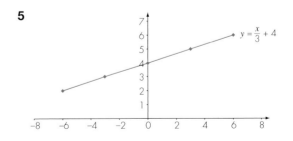

5

6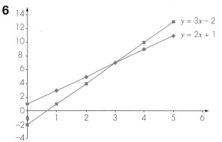

b (3, 7)

7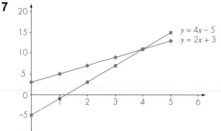

b (4, 11)

8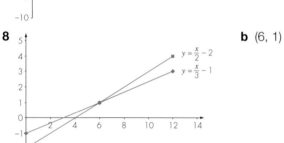

b (6, 1)

9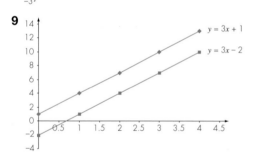

b No, because the lines are parallel.

10

x	0	1	2	3	4	5
y	5	4	3	2	1	0

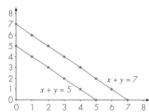

Exercise 16B

1 a 2 **b** $\frac{1}{3}$ **c** –3 **d** 1 **e** –2 **f** $-\frac{1}{3}$ **g** 5 **h** –5 **i** $\frac{1}{5}$ **j** $-\frac{3}{4}$

2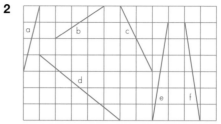

3 a 1 **b** –1 They are perpendicular and symmetrical about the axes.

4 a 0.5 **b** 0.4 **c** 0.2 **d** 0.1 **e** 0

5 a $1\frac{2}{3}$ **b** 2 **c** $3\frac{1}{3}$ **d** 10 **e** ∞

Exercise 16C

1

$y = 2x + 6,\ y = 3x - 4,\ y = \frac{1}{2}x + 5,\ y = x + 7$

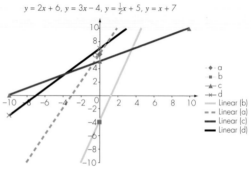

$y = 4x - 3,\ y = 2x - 7,\ y = \frac{1}{4}x - 3,\ y = \frac{2}{3}x + 4$

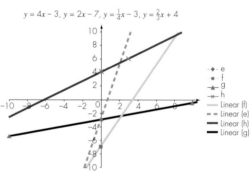

$y = 6x - 5,\ y = x + 8,\ y = \frac{4}{3}x - 2,\ y = 3x - 9$

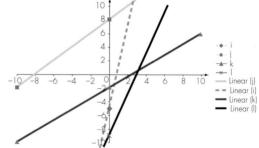

2 a

$y = 3x + 1, y = 2x + 3$

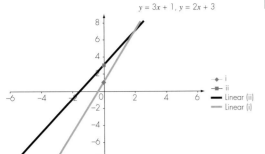

b (2, 7)

$6x + 5y = 30, x + y = -5, x + y = 3, x - y = -4$

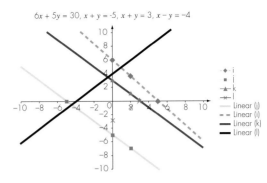

3 a

$y = \frac{x}{3} + 3, y = \frac{x}{4} + 2$

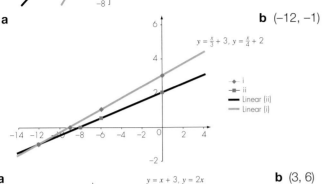

b (−12, −1)

2 a

$2x + y = 4, x - 2y = 2$

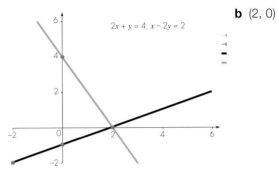

b (2, 0)

4 a

$y = x + 3, y = 2x$

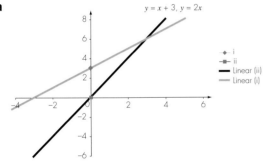

b (3, 6)

3 a

$x + 2y = 6, 2x - y = 2$

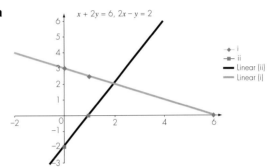

Exercise 16D

1 $3x + 2y = 6, 4x + 3y = 12, 4x - 5y = 20, x + y = 10$

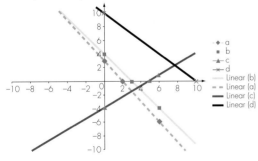

b (2, 2)

4 a

$x + y = 6, x - y = 2$

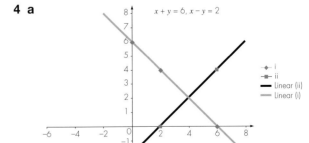

$3x - 2y = 18, x - y = 4, 5x - 2y = 15, 2x - 3y = 15$

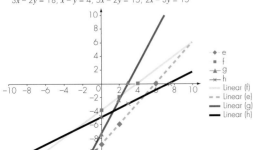

b (4, 2)

Exercise 16E

1 a $y = \frac{4}{3}x - 2$ or $3y = 4x - 6$ **b** $y = x + 1$ **c** $y = 2x - 3$ **d** $2y = x + 6$ **e** $y = x$ **f** $y = 2x$

2 a i $y = 2x + 1$, $y = -2x + 1$ **ii** reflection in y-axis (and $y = 1$)   **iii** different sign
  b i $5y = 2x - 5$, $5y = -2x - 5$ **ii** reflection in y-axis (and $y = -1$)   **iii** different sign
  c i $y = x + 1$, $y = -x + 1$ **ii** reflection in y-axis (and $y = 1$)   **iii** different sign

3 a $y = -2x + 1$ **b** $2y = -x$ **c** $y = -x + 1$ **d** $5y = -2x - 5$ **e** $y = \frac{3}{2}x - 3$

4 a i $2y = -x + 1$, $y = -2x + 1$ **ii** reflection in $x = y$ **iii** reciprocal of each other
  b i $2y = 5x + 5$, $5y = 2x - 5$ **ii** reflection in $x = y$ **iii** reciprocal of each other
  c i $y = 2$, $x = 2$ **ii** reflection in $x = y$ **iii** reciprocal of each other (reciprocal of zero is infinity)

Exercise 16F

1 a 32°F   **b** $\frac{9}{5}$ (Take gradient at C =10° and 30°.)   **c** $F = \frac{9}{5}C + 32$

2 a 0.07 (Take gradient at U = 0 and 500.)   **b** £10   **c** $C = £(10 + 0.07U)$ or Charge = £10 + 7p/unit

3 a $\frac{5}{2}$ (Take gradient at D = 0 and 40.)   **b** £20   **c** $C = £(20 + \frac{5D}{2})$ or Charge = £20 + £2.50/day

4 a $\frac{1}{2}$ (Take gradient at N = 0 and 500.)   **b** £50   **c** $C = £(50 + \frac{N}{2})$ or £50 + 50p/person

5 a $\frac{4}{10}$ **b** 24.5 cm   **c** 0.1 cm or 1 mm   **d** $\angle = 24.5 + \frac{W}{10}$ or Length = 24.5 + 1 mm/kg

Exercise 16G

1 (4, 1)   **2** (2, 3)   **3** (3, 10)
4 (5, 5)   **5** (1, 5)   **6** (3, 16)
7 (–2, 6)   **8** (–6, –9)   **9** (1, –1)
10 (2, 6)   **11** (2, 8)   **12** $(7\frac{1}{2}, 3\frac{1}{2})$

4 a $y = -\frac{1}{3}x - 1$ **b** $y = 3x + 5$ **c** $y = -x + 1$
5 a $y = -x + 14$ **b** $y = x + 2$
6 $y = 2x + 6$
7 $y = -\frac{1}{4}x + 2$
8 a (0, –20)   **b** $y = -\frac{1}{5}x + 6$ **c** $y = 5x - 20$
9 $y = -\frac{1}{2}x + 5$
10 a $y = 3x - 6$
   b Bisector of AB is $y = -2x + 9$, bisector of AC is
      $y = \frac{x}{2} + \frac{3}{2}$, solving these equations shows the lines
      intersect at (3, 3)
   c (3, 3) lies on $y = 3x - 6$ because $(3 \times 3) - 6 = 3$

Exercise 16H

1 a $-\frac{1}{2}$ **b** $\frac{1}{3}$ **c** $-\frac{1}{5}$ **d** 1   **e** –2   **f** –4
  g 3   **h** $\frac{3}{2}$ **i** $-\frac{2}{3}$ **j** $-\frac{1}{10}$ **k** $\frac{1}{6}$ **l** $-\frac{3}{4}$

2 a $y = -\frac{1}{2}x - 1$ **b** $y = \frac{1}{3}x + 1$ **c** $y = -x + 2$ **d** $y = x + 2$
  e $y = -2x + 3$ **f** $y = -4x - 3$ **g** $y = 3x$ **h** $y = 1.5x - 5$

3 a $y = 4x + 1$ **b** $y = \frac{1}{2}x - 2$ **c** $y = -x + 3$

ANSWERS TO CHAPTER 17

Quick check

1

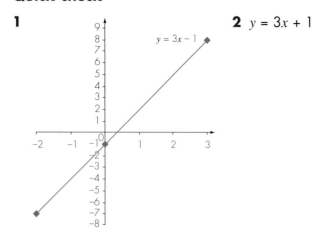

2 $y = 3x + 1$

Exercise 17A

1 a Values of y: 27, 12, 3, 0, 3, 12, 27
  b 6.8   **c** 1.8 or –1.8
2 a Values of y: 27, 18, 11, 6, 3, 2, 3, 6, 11, 18, 27
  b 8.3   **c** 3.5 or –3.5
3 a Values of y: 27, 16, 7, 0, –5, –8, –9, –8, –5, 0, 7
  b –8.8   **c** 3.4 or –1.4

4 a Values of y: 2, –1, –2, –1, 2, 7, 14   **b** 0.25
  c 0.7 or –2.7   **e** (1.1, 2.6) and (–2.6, 0.7)
5 a Values of y: 18, 12, 8, 6, 6, 8, 12   **b** 9.75   **c** 2 or –1
  d Values of y: 14, 9, 6, 5, 6, 9, 14   **e** (1, 6)
6 a Values of y: 4, 1, 0, 1, 4, 9, 16   **b** 7.3   **c** 0.4 or –2.4
  e (1, 4) and (–1, 0)
7 a Values of y: 15, 9, 4, 0, –3, –5, –6, –6, –5, –3, 0, 4, 9
  b –0.5 and 3

Exercise 17B

1 a Values of y: 12, 5, 0, –3, –4, –3, 0, 5, 12   **b** 2 and –2
2 a Values of y: 7, 0, –5, –8, –9, –8, –5, 0, 7   **b** 3 and –3
3 c Values of y: 15, 8, 3, 0, –1, 0, 3, 8, 15
  d Values of y: 11, 4, –1, –4, –5, –4, –1, 4, 11
  e 1 and –1, 2.2 and –2.2
4 a Values of y: 5, 0, –3, –4, –3, 0, 5, 12   **b** –4 and 0
5 a Values of y: 16, 7, 0, –5, –8, –9, –8, –5, 0, 7, 16
  b 0 and 6
6 a Values of y: 10, 4, 0, –2, –2, 0, 4, 10, 18   **b** –3 and 0
7 c Values of y: 10, 4, 0, –2, –2, 0, 4, 10
  d Values of y: 6, 0, –4, –6, –6, –4, 0, 6, 14
  e 0 and 3, –5 and 0
8 a Values of y: 9, 4, 1, 0, 1, 4, 9   **b** +2   **c** Only 1 root
9 a Values of y: 10, 3, –2, –5, –6, –5, –2, 3, 10
  b 0.6 and 5.4

10 a Values of y: 19, 6, –3, –8, –9, –6, 1, 12 **b** 0.9 and –3.4
11 a –4, –9, –1, –5, 0, 0, 0, 0, 0
  b (0, –4), (0, –9), (0, –1), (0, –5), (–2, –4), (3, –9), (–1.5, –2.25), (1.5, –2.25), (–2.5, –6.25)
12 a $y = (x - 2)^2$ **b** 0
13 a $y = (x - 3)^2 - 6$ **b** –6
14 a $y = (x - 4)^2 - 14$ **b** –14
15 a $y = -(x - 1)^2 - 5$ **b** –5

Exercise 17C

1 a Values of y: 10, 5, 4, 2.5, 2, 1.33, 1, 0.67, 0.5
  b i 0.8 **ii** –1.6
2 a Values of $5\sqrt{x}$: 0, 5 and –5, 7.1 and –7.1, 8.7 and –8.7, 10 and –10, 11.2 and –11.2
  b i 9.4 and –9.4 **ii** 2.6
3 a Values of $\frac{1}{2}\sqrt{x}$: 0, $\frac{1}{2}$ and $-\frac{1}{2}$, 0.71 and –0.71, 0.87 and –0.87, 1 and –1, 1.1 and –1.1
  b i 0.8 and –0.8 **ii** 2.25
4 a Values of y: 10, 5, 2.5, 2, 1, 0.5, 0.4, 0.25, 0.2
  c 4.8 and 0.2
5 a Values of y: 25, 12.5, 10, 5, 2.5, 1, 0.5, 0.33, 0.25
  c 0.48 and –10.48

Exercise 17D

1 a Values of y: –24, –12.63, –5, –0.38, 2, 2.9, 3, 3.13, 4, 6.38, 11, 18.63, 30 **b** 4.7
2 a Values of y: –54, –31.25, –16, –6.75, –2, –0.25, 0, 0.25, 2, 6.75, 16, 31.25, 54 **b** 39.4
3 a Values of y: 27, 15.63, 8, 3.38, 1, 0.13, 0, –0.13, –1, –3.38, –8, –15.63, –27 **b** 0.2
4 a Values of y: –36, –23.13, –14, –7.88, –4, –1.63, 0, 1.63, 4, 7.88, 14, 23.13, 36 **b** 0.6
5 a Values of y: –45, –26.88, –14, –5.63, –1, 0.63, 0, –2.13, –5, –7.88, –10, –10.63, –9 **b** –9.3
6 a Values of y: –16, –5.63, 1, 4.63, 6, 5.88, 5, 4.13, 4, 5.38, 9, 15.63, 26 **c** –1.6, –0.4, 1.9
7 a Values of y: –20, –9.63, –3, 0.63, 2, 1.88, 1, 0.13, 0, 1.38, 5, 11.63, 22 **c** –1.9, 0.4, 1.5
8 a Quadratic **b** Linear **c** None
  d Reciprocal **e** None **f** Cubic
  g Linear **h** None **i** Quadratic

Exercise 17E

1 a Values of y: 0.01, 0.04, 0.11, 0.33, 1, 3, 9, 27
  c 15.6 **d** –0.63

2 a Values of y: 32, 16, 8, 4, 2, 1, 0.5, 0.25, 0.13, 0.06, 0.03
  c 0.18 **d** 0.42
3 b Values of y: 1, 2, 4, 8, 16, 32, 64, 128, 256, 512
  c 9.2×10^{18} **d** £4.61×10^{14}
4 a Number of pieces: 2, 4, 8, 16, 32, 64, 128, 256
  b number of pieces = 2^n **c** 1.1×10^{15} pieces
  d 1.1×10^8 km

Exercise 17F

1 115° **2** 327°
3 324° **4** 195°
5 210°, 330° **6** 135°, 225°
7 a 64° **b** 206°, 334° **c** 116°, 244°

Exercise 17G

1 a i –1.4, 4.4 **ii** –2, 5 **iii** –0.6, 3.6 **b** 2.6, 0.4
2 a –5, 1 **b i** –5.3, 1.3 **ii** –4.8, 0.8 **iii** –3.4, –0.6
3 a i 0, 6 **ii** 4.3, 0.7 **b i** 4.8, 0.2 **ii** 5.4, –0.4
4 a i –1.6, 2.6 **ii** 1.4, –1.4 **b i** 2.3, –2.3 **ii** 2, –2
5 a 0, 2 **b** 2.5 **c** –0.6, 1, 1.6 **d** 2.8 **e** –0.8, 0.6, 2.2

6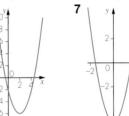
  a –0.4, 4.4
  b –1, 5

7
  a 1.6, –1.6
  b –1.2, 1.2

8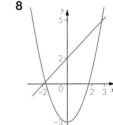
  a 2.2, –2.2
  b –1.8, 2.8

9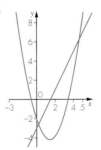
  a 3.3, –0.3
  b 4.8, 0.2

10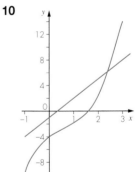
  a 2 **b** 2.5

ANSWERS TO CHAPTER 18

Quick check

1 29.0

Exercise 18A

1 b About 328 million **c** Between 1980 and 1985
  d Rising living standards
2 b Smallest difference Wednesday (7°), greatest difference Friday (10°)

Exercise 18B

1 a
```
2 | 8 9
3 | 4 5 6 8 8 9
4 | 1 1 3 3 3 8 8
```
  b 43 cm **c** 39 cm **d** 20 cm
2 a
```
0 | 2 8 9 9 9
1 | 2 3 7 7 8
2 | 0 1 2 3
```
  b 9 messages **c** 15 messages

239

Exercise 18C

1 a Positive correlation, reaction time increases with amount of alcohol drunk.

b Negative correlation, you drink less alcohol as you get older.

c No correlation, speed of cars on MI is not related to the temperature.

d Weak, positive correlation, older people generally have more money saved in the bank.

2 c ≈ 19 cm/s **d** ≈ 34 cm

3 c Greta **d** ≈ 67 **e** ≈ 72

4 b Yes, usually (good correlation)

5 b No correlation, so cannot draw a line of best fit

Exercise 18D

1 a cumulative frequency 1, 4, 10, 22, 25, 28, 30

c 54 secs, 16 secs

2 a cumulative frequency 1, 3, 5, 14, 31, 44, 47, 49, 50

c 56 secs, 17 secs **d** Pensioners, median closer to 60 secs

3 a cumulative frequency 12, 30, 63, 113, 176, 250, 314, 349, 360

c 605 pupils, 280 pupils **d** 46–47 schools

4 a cumulative frequency 2, 5, 10, 16, 22, 31, 39, 45, 50

c 20.5°C, 10°C

5 a cumulative frequency 9, 22, 45, 60, 71, 78, 80

c 56, 43 **d** 17.5%

6 a cumulative frequency 6, 16, 36, 64, 82, 93, 98, 100

c 225p, 110p

7 a cumulative frequency 8, 22, 47, 82, 96, 100

c £1605, £85 **d** 13%

Exercise 18E

1 a

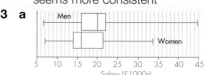

b The students are much slower than the pensioners. Although both distributions have the same inter-quartile range, the students' median and upper quartile are 1 minute, 35 seconds higher. The fastest person to compete the calculations was a student, but so was the slowest

2 a The resorts have similar median temperatures, but Resort B has a much wider temperature range. The greatest extremes of temperature are recorded in Resort B

b Resort A is probably a better choice as the weather seems more consistent

3 a

b Both distributions have a similar inter-quartile range, and there is little difference between the upper quartile values. Men have a wider range of salaries, but the higher men's median and the fact that the men's distribution is negatively skewed and the women's distribution is positively skewed indicates that men are better paid than women.

4 b £1605, £85

c ii symmetric

5 a Symmetric **b** Negatively skewed

c Negatively skewed **d** Symmetric

e Negatively skewed **f** Positively skewed

g Negatively skewed **h** Positively skewed

i Positively skewed **j** Symmetric

ANSWERS TO CHAPTER 19

Quick check

1 a Perhaps around 0.6 **b** Very close to 1

c Very close to 0 **d** 1 **e** 1

Exercise 19A

1 a $\frac{1}{5}, \frac{2}{25}, \frac{1}{10}, \frac{21}{200}, \frac{37}{250}, \frac{163}{1000}, \frac{329}{2000}$ **b** 6 **c** 1

d $\frac{1}{6}$ **e** 1000

2 a $\frac{19}{200}, \frac{27}{200}, \frac{4}{25}, \frac{53}{200}, \frac{69}{200}$ **b** 40

c No, it is weighted towards the side with numbers 4 and 5

3 a 32 is too high, 20 of the 50 throws between 50 and 100 unlikely to be 5

b Yes

4 a $\frac{1}{5}, \frac{1}{4}, \frac{38}{100}, \frac{21}{50}, \frac{77}{200}, \frac{1987}{5000}$ **b** 8

5 a 0.346, 0.326, 0.294, 0.305, 0.303, 0.306

b 0.231, 0.168, 0.190, 0.16, 0.202, 0.201

c Red 0.5, white 0.3, blue 0.2

d 1

e Red 10, white 6, blue 4

6 b 20

7 a 6

8 a Caryl, most throws **b** $\frac{107}{275}, \frac{169}{550}, \frac{91}{550}, \frac{38}{275}$ **c** Yes

9 a Method B **b** B **c** C **d** A **e** B **f** A **g** B **h** B

10 a Not likely **b** Impossible **c** Not likely

d Certain **e** Impossible **f** 50–50 chance

g 50–50 chance **h** Certain **i** Quite likely

Exercise 19B

1　a Yes　b Yes　c No　d Yes　e Yes　f Yes
2　Events a and f
3　$\frac{3}{5}$
4　a i $\frac{3}{10}$　ii $\frac{3}{10}$　iii $\frac{3}{10}$　b All except iii　c Event iv
5　b i $\frac{1}{10}$　ii $\frac{3}{10}$　iii $\frac{3}{10}$　iv $\frac{7}{10}$　c All except iii　d Event ii
6　a $\frac{3}{8}$　b $\frac{1}{8}$　c All except ii　d Outcomes overlap
7　$\frac{3}{20}$
8　Not mutually exclusive events
9　a i 0.25　ii 0.4　iii 0.7
　　b Events not mutually exclusive
　　c Man/woman, American man/American woman
　　d Man/woman

Exercise 19C

1　25
2　1000
3　a 260　b 40　c 130　d 10
4　5
5　a 150　b 100　c 250　d 0
6　167　b 833
7　1050
8　a Each score expected 10 times　b 3.5
　　c Find the average of the scores,
　　 which is 21 (1 + 2 + 3 + 4 + 5 + 6) divided by 6
9　400

Exercise 19D

1　a 23　b 20%　c $\frac{4}{25}$　d 480
2　a 10　b 7　c 14%　d 15%
3　b 4　c i $\frac{1}{4}$　ii $\frac{3}{16}$　iii $\frac{1}{4}$
4　a 16　b 16　c 73　d $\frac{51}{73}$
5　b 3　c $\frac{1}{4}$
6　a The greenhouse sunflowers are bigger on average
　　b The garden sunflowers have a more consistent size
　　 (smaller range)
7　a 40%　b 45%
　　c No as you don't know how much the people who get
　　 over £350 actually earn

Exercise 19E

1　a $\frac{1}{6}$　b $\frac{1}{6}$　c $\frac{1}{3}$
2　a $\frac{1}{4}$　b $\frac{1}{4}$　c $\frac{1}{2}$
3　a $\frac{1}{13}$　b $\frac{1}{13}$　c $\frac{2}{13}$
4　a $\frac{2}{11}$　b $\frac{4}{11}$　c $\frac{6}{11}$
5　a $\frac{1}{3}$　b $\frac{2}{5}$　c $\frac{11}{15}$　d $\frac{11}{15}$　e $\frac{1}{3}$
6　a 0.6　b 120
7　a 0.8　b 0.2
8　a 0.75　b 0.6　c 0.5　d 0.6
　　e i Cannot add P(red) and P(1) as events are not
　　　 mutually exclusive　ii 0.75
9　a $\frac{17}{20}$　b $\frac{2}{5}$　c $\frac{3}{4}$
10　Probability cannot exceed 1, and probabilities cannot be
　　 summed in this way as events are not mutually exclusive

Exercise 19F

1　a 7　b 2, 12
　　c P(2) = $\frac{1}{36}$, P(3) = $\frac{1}{18}$, P(4) = $\frac{1}{12}$, P(5) = $\frac{1}{9}$, P(6) = $\frac{5}{36}$,
　　 P(7) = $\frac{1}{6}$, P(8) = $\frac{5}{36}$, P(9) = $\frac{1}{9}$, P(10) = $\frac{1}{12}$, P(11) = $\frac{1}{18}$,
　　 P(12) = $\frac{1}{36}$
　　d i $\frac{1}{12}$　ii $\frac{1}{3}$　iii $\frac{1}{2}$　iv $\frac{7}{36}$　v $\frac{5}{12}$　vi $\frac{5}{18}$
2　a $\frac{1}{12}$　b $\frac{11}{36}$　c $\frac{1}{6}$　d $\frac{5}{9}$
3　a $\frac{1}{36}$　b $\frac{11}{36}$　c $\frac{5}{18}$
4　a $\frac{5}{18}$　b $\frac{1}{6}$　c $\frac{1}{9}$　d 0　e $\frac{1}{2}$
5　a $\frac{1}{4}$　b $\frac{1}{2}$　c $\frac{3}{4}$　d $\frac{1}{4}$
6　a 6　b i $\frac{4}{25}$　ii $\frac{13}{25}$　iii $\frac{1}{5}$　iv $\frac{3}{5}$
7　a $\frac{1}{8}$　b $\frac{3}{8}$　c $\frac{7}{8}$　d $\frac{1}{8}$
8　a 16　b 32　c 1024　d 2^n
9　a $\frac{1}{12}$　b $\frac{1}{4}$　c $\frac{1}{6}$

Exercise 19G

1　a $\frac{1}{4}$　b $\frac{1}{2}$　c $\frac{3}{4}$
2　a $\frac{1}{13}$　b $\frac{12}{13}$　c i $\frac{1}{169}$　ii $\frac{25}{169}$
3　a $\frac{2}{3}$　b $\frac{1}{2}$　d i $\frac{1}{6}$　ii $\frac{1}{2}$　iii $\frac{5}{6}$　e 15 days
4　a $\frac{2}{5}$　b i $\frac{4}{25}$　ii $\frac{12}{25}$
5　a $\frac{1}{8}$　b $\frac{3}{8}$　c $\frac{7}{8}$
6　a 0.14　b 0.41　c 0.09
7　a $\frac{3}{5}$　c i $\frac{1}{3}$　ii $\frac{7}{15}$　iii $\frac{8}{15}$
8　a 1　b 1　c

	$\frac{1}{4}$	$\frac{1}{4}$	$\frac{1}{10}$
$\frac{3}{5}$	$\frac{1}{3}$	$\frac{3}{5}×\frac{1}{3}$	
$\frac{2}{3}$	$\frac{3}{5}×\frac{2}{3}$	$\frac{2}{5}$	

Exercise 19H

1　a $\frac{4}{9}$　b $\frac{4}{9}$
2　a $\frac{1}{169}$　b $\frac{2}{169}$
3　a $\frac{1}{4}$　b $\frac{1}{2}$
4　$\frac{1}{216}$
5　a $\frac{4}{25}$　b $\frac{12}{25}$
6　a 0.08　b 0.32　c 0.48
7　a 0.336　b 0.452　c 0.024

Exercise 19I

1　a $\frac{125}{216}$ (0.579)　b $\frac{91}{216}$ (0.421)
2　a $\frac{1}{16}$　b $\frac{15}{16}$
3　a 0.378　b 0.162　c 0.012　d 0.988
4　a $\frac{4}{25}$　b $\frac{9}{25}$　c $\frac{16}{25}$
5　a i $\frac{1}{216}$ (0.005)　ii $\frac{125}{216}$ (0.579)　iii $\frac{91}{216}$ (0.421)
　　b i $\frac{1}{1296}$ (0.00077)　ii $\frac{625}{1296}$ (0.482)　iii $\frac{671}{1296}$ (0.518)
　　c i $\frac{1}{7776}$ (0.00013)　ii $\frac{3125}{7776}$ (0.402)　iii $\frac{4651}{7776}$ (0.598)
　　d i $\frac{1}{6^n}$　ii $\frac{5^n}{6^n}$　iii $1 - \frac{5^n}{6^n}$
6　a $\frac{32}{243}$ (0.132)　b $\frac{1}{243}$ (0.004)　c $\frac{242}{243}$ (0.996)
7　a $\frac{3}{8}$　b $\frac{1}{120}$　c $\frac{119}{120}$

Exercise 19J

1　a $\frac{27}{1000}$　b $\frac{189}{1000}$　c $\frac{441}{1000}$　d $\frac{343}{1000}$
2　a $\frac{1}{1296}$ (0.00077)　b $\frac{625}{1296}$ (0.482)　c $\frac{125}{324}$

3 a $\frac{1}{9}$ **b** $\frac{7}{18}$ **c** $\frac{7}{18}$ **d** $\frac{1}{9}$ **e** $\frac{8}{9}$
4 a 0.154 **b** 0.456
5 a 0.3024 **b** 0.4404 **c** 0.7428
6 a 0.9 **b** 0.6 **c** 0.54 **d** 0.216
7 a 0.6 **b** 0.6 **c** 0.432 **d** Independent events
8 a $\frac{1}{9}$ **b** $\frac{1}{9}$ **c** $\frac{7}{27}$ **d** $\frac{1}{27}$
9 a 0.126 **b** 0.4 **c** 0.42 **d** 0.054

Exercise 19K
1 a $\frac{1}{60}$ **b** 50
2 a $\frac{1}{6}$ **b** 0 **c i** $\frac{2}{3}$ **ii** $\frac{1}{3}$ **iii** 0

3 a i $\frac{3}{8}$ **ii** $\frac{5}{8}$ **b i** $\frac{5}{12}$ **b ii** $\frac{7}{12}$
4 a i $\frac{5}{13}$ **ii** $\frac{8}{13}$ **b i** $\frac{15}{91}$ **ii** $\frac{4}{13}$
5 a i $\frac{1}{3}$ **ii** $\frac{2}{15}$ **b** $\frac{4}{15}$ **c** $\frac{1}{6}$ **d** 1
6 Both events are independent
7 a $\frac{1}{120}$ **b** $\frac{7}{40}$ **c** $\frac{21}{40}$ **d** $\frac{7}{24}$
8 a $\frac{1}{9}$ **b** $\frac{2}{9}$ **c** $\frac{2}{3}$ **d** $\frac{7}{9}$
9 a 0.000495 **b** 0.00198 **c** 0.000018 **d** 0.00024
10 a 0.54 **b** 0.38 **c** 0.08 **d** 1
11 a RFC, FRC, CFC, CRC **b** $\frac{1}{3}$ **c** $\frac{1}{3}$ **d** $\frac{1}{3}$ **e**
Probability is the same regardless of which day he chooses

ANSWERS TO CHAPTER 20

Quick check

1 a 17, 20, 23 **b** 28, 36, 45 **c** 15, 10, 5
  d 49, 64, 81
2 a 1 **b** 4 **c** 7
3 a $2(x + 3)$ **b** $x(x - 1)$ **c** $2x(5x + 1)$
4 a $x^2 + 8x + 12$ **b** $2x^2 - 5x - 3$ **c** $x^2 - 4x + 4$
5 a $x = 3 - 2y$ **b** $x = 4 + 3y$ **c** $x = 4y - 3$

Exercise 20A

1 a $\frac{5x}{6}$ **b** $\frac{19x}{20}$ **c** $\frac{23x}{20}$ **d** $\frac{3x + 2y}{6}$ **e** $\frac{x^2y + 8}{4x}$

  f $\frac{5x + 7}{6}$ **g** $\frac{7x - 3}{4}$ **h** $\frac{13x - 5}{15}$ **i** $\frac{3x - 1}{4}$

  j $\frac{12x - 23}{10}$

2 a $\frac{x}{6}$ **b** $\frac{11x}{20}$ **c** $\frac{7x}{20}$ **d** $\frac{3x - 2y}{6}$ **e** $\frac{xy^2 - 8}{4y}$

  f $\frac{x - 1}{6}$ **g** $\frac{x - 1}{4}$ **h** $\frac{-7x - 5}{15}$

  i $\frac{x - 1}{4}$ **j** $\frac{-8x + 7}{10}$

3 a 3 **b** 6 **c** 2 **d** 5 **e** 0.75 **f** 3
4 a $\frac{x^2}{6}$ **b** $\frac{3xy}{14}$ **c** $\frac{8}{3}$ **d** $\frac{2xy}{3}$ **e** $\frac{x^2 - 2x}{10}$

  $\frac{1}{6}$ **f** **g** $\frac{6x^2 + 5x + 1}{8}$

  h $\frac{2x^2 + x}{15}$ **i** $\frac{2x - 4}{x - 3}$ **j** $\frac{1}{2x}$

5 a $\frac{3}{2}$ **b** $\frac{x}{y}$ **c** $\frac{8}{3}$ **d** $\frac{2xy}{3}$ **e** $\frac{5x}{2x - 4}$

  f $\frac{2x^2 - 12x + 18}{75}$ **g** 1 **h** $\frac{1}{4x + 2}$

  i $\frac{x^2 - 5x + 6}{48}$ **j** $\frac{1}{2x}$

6 a x **b** $\frac{x}{2}$ **c** $\frac{3x^2}{16}$ **d** 3

  e $\frac{17x + 1}{10}$ **f** $\frac{13x + 9}{10}$ **g** $\frac{3x^2 - 5x - 2}{10}$

  h $\frac{x + 3}{2}$ **i** $\frac{2}{3}$ **j** $\frac{2x^2 - 6y^2}{9}$

8 a 3, −1.5 **b** 4, −1.25 **c** 3, −2.5 **d** 0, 1
  i $\frac{x - 1}{4}$ **j** $\frac{-8x + 7}{10}$

9 a $\frac{x - 1}{2x + 1}$ **b** $\frac{2x + 1}{x + 3}$ **c** $\frac{2x - 1}{3x - 2}$

  d $\frac{x + 1}{x - 1}$ **e** $\frac{2x + 5}{4x - 1}$

Exercise 20B

1 a (5, −1) **b** (4, 1) **c** (8, −1)
2 a (1, 2) and (−2, −1) **b** $x = -4, y = 1; x = -2, y = 2$
3 a (3, 4) and (4, 3) **b** (0, 3) and (−3, 0) **c** (3, 2) and (−2, 3)
4 a (2, 5) and (−2, −3) **b** (−1, −2) and (4, 3) **c** (3, 3) and (1, −1)
5 a (2, 4) **b** (1, 0) **c** The line is a tangent to the curve

Exercise 20C

1 a 21, 34: add previous 2 terms **b** 49, 64: next square number **c** 47, 76: add previous 2 terms
2 15, 21, 28, 36
3 61, 91, 127
4 $\frac{1}{2}, \frac{3}{5}, \frac{2}{3}, \frac{5}{7}, \frac{3}{4}$
5 a 6, 10, 15, 21, 28 **b** It is the sums of the natural numbers, or the numbers in Pascal's Triangle.
6 a 2, 6, 24, 720 **b** 69!

Exercise 20D

1 a 13, 15, $2n + 1$ **b** 25, 29, $4n + 1$
  c 33, 38, $5n + 3$ **d** 32, 38, $6n - 4$
  e 20, 23, $3n + 2$ **f** 37, 44, $7n - 5$
  g 21, 25, $4n - 3$ **h** 23, 27, $4n - 1$
  i 17, 20, $3n - 1$ **j** 42, 52, $10n - 8$
  k 24, 28, $4n + 4$ **l** 29, 34, $5n - 1$

2 **a** $3n + 1$, 151 **b** $2n + 5$, 105 **c** $5n - 2$, 248
  d $4n - 3$, 197 **e** $8n - 6$, 394 **f** $n + 4$, 54
  g $5n + 1$, 251 **h** $8n - 5$, 395 **i** $3n - 2$, 148
  j $3n + 18$, 168 **k** $7n + 5$, 355 **l** $8n - 7$, 393
3 **a** 33rd **b** 30th **c** 100th = 499
4 **a i** $4n + 1$ **ii** 401 **iii** 101, 25th
  b i $2n + 1$ **ii** 201 **iii** 99 or 101, 49th and 50th
  c i $3n + 1$ **ii** 301 **iii** 100, 33rd
  d i $2n + 6$ **ii** 206 **iii** 100, 47th
  e i $4n + 5$ **ii** 405 **iii** 101, 24th
  f i $5n + 1$ **ii** 501 **iii** 101, 20th
  g i $3n - 3$ **ii** 297 **iii** 99, 34th
  h i $6n - 4$ **ii** 596 **iii** 98, 17th
  i i $8n - 1$ **ii** 799 **iii** 103, 13th
  j i $2n + 23$ **ii** 223 **iii** 99 or 101, 38th and 39th
5 a $\dfrac{2n + 1}{3n + 1}$ **b** Getting closer to $\frac{2}{3}$ ($0.\dot{6}$)
  c i 0.667 774 (6dp) **ii** 0.666 778 (6dp)

  d 0.666 678 (6dp), 0.666 667 (6dp)
6 a $\dfrac{4n - 1}{5n + 1}$ **b** Getting closer to $\frac{4}{5}$ (0.8)
  c i 0.796 407 (6dp) **ii** 0.799 640 (6dp)

  d 0.799 964 (6dp), 0.799 9996 (7dp)
7 a 64, 128, 256, 512, 1024 **b i** $2^n - 1$ **ii** $2^n + 1$ **iii** 3×2^n
8 a The number of zeros equals the power. **b** 6
  c i $10^n - 1$ **ii** 2×10^n
9 a Even,   **b** Odd,

+	**Odd**	**Even**
Odd	Even	Odd
Even	Odd	Even

×	**Odd**	**Even**
Odd	Odd	Even
Even	Even	Even

10 a 36, 49, 64, 81, 100 **b i** $n^2 + 1$ **ii** $2n^2$ **iii** $n^2 - 1$
11 $1 + 3 + 5 + 7 = 16 = 4^2$, $1 + 3 + 5 + 7 + 9 = 25 = 5^2$
12 a 28, 36, 45, 55, 66 **b i** 210 **ii** 5050 **c** You
  get the square numbers.
13 a Even **b** Odd **c** Odd **d** Odd **e** Odd
  f Odd **g** Even **h** Odd **i** Odd
14 a Odd or even **b** Odd or even **c** Odd or even
  d Odd **e** Odd or even **f** Even

Exercise 20E
1 b $4n - 3$ **c** 97 **d** 50th diagram
2 b $2n + 1$ **c** 121 **d** 49th set

3 **a** 18 **b** $4n + 2$ **c** 12
4 **a i** 24 **ii** $5n - 1$ **iii** 224 **b** 25
5 **a i** 20 cm **ii** $(3n + 2)$ cm **iii** 152 cm **b** 332
6 **a i** 20 **ii** 162 **b** 79.8 km
7 **a i** 14 **ii** $3n + 2$ **iii** 41 **b** 66
8 **a i** 5 **ii** n **iii** 18 **b** 20
9 **a** 2^n **b i** $100 \times 2^{n-1}$ ml **ii** 1600 ml

Exercise 20F
1 a i 35, 48 **ii** $n^2 - 1$ **b i** 38, 51 **ii** $n^2 + 2$ **c i**
39, 52 **ii** $n^2 + 3$ **d i** 34, 47 **ii** $n^2 - 2$
  e i 35, 46 **ii** $n^2 + 10$
2 a i 37, 50 **ii** $(n + 1)^2 + 1$ **b i** 35, 48 **ii** $(n + 1)^2$
  $- 1$ **c i** 41, 54 **ii** $(n + 1)^2 + 5$
  d i 50, 65 **ii** $(n + 2)^2 + 1$ **e i** 48, 63 **ii** $(n + 2)^2 - 1$
3 a i $n^2 + 4$ **ii** 2504 **b i** $3n + 2$ **ii** 152 **c i** $(n$
  $+ 1)^2 - 1$ **ii** 2600 **d i** $n(n + 4)$ **ii** 2700
  e i $n^2 + 2$ **ii** 2502 **f i** $5n - 4$ **ii** 246
4 a $2n^2 - 3n + 2$ **b** $3n^2 + 2n - 3$ **c** $\frac{1}{2}n^2 + \frac{5}{2}n + 1$

Exercise 20G
1 $-8y$ **2** $\dfrac{-x}{8}$ **3** $\dfrac{b + 5c}{4}$
4 $\dfrac{b(q + p)}{q - p}$ **5** $\dfrac{a(q - p)}{q + p}$ **6** $\dfrac{A}{\pi(2h + k)}$
7 $\dfrac{u}{\sqrt{(1 - a)}}$ **8** $\dfrac{3 + st}{2 + s}$ **9** $\dfrac{6 + st}{2 + s}$
10 $\dfrac{2R - 3}{R - 1}$ **11 a** $\dfrac{P}{\pi + 2k}$ **b** $\sqrt{\dfrac{2A}{\pi + \sqrt{(k^2 - 1)}}}$
12 $\dfrac{100A}{100 + RY}$ **13 a** $b = \dfrac{Ra}{a - R}$ **b** $a = \dfrac{Rb}{b - R}$
14 a $\dfrac{2 + 2y}{y - 1}$ **c** $x = \dfrac{2W + 2zy}{z + y}$

  d Same formula as in **a**
15 a Cannot factorise the expression.

  b $\dfrac{3V}{r^2(2r + 3h)}$ **c** Yes, $\sqrt[3]{\dfrac{3V}{5\pi}}$

16 $x = \dfrac{2W - 2zy}{z + y}$

ANSWERS TO CHAPTER 21

Quick check

1 $P = 4l$ **2** $C = \pi d$ **3** $A = \frac{1}{2}bh$
4 $A = \pi r^2$ **5** $V = l^3$ **6** $V = \pi r^2 h$

Exercise 21A
1 $P = 2a + 2b$ **2** $P = a + b + c + d$
3 $P = 4x$ **4** $P = p + 2q$
5 $P = 4x + 4y$ **6** $P = a + 3b$
7 $P = 5x + 2y + 2z$ **8** $P = 2\pi r$
9 $P = 2h + (2 + \pi)r$ **10** $P = 2l + \pi d$

Exercise 21B
1 $A = a^2 + ab$ **2** $A = \frac{1}{2}bh$
3 $A = bh$ **4** $A = \frac{1}{2}(a + b)h$
5 $A = \pi r^2$ **6** $A = 2ad - a^2$
7 $A = \frac{1}{2}bh + \frac{1}{2}bw$ **8** $A = 2rh + \pi r^2$
9 $A = \frac{1}{8}\pi d^2 + \frac{1}{2}dh$ **10** $A = \frac{1}{8}\pi D^2 + \frac{1}{2}(b + D)w$

Exercise 21C
1 $V = 6p^3$ **2** $V = \pi r^2 h$
3 $V = \frac{1}{2}bhw$ **4** $V = \frac{1}{2}bhl$
5 $V = aqt + bpt - apt$ **6** $V = abl + adl + 2cdl$

Exercise 21D

1 a A b L c L d A e V f V g V
   h A i L j V k A l L m V n A
   o V p A q V r A s A t A u L
   v A w A x A y V z V
2 a C b I c C d I e C f I g C
   h I i C j I k C l C m C n C
   o C p I q C r C s I t C u C
   v C w C x C y C

3 a C, L b I c C, V d C, L e I
   f I g C, V h C, V i C, V j C, V
   k C, L l I m C, V
4 a 2 b 2, 3 c 2 d 2, 2
5 Inconsistent
6 a A is F_2, B is F_4, C is F_3
   b F_1 is the total length of the curved edges

ANSWERS TO CHAPTER 22

Quick check

1 a 25 b 9 c 27 d 4 2 a 48 b $\frac{1}{2}$

Exercise 22A

1 a 15 b 2
2 a 75 b 6
3 a 150 b 6
4 a 22.5 b 12
5 a 175 miles b 8 hours
6 a £66.50 b 175 kg
7 a 44 b 84 m^2

Exercise 22B

1 a 100 b 10
2 a 27 b 5
3 a 56 b 1.69
4 a 192 b 2.25
5 a 25.6 b 5

6 a £50 b 225
7 a 3.2 °C b 10 atm
8 a 388.8 g b 3 mm
9 a 2 J b 40 m/s
10 a £78 b 400 miles

Exercise 22C

1 $Tm = 12$ a 3 b 2.5
2 $Wx = 60$ a 20 b 6
3 $Q(5 - t) = 16$ a −3.2 b 4
4 $Mt^2 = 36$ a 4 b 5
5 $W\sqrt{T} = 24$ a 4.8 b 100
6 $gp = 1800$ a £15 b 36
7 $td = 24$ a 3 °C b 12 km
8 $ds^2 = 432$ a 1.92 km b 8 m/s
9 $p\sqrt{h} = 7.2$ c 2.4 atm b 100 m
10 $W\sqrt{F} = 0.5$ a 5 t/h b 0.58 t/h

ANSWERS TO CHAPTER 23

Quick check

1 a 6370 b 6400 c 6000

2 a 2.4 b 2.39

3 a 50 b 47.3

Exercise 23A

1 a $6.5 \leqslant 7 < 7.5$ b $115 \leqslant 120 < 125$
   c $3350 \leqslant 3400 < 3450$ d $49.5 \leqslant 50 < 50.5$
   e $5.50 \leqslant 6 < 6.49$ f $16.75 \leqslant 16.8 < 16.85$
   g $15.5 \leqslant 16 < 16.5$ h $14\,450 \leqslant 14\,500 < 14\,549$
   i $54.5 \leqslant 55 < 55.5$ j $52.5 \leqslant 55 < 57.5$
2 a $5.5 \leqslant 6 < 6.5$ b $16.5 \leqslant 17 < 17.5$
   c $31.5 \leqslant 32 < 32.5$ d $237.5 \leqslant 238 < 238.5$
   e $7.25 \leqslant 7.3 < 7.35$ f $25.75 \leqslant 25.8 < 25.85$
   g $3.35 \leqslant 3.4 < 3.45$ h $86.5 \leqslant 87 < 87.5$
   i $4.225 \leqslant 4.23 < 4.235$ j $2.185 \leqslant 2.19 < 2.195$
   k $12.665 \leqslant 12.67 < 12.675$ l $24.5 \leqslant 25 < 25.5$
   m $35 \leqslant 40 < 45$ n $595 \leqslant 600 < 605$
   o $25 \leqslant 30 < 35$ p $995 \leqslant 1000 < 1050$
   q $3.95 \leqslant 4.0 < 4.05$ r $7.035 \leqslant 7.04 < 7.045$
   s $11.95 \leqslant 12.0 < 12.05$ t $6.995 \leqslant 7.00 < 7.005$

Exercise 23B

1 a 7.5, 8.5 b 25.5, 26.5 c 24.5, 25.5
   d 84.5, 85.5 e 2.395, 2.405 f 0.15, 0.25

   g 0.055, 0.065 h 250 g, 350 g i 0.65, 0.75
   j 365.5, 366.5 k 165, 175 l 205, 215
2 a <65.5 g b 64.5 g c <2620 g d 2580 g

Exercise 23C

1 a 38.25 cm^2 $\leqslant$ area < 52.25 cm^2
   b 37.1575 cm^2 $\leqslant$ area < 38.4475 cm^2
   c 135.625 cm^2 $\leqslant$ area < 145.225 cm^2
2 a 5.5 m $\leqslant$ length < 6.5 m, 3.5 m $\leqslant$ width < 4.5 m
   b 29.25 m^2 c 18 m
3 79.75 m^2 $\leqslant$ area < 100.75 m^2
4 216.125 m^3 $\leqslant$ volume < 354.375 m^3
5 20.9 m $\leqslant$ length < 22.9 m (3 sf)
6 16.4 cm^2 $\leqslant$ area < 21.7 cm^2 (3 sf)
7 a i 64.1 cm^3 $\leqslant$ volume < 69.6 cm^3 (3 sf)
     ii £22 569 $\leqslant$ price $<$ £24 506 (nearest £)
   b $23\,643 \leqslant$ price $< 23\,661$ (nearest £)
   c Errors in length are compounded by being used 3 times
     in **a**, but errors in weight are only used once in **b**.
8 a 14.65 s $\leqslant$ time < 14.75 s
   b 99.5 m $\leqslant$ length < 100.5 m
   c 6.86 m/s (3 sf)
9 a +2.53% (3 sf) b +3.82% (3 sf)
10 3.41 cm $\leqslant$ length < 3.43 cm (3 sf)
11 5.80 cm $\leqslant$ length < 5.90 cm (3 sf)
12 14 s $\leqslant$ time < 30 s

Quick check

1 a 8   **b** 10

2 a 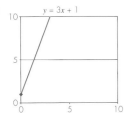   **b**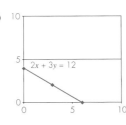

Exercise 24A

1 a $x < 3$ **b** $t > 8$ **c** $p \geqslant 10$ **d** $x < 5$
   e $y \leqslant 3$ **f** $t > 5$ **g** $x < 6$ **h** $y \leqslant 15$
   i $t \geqslant 18$ **j** $x < 7$ **k** $x \leqslant 3$ **l** $t \geqslant 5$

2 a 8   **b** 6   **c** 16   **d** 3   **e** 7

3 a 11   **b** 16   **c** 16

4 a $x \geqslant -6$ **b** $t \leqslant \frac{8}{3}$ **c** $y \leqslant 4$ **d** $x \geqslant -2$
   e $w \leqslant 5.5$ **f** $x \leqslant \frac{14}{5}$

5 a $x \leqslant 2$ **b** $x > 38$ **c** $x < 6\frac{1}{2}$ **d** $x \geqslant 7$
   e $t > 10$ **f** $y \leqslant \frac{7}{5}$

6 a $3 < x < 6$ **b** $2 < x < 5$ **c** $-1 < x < 3$
   d $1 \leqslant x < 4$ **e** $2 \leqslant x < 4$ **f** $0 \leqslant x \leqslant 5$

Exercise 24B

1 a $x > 1$ **b** $x \leqslant 3$ **c** $x < 2$ **d** $x \geqslant -1$ **e** $x \leqslant -1$ **f** $x \geqslant 1$

2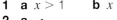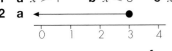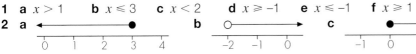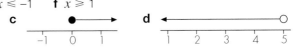

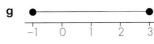 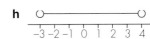

3 a $x \geqslant 4$ **b** $x < -2$

c $x \geqslant 3\frac{1}{2}$ **d** $x < -1$

e $x < 1\frac{1}{2}$ **f** $x \leqslant -2$

g $x > 50$ **h** $x \geqslant -6$

4 a $x > 2$ **b** $x \geqslant 6$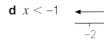

c $x \leqslant -1$ **d** $x \geqslant -4$

Exercise 24C

1 $-2 \leqslant x \leqslant 2$ **2** $x > 5, x < -5$

3 $-7 < x < 7$ **4** $x \geqslant 1, x \leqslant -1$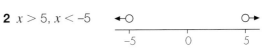

5 $x \geqslant 3, x \leqslant -3$ **6** $x > 3, x < -3$

7 $-2 \leqslant x \leqslant 2$ **8** $-4 < x < 4$

9 $x > 1, x < -1$ 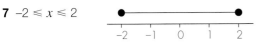   **10** $x \geqslant 3, x \leqslant -3$

11 $x > 2, x < -2$ 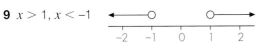   **12** $-3 < x < 3$

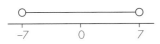

13 $-1 \leqslant x \leqslant 1$

14 $-4 < x < 4$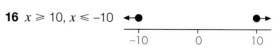

15 $x \geqslant 5, x \leqslant -5$

16 $x \geqslant 10, x \leqslant -10$

17 $-1.5 < x < 1.5$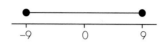

18 $x \geqslant \frac{1}{2}, x \leqslant -\frac{1}{2}$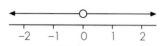

19 $-9 \leqslant x \leqslant 9$

20 $x > 0, x < 0$

Exercise 24D

1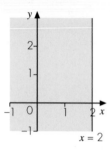

2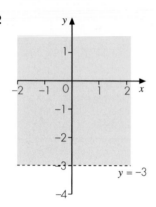

3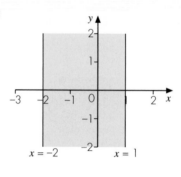

4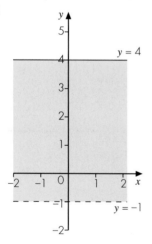

5 a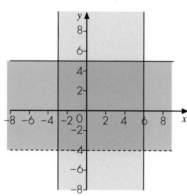

b i Yes **ii** Yes **iii** No

6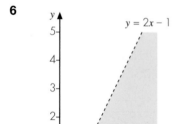

7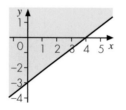

8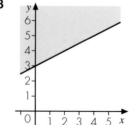

9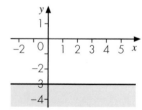

10 a–d 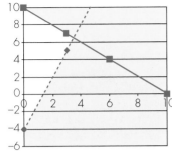 **11 a–f** 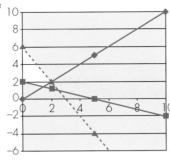 **12**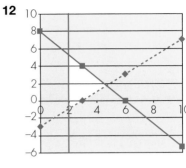

e i No **ii** No **iii** Yes **g i** No **ii** No **iii** Yes **b i** No **ii** Yes **iii** No **iv** No

Exercise 24E

1 a £148*x* **b** £125*y* **c** £(148*x* + 125*y*)

2 a £(*Ax* + *By*) **b** £(*Ax* + 2*Bx*) **c** £(9*A* + (9 + *y*)*B*)

3 a May be true **b** Must be false **c** May be true, e.g. *x* = 30, *y* = 20 **d** May be true, e.g. *x* = 3, *y* = 40

4 a May be true **b** May be true **c** Must be false

5 *E* Excels hold 40*E*; *S* Storms hold 50*S*. There must be at least 1500 seats, so 40*E* + 50*S* ⩾ 1500. Cancelling through by 10 gives 4*E* + 5*S* ⩾ 150

6 a *W* rides cost £1.50*W*. This cannot exceed £6.00, so 1.50*W* ⩽ 6.00. Cancelling through by 1.5 gives *W* ⩽ 4

 b Likewise 2*D* ⩽ 6, giving *D* ⩽ 3

 c Total cost is 1.50*W* + 2*D* ⩽ 6.00. Multiplying through by 2 gives 3*W* + 4*D* ⩽ 12

 d *D* ⩽ 2 **e i** Yes **ii** No **iii** No **iv** Yes

7 a 45*x* + 25*y* ⩽ 200 ⟹ 9*x* + 5*y* ⩽ 40 **b** *y* ⩾ *x* + 2

8 a i Cost 30*x* + 40*y* ⩽ 300 ⟹ 3*x* + 4*y* ⩽ 30 **ii** At least 2 apples, so *x* ⩾ 2 **iii** At least 3 pears, so *y* ⩾ 3

 iv At least 7 fruits, so *x* + *y* ⩾ 7

 b i No **ii** No **iii** No **iv** Yes

9 a i Space 4*x* + 3*y* ⩽ 48 **ii** Cost 300*x* + 500*y* ⩽ 6000 ⟹ 3*x* + 5*y* ⩽ 60 **b i** Yes **ii** No **iii** No **iv** Yes

10 a i Number of seats required is 40*x* + 50*y* ⩾ 300 ⟹ 4*x* + 5*y* ⩾ 30 **ii** Number of 40-seaters *x* ⩽ 6

 iii Number of 50-seaters *y* ⩽ 5

 b i Yes **ii** Yes **iii** Yes **iv** Yes

 c Combination iii, which costs £760

 d Five 40-seaters and two 50-seaters cost £740

ANSWERS TO CHAPTER 25

Quick check

a $\begin{pmatrix} 1 \\ 3 \end{pmatrix}$ **b** $\begin{pmatrix} 3 \\ 0 \end{pmatrix}$ **c** $\begin{pmatrix} 2 \\ -1 \end{pmatrix}$ **d** $\begin{pmatrix} -1 \\ -2 \end{pmatrix}$

Exercise 25A

1 a Any 3 of $\overrightarrow{AC}$, $\overrightarrow{CF}$, $\overrightarrow{BD}$, $\overrightarrow{DG}$, $\overrightarrow{GI}$, $\overrightarrow{EH}$, $\overrightarrow{HJ}$, $\overrightarrow{JK}$ **b** Any 3 of $\overrightarrow{BE}$, $\overrightarrow{AD}$, $\overrightarrow{DH}$, $\overrightarrow{CG}$, $\overrightarrow{GJ}$, $\overrightarrow{FI}$, $\overrightarrow{IK}$

 c Any 3 of $\overrightarrow{AO}$, $\overrightarrow{CA}$, $\overrightarrow{FC}$, $\overrightarrow{IG}$, $\overrightarrow{GD}$, $\overrightarrow{DB}$, $\overrightarrow{KJ}$, $\overrightarrow{JH}$, $\overrightarrow{HE}$ **d** Any 3 of $\overrightarrow{BO}$, $\overrightarrow{EB}$, $\overrightarrow{HD}$, $\overrightarrow{DA}$, $\overrightarrow{JG}$, $\overrightarrow{GC}$, $\overrightarrow{KI}$, $\overrightarrow{IF}$

2 a 2**a** **b** 2**b** **c a** + **b** **d** 2**a** + **b** **e** 2**a** + 2**b** **f a** + 2**b** **g a** + **b** **h** 2**a** + 2**b** **i** 3**a** + **b**

 j 2**a** **k b** **l** 2**a** + **b**

3 a Equal **b** $\overrightarrow{AI}$, $\overrightarrow{BJ}$, $\overrightarrow{DK}$

4 a $\overrightarrow{OJ}$ = 2$\overrightarrow{OD}$ and parallel **b** $\overrightarrow{AK}$ **c** $\overrightarrow{OF}$, $\overrightarrow{BI}$, $\overrightarrow{EK}$ **5**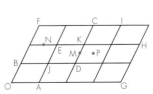

6 a Lie on same straight line **b** All multiples of **a** + **b** and start at O **c** H **d i** $\overrightarrow{OQ}$ = **a** + $\frac{1}{2}$**b** **ii** $\overrightarrow{OR}$ = 3**a** + $\frac{3}{2}$**b**

 e *n***a** + $\frac{n}{2}$**b**

7 a – **b** **b** 3**a** – **b** **c** 2**a** – **b** **d a** – **b** **e a** + **b** **f** –**a** – **b** **g** 2**a** – **b** **h** –**a** – 2**b** **i a** + 2**b**

 j –**a** + **b** **k** 2**a** – 2**b** **l a** – 2**b**

8 a Equal but in opposite directions **b** Any 3 of $\overrightarrow{DA}$, $\overrightarrow{EF}$, $\overrightarrow{GJ}$, $\overrightarrow{FI}$, $\overrightarrow{AH}$

9 a Opposite direction and $\overrightarrow{AB} = -\frac{1}{2}\overrightarrow{CK}$ **b** $\overrightarrow{BJ}$, $\overrightarrow{CK}$ **c** $\overrightarrow{EB}$, $\overrightarrow{GO}$, $\overrightarrow{KH}$

10 a

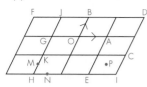

11 a Any 3 of $\overrightarrow{MJ}$, $\overrightarrow{AG}$, $\overrightarrow{HC}$, $\overrightarrow{BD}$, $\overrightarrow{OH}$, $\overrightarrow{NA}$, $\overrightarrow{PO}$, $\overrightarrow{KB}$, $\overrightarrow{IE}$ **b** Any 3 of $\overrightarrow{DG}$, $\overrightarrow{HJ}$, $\overrightarrow{AL}$, $\overrightarrow{EH}$, $\overrightarrow{BA}$, $\overrightarrow{OM}$, $\overrightarrow{FB}$, $\overrightarrow{IO}$, $\overrightarrow{KN}$

  c Any 3 of $\overrightarrow{GD}$, $\overrightarrow{HE}$, $\overrightarrow{BF}$, $\overrightarrow{JH}$, $\overrightarrow{AB}$, $\overrightarrow{OI}$, $\overrightarrow{LA}$, $\overrightarrow{MO}$, $\overrightarrow{NK}$ **d** Any 3 of $\overrightarrow{CH}$, $\overrightarrow{DB}$, $\overrightarrow{EI}$, $\overrightarrow{GA}$, $\overrightarrow{HO}$, $\overrightarrow{BK}$, $\overrightarrow{JM}$, $\overrightarrow{AN}$, $\overrightarrow{OP}$

  e Any 3 of $\overrightarrow{FH}$, $\overrightarrow{EG}$, $\overrightarrow{IA}$, $\overrightarrow{BJ}$, $\overrightarrow{KM}$, $\overrightarrow{OL}$ **f** Any 3 of $\overrightarrow{JD}$, $\overrightarrow{AE}$, $\overrightarrow{OF}$, $\overrightarrow{LH}$, $\overrightarrow{MB}$, $\overrightarrow{NI}$

  g i $\overrightarrow{FG}$, $\overrightarrow{IJ}$ or $\overrightarrow{KL}$ **ii** $\overrightarrow{OC}$, $\overrightarrow{KD}$, $\overrightarrow{NG}$, $\overrightarrow{PH}$ **iii** $\overrightarrow{FJ}$ or $\overrightarrow{IL}$ **iv** $\overrightarrow{FL}$ **v** $\overrightarrow{LF}$ **vi** $\overrightarrow{PC}$ **vii** $\overrightarrow{CP}$

  viii Same as part **d** **ix** Same as part **a**

12 Parts **b** and **d** could be, parts **a** and **c** could not be

13 a Any multiple (positive or negative) of 3**a**–**b** **b** Will be a multiple of 3**a**–**b**

Exercise 25B

1 a i –**a** + **b** **ii** $\frac{1}{2}$(–**a** + **b**) **iii**   **iv** $\frac{1}{2}$**a** + $\frac{1}{2}$**b** **b i** **a** – **b** **ii** $\frac{1}{2}$**a** – $\frac{1}{2}$**b** **iii**

  iv $\frac{1}{2}$**a** + $\frac{1}{2}$**b** **c** 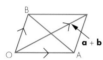 **d** M is midpoint of parallelogram of which OA and OB are two sides

2 a i –**a** – **b** **ii** $-\frac{1}{2}$**a** – $\frac{1}{2}$**b** **iii**   **iv** $\frac{1}{2}$**a** – $\frac{1}{2}$**b** **b i** **b** + **a** **ii** $\frac{1}{2}$**b** + $\frac{1}{2}$**a** **iii**

  iv $\frac{1}{2}$**a** – $\frac{1}{2}$**b** **c** 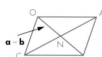 **d** N is midpoint of parallelogram of which OA and OC are two sides

3 a 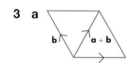 **b**

4 a i –**a** + **b** **ii** $\frac{1}{3}$(–**a** + **b**) **iii** $\frac{2}{3}$**a** + $\frac{1}{3}$**b** **b** $\frac{3}{4}$**a** + $\frac{1}{4}$**b**

5 a i $\frac{2}{3}$**b** **ii** $\frac{1}{2}$**a** + $\frac{1}{2}$**b** **iii** $-\frac{2}{3}$**b** **b** $\frac{1}{2}$**a** – $\frac{1}{6}$**b** **c** $\overrightarrow{DE} = \overrightarrow{DO} + \overrightarrow{OE} = \frac{3}{2}$**a** – $\frac{1}{2}$**b**

  d $\overrightarrow{DE}$ parallel to $\overrightarrow{CD}$ (multiple of $\overrightarrow{CD}$) and D is a common point

6 a $\overrightarrow{CD} = -$**a** + **b** = **b** – **a** **b i** –**a** **ii** –**b** **iii** **a** – **b** **c** 0, vectors return to starting point

  d i 2**b** **ii** 2**b** – 2**a** **iii** –2**a** **iv** 2**b** – **a** **v** –**a** – **b**

7 a 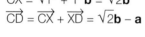 $\overrightarrow{CX} = \sqrt{1^2 + 1^2}\,$**b** = $\sqrt{2}$**b** **b** $\overrightarrow{YE} = \sqrt{1^2 + 1^2}\,$**a** = $\sqrt{2}$**a**.

  $\overrightarrow{CD} = \overrightarrow{CX} + \overrightarrow{XD} = \sqrt{2}$**b** – **a** $\overrightarrow{DE} = \overrightarrow{DY} + \overrightarrow{YE} = $**b** – $\sqrt{2}$**a**

  c i –**a** **ii** –**b** **iii** **a** – $\sqrt{2}$**b** **iv** $\sqrt{2}$**a** – **b** **v** $\sqrt{2}$**a** + **a** **vi** $\sqrt{2}$**b** + **b** **vii** 2**b** + $\sqrt{2}$**b** – **a** – $\sqrt{2}$**a**

  viii 2**b** + $\sqrt{2}$**b** – 2**a** – $\sqrt{2}$**a**

8 a i –**a** + **b** **ii** $\frac{1}{2}$(–**a** + **b**) = $-\frac{1}{2}$**a** + $\frac{1}{2}$**b** **iii** $\frac{1}{2}$**a** + $\frac{1}{2}$**b** **b i** $\frac{1}{2}$**b** + $\frac{1}{2}$**c** **ii** $-\frac{1}{2}$**a** + $\frac{1}{2}$**c** **c i** $-\frac{1}{2}$**a** + $\frac{1}{2}$**c**

  ii Equal **iii** Parallelogram

9 a i $\frac{1}{2}$**a** **ii** **c** – **a** **iii** $\frac{1}{2}$**a** + $\frac{1}{2}$**c** **iv** $\frac{1}{2}$**c** **b i** $-\frac{1}{2}$**a** + $\frac{1}{2}$**b** **ii** $-\frac{1}{2}$**a** + $\frac{1}{2}$**b**

  c Opposite sides are equal and parallel **d** NMRQ and PNLR

Quick check

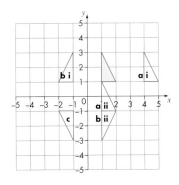

Exercise 26A

1 a–d

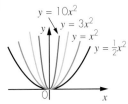

e Stretch sf in y-direction: 3, $\frac{1}{2}$, 10

2 a–d

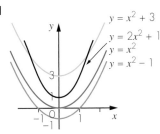

e b Translation $\begin{pmatrix} 0 \\ 3 \end{pmatrix}$ c Translation $\begin{pmatrix} 0 \\ -1 \end{pmatrix}$

d Stretch sf 2 in y-direction, followed by translation $\begin{pmatrix} 0 \\ 1 \end{pmatrix}$

3 a–d

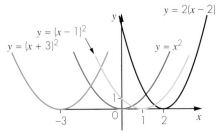

e b Translation $\begin{pmatrix} -3 \\ 0 \end{pmatrix}$ c Translation $\begin{pmatrix} 1 \\ 0 \end{pmatrix}$

d Stretch sf 2 in y-direction, followed by translation $\begin{pmatrix} 2 \\ 0 \end{pmatrix}$

4 a–c

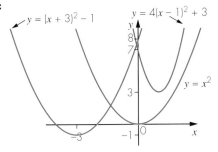

d b Translation $\begin{pmatrix} -3 \\ -1 \end{pmatrix}$

c Translation $\begin{pmatrix} 1 \\ 3 \end{pmatrix}$ followed by stretch sf 4 in y-direction

5 a–d

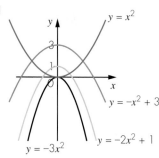

e *b* Reflection in *x*-axis, followed by translation $\begin{pmatrix} 0 \\ 3 \end{pmatrix}$

  c Reflection in the *x*-axis, followed by stretch sf 3 in *y*-direction
  d Reflection in *x*-axis, followed by stretch sf 2 in *y*-direction and translation $\begin{pmatrix} 0 \\ 1 \end{pmatrix}$

6 a–d

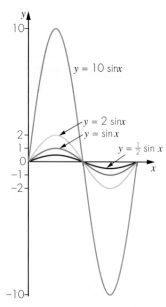

7 a–d

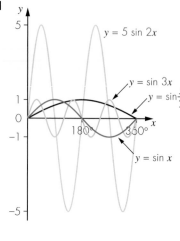

e *b* Stretch sf $\frac{1}{3}$ in *x*-direction
  c Stretch sf 2 in *x*-direction
  d Stretch sf 5 in *y*-direction, followed by stretch sf $\frac{1}{2}$ in *x*-direction

e Stretch sf in *y*-direction: 2, $\frac{1}{2}$, 10

8 a–d

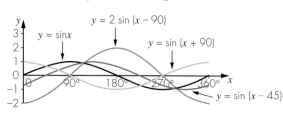

e *b* Translation $\begin{pmatrix} -90 \\ 0 \end{pmatrix}$ *c* Translation $\begin{pmatrix} 40 \\ 0 \end{pmatrix}$

  d Stretch sf 2 in *y*-direction followed by

  translation $\begin{pmatrix} 90 \\ 0 \end{pmatrix}$

9 a–d

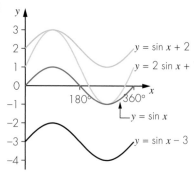

e *b* Translation $\begin{pmatrix} 0 \\ 2 \end{pmatrix}$ *c* Translation $\begin{pmatrix} 0 \\ -3 \end{pmatrix}$

  d Stretch sf 2 in *y*-direction followed by translation $\begin{pmatrix} 0 \\ 1 \end{pmatrix}$

10 a–d

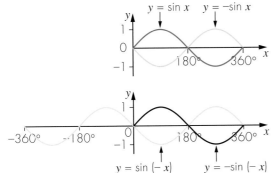

e *b* Reflection in *x*-axis   *c* Reflection in *y*-axis
  d This leaves the graph in the same place and is the identity transform

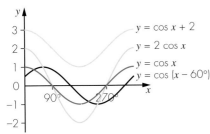

11 a–d

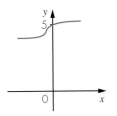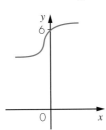

e *b* Stretch sf 2 in *y*-direction   *c* Translation $\begin{pmatrix} 60 \\ 0 \end{pmatrix}$

  d Translation $\begin{pmatrix} 0 \\ 2 \end{pmatrix}$

12 a i Stretch sf 4 in *y*-direction   **ii** Stretch sf 9 in *y*-direction   **iii** Stretch sf 16 in *y*-direction
  b i Stretch sf $\frac{1}{2}$ in *x*-direction   **ii** Stretch sf $\frac{1}{3}$ in *x*-direction   **iii** Stretch sf $\frac{1}{4}$ in *x*-direction

  c Stretch sf a^2 in *y*-direction, or stretch sf $\dfrac{1}{a}$ in *x*-direction

13 a   **b**   **c**   **d**

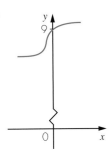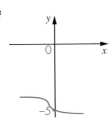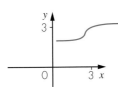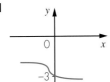

e   **f**

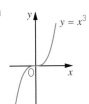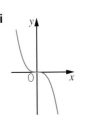

14 a $y = 5x^2$ **b** $y = x^2 + 7$ **c** $y = (x + 3)^2$
  d $y = 3x^2 + 4$ **e** $y = (x + 2)^2 - 3$ **f** $y = -3x^2$
15 a $y = 6\cos x$ **b** $y = \cos x + 3$ **c** $y = \cos (x + 30°)$ **d**
  $y = 3\cos x - 2$ **e** $y = \cos (x - 45°) - 2$

16 a   **b i**   **ii**   **iii**   **iv**

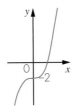

  c i $y = -x^3$ **ii** $y = x^3 - 2$ **iii** $y = 3x^3$ **iv** $y = (x + 2)^3$

17 a

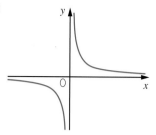

b i

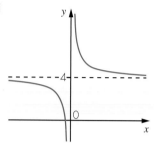

ii

(graph)

iii

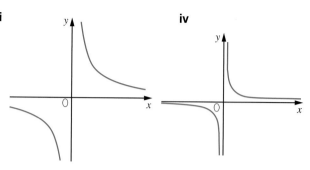

iv

(graph)

c i $y = \dfrac{1}{x} + 4$ **ii** $y = \dfrac{1}{x-4}$

iii $y = \dfrac{3}{x}$ **iv** $y = \dfrac{1}{2x}$

18 a $y = x^2 + 2$ **b** $y = (x-2)^2$
   c $y = 2x^2$ **d** $y = -x^2 + 4$

19 a $y = 2\sin x$ **b** $y = \sin(x-30°)$
   c $y = 2\sin(x-60°)$ **d** $y = \sin 2x$

20 a Translation $\begin{pmatrix} 0 \\ -90 \end{pmatrix}$

   b i Equivalent   **ii** Equivalent   **iii** Not equivalent

21 i A   **ii** D   **iii** E   **iv** C   **v** B

ANSWERS TO CHAPTER 27

Quick check

1 $z = x + y$

2 $p^2 = q^2 + r^2$

3

+	**Even**	**Odd**
even	even	odd
odd	odd	even

Exercise 27A

6 a 3, 5, 8, 13, 21, 34, 55
   b $3a + 5b$, $5a + 8b$, $8a + 13b$, $13a + 21b$, $21a + 34b$

8 a i $40°$

9 a i 10

Index